■ ■ ■

DECIDING
ETHICALLY

A Practical Approach to Nursing Challenges

■ ■

VERENA TSCHUDIN
BSc (Hons), RGN, RM, Dip Couns
Honorary Lecturer, University of East London

■

Baillière Tindall
London   Philadelphia   Toronto   Sydney   Tokyo

Baillière Tindall   24–28 Oval Road
W. B. Saunders   London NW1 7DX

The Curtis Center
Independence Square West
Philadelphia, PA 19106-3399, USA

Harcourt Brace & Company
55 Horner Avenue
Toronto, Ontario, M8Z 4X6, Canada

Harcourt Brace & Company, Australia
30–52 Smidmore Street
Marrickville
NSW 2204, Australia

Harcourt Brace & Company, Japan
Ichibancho Central Building
22-1 Ichibancho
Chiyoda-ku, Tokyo 102, Japan

© 1994 Baillière Tindall

This book is printed on acid-free paper

A catalogue record for this book is available from the British Library

ISBN 0-7020-1721-3

Typeset by Paston Press Ltd, Loddon, Norfolk
Printed and bound in Great Britain by Mackays of Chatham PLC, Chatham, Kent

NB still in
print JAN
2005.

DECIDING
ETHICALLY

Contents

Preface

Making decisions can be difficult; it can also be exciting. It is certainly what real life is about.

Helping people to make decisions has been a central aspect of much of my professional life. In the 1970s I trained as a counsellor, and practising and teaching that discipline led me into ethics. The two subjects have complemented each other to the point that I often feel that when I am talking about counselling I am really talking about ethics, and when I am talking about ethics I am really talking about counselling. The idea for this book came about in just such a situation.

I have been using Niebuhr's *Response Ethics* for some time now as a basis for teaching ethics in lectures and workshops. But it was a person I counsel who told me that she uses our counselling sessions to find out what is happening and to come to the point of insight or meaning. She can then find it in herself to give the fitting answer and live 'in a more satisfying and resourceful way' (BAC, 1990). Over the time that I have worked with her she has had to make some major ethical decisions – although the word 'ethics' has never been mentioned. Similarly, I have been with nurses who had to make ethical decisions and we used the same approach – and the word 'counselling' was never mentioned.

But clearly, ethics and counselling are not the same and one does not replace the other. Counselling is more directly concerned with attitudes, with finding meaning and purpose and achieving certain goals so as to live more satisfyingly and resourcefully. Ethics is directly concerned with what is good and right and how to achieve that. The skills of counselling – which are essentially nothing more than good communication – are, however, useful in understanding our values, how they are formed and how they can and do change.

So it is that this book is about ethical decision making with a strong input of counselling aspects and insights. Although this reflects where I am and where I come from, my experience teaches me that it is a useful way of presenting the subject. Where there are shortcomings and limitations in the presentation, I hope that readers will note them and use them consciously to improve their own practice.

The stories which summarise each chapter are focuses for the particular topic under discussion. Because of this, they become 'universal' stories or examples for any number of similar stories. With details changed here and there they could be told by most nurses. At the same time, because one story is told, another is left out. I am very conscious that vast areas of nursing care are therefore not covered. I would hope, however, that for any readers who find that their own 'story' is not recounted, the framework of the questions will help them to address their own problems and situations.

Ethics is a difficult subject in itself and the more one understands of it, the more one is sometimes aware of what one does not yet understand of it. Niebuhr's *Response Ethics* is not simplistic because it has only two main questions, but it is simple in that it addresses the main points of ethics very clearly with these questions. They are powerful questions which, when used responsibly, lead to fitting answers.

I hope that readers may catch some of the excitement which ethics as a study and a practice never fails to have for me.

VERENA TSCHUDIN

Chapter 1
Response ethics

Story

Elsie was a resident in a psychogeriatric unit attached to a large hospital which had recently become a trust. Elsie was something of a legend: small, softly spoken and very good-natured, she managed to get round any obstacles – whether staff or doors – when her mind was fixed on something. She charmed her way into or out of any situation to her advantage. Sometimes it was difficult to believe that she was really mentally ill and confused. Legend also had it that she was as old as the building, but nobody knew quite how old the building was.

Because Elsie was mobile, she wandered around a great deal. She was frequently brought back by nurses from other parts of the hospital, by shopkeepers, pub owners or local people worried that she might have an accident. The staff had on many occasions discussed what could or should be done to prevent her being hurt. Each time the decision was the same: nothing could be done that would stop only her. If Elsie would be stopped by locking doors, everybody else would be stopped too. She might also become more confused if she could not wander, and that might only aggravate the problem.

Along with the new trust management came new regulations and directives for the staff to follow. Management was keen to be seen to be active, and one by one the leaders of the various units were invited for policy discussions. When it was the turn of the manager of the psychogeriatric unit, it was put to her that electronic tagging

1

was a simple and effective way of stopping patients getting lost. Doors and limits could be put around the buildings in such a way that there would still be ample movement for patients and staff, but people like Elsie would be much safer. All the senior staff and social workers concerned were against this idea and argued their case strongly. But it seemed as if the doors had already been shut in the minds of the senior managers and they all but insisted that the scheme would at least be given a try. That seemed fair enough, at face value, and staff agreed to cooperate.

The staff were aware of ethical issues concerned with tagging, such as restrictions of freedom, consent to be tagged, where and how tags are worn, reviews of decisions to place tags and what actions should be taken by staff when an alarm was activated. These issues were all discussed, including the equally difficult point of whether this was meant to be a ploy to reduce staff in the unit.

When the staff came to discuss details, Elsie presented them with a particular difficulty: she had no relatives or friends who visited her from whom advice or consent could be sought. Occasionally, someone from the local church brought her a little parcel of food, but it was not always the same person. Elsie would have to have a tag fitted to her body, as she would certainly remove anything worn around her neck or in her handbag. A tag would not stop her from wandering, and staff might have to go several times a day to 'rescue' her when she had triggered an alarm. This in itself might be very distressing to Elsie. If Elsie had to wear a device on her ankle or arm she might just refuse to have a bath with the device in place. She would therefore really need an implanted tag. What are the implications in this situation?

This story, concerning one elderly person, encapsulates ethics in all its aspects: the personal and the general; the rightness or wrongness of a situation or act; obedience to rules or professional freedom; the dignity of the person or the convenience of a system limited by scarce resources. Questions of ethics generally arise at the intersection of two or more not totally straightforward ways of being or acting.

'Response ethics', the ethical theory used in this book, was put forward by H. Richard Niebuhr in a slim volume entitled *The Responsible Self*, published in 1963. Niebuhr (1894–1962) was Sterling Professor of Theology and Christian Ethics at Yale Divinity School. He and his more famous brother Reinhold together produced an impressive array of books which have influenced people profoundly, both in America and Europe. *The Responsible Self* comprises the Robertson Lectures which Richard Niebuhr delivered at the University of Glasgow in the spring of 1960.

Niebuhr does not deny the great ethical theories of teleology and deontology, but he starts from a very different point from these theories. He sums up teleology by saying that it is characterised by the question 'What is the goal, ideal, or telos?'; and deontology by the question 'What is the law and what is the first law of my life?' Response ethics always starts with 'What is happening?' and proceeds to 'What is the fitting answer to what is happening?' Thus, teleology is concerned with the highest good, to which it subordinates what is right; deontology is concerned with the right, no matter what may happen to the 'good': but for the ethics of responsibility the *fitting* answer is the only one which is conducive to the good and therefore the only one which is 'right'.

A simple example here is the case, in the late 1980s, of an 18-year-old mentally handicapped woman whose mother had asked that she be sterilised. The young woman was then living in a home and beginning to show sexual attraction to a man of about her own age. The mother feared that should the daughter become pregnant she would not be able to cope with the pregnancy nor with a child. Deontology would consider if such an operation is right in itself and if the mother has a duty to her daughter to ensure that a pregnancy be avoided. Teleology would consider first the consequences: if a sterilisation operation is performed in this one case, would this mean that every other 18-year-old mentally handicapped woman would be able to have a sterilisation as a precaution? Response ethics starts by asking *What is happening* here, with these persons, in this situation, given these circumstances. Response ethics is concerned with the relationships among all the people involved and how the various people respond to one another. It does not overlook duty and goals, but it does ask for the *fitting answer* rather than the theoretically correct one.

The story of Elsie was left at the point where her carers were asking *What is happening?*, and were beginning to consider all the various problems, issues, aspects and people. The *fitting answer* will only come to light when they also consider their own rights and responsibilities, personal and professional issues of relationships, the needs of all the people and systems involved.

Teleology is characterised by the need to achieve some goal. Niebuhr equates this with the symbol of the 'maker'. The purpose of life as understood in teleology is to make something of it and of oneself in it. The symbol which is applicable to deontology is that of the 'citizen'. Here the purpose of life is to live together in harmony. Life is more like politics than art. These two symbols do not exclude each other; on the contrary, they complement each other, and when this happens, they point to justice. Responsibility, says Niebuhr, is a new symbol which points to an alternative or additional way of defining the purpose of life: that of being an 'answerer'; that is, one who responds to another in answer to action taken in regard to him or her. The team around Elsie responds – to one another and to what is happening to her, to themselves and to their ideas of caring.

Niebuhr uses the word 'response' a great deal and almost plays with it. He writes about *response-ability* which leads to *responsibility*, about *responsiveness, response* and *responses*.

The two great ethical theories arose out of philosophical enquiry and are therefore inclined to be abstract; the idea of responding – being engaged in dialogue, answering questions, meeting challenges – is a daily experience and therefore immediately understandable. We act in reaction to stimuli; we respond to others out of an understanding that we are responsive beings. In order to be human and remain human we have to express ourselves, and we do this by responding to the people, objects and events around us. We interpret what is happening to us and we respond. Generally this is most notable in two particular situations: in social emergencies and in personal suffering. These situations pose a challenge and the interpretation we make of this challenge determines our response.

The simple choices of daily life require little deliberate thought. However, more and more of our daily challenges have ethical components. This is true even when we are shopping. You are faced with a delicacy which is appealing: do you have enough money to buy it, and if you buy a delicacy, does this mean that you still have enough money next week to pay the mortgage? Or perhaps outside the shop is someone rattling a collection tin with a photo of a little girl on it with the indication '£5 will save her life'. Do you give yourself a treat (which you do not need) or save a child's life with the same money? Our choices are constantly growing and therefore also constantly becoming more complex.

The challenges in health care are no less difficult, and perhaps a simple response made to a challenge can have very widespread consequences. Niebuhr considered the 'social emergencies' of his day to be famine and floods; they are still – or even more – with us today and need to be acknowledged; but the purpose of this book is to concentrate on health care.

The stories at the head of this and each chapter tell a personal story, but they are also universal stories. Readers may not have had the same experience as any particular story, but it should not be too difficult to compare them with their own experiences and events.

What is happening?

Niebuhr starts his theory with this question. It is such a simple question that it is remarkable that other ethical systems do not seem to give it the same prominence.

Nurses are very familiar, though, with this kind of question. Any process, in particular any process of change, has to start with where we are. The nursing process is only one among many other such processes, and the four steps of

Assessment, Planning, Implementation, Evaluation

are second nature to any nurse. The assessment is nothing other than asking, *What is happening?* Unless that question is asked we would be starting from somewhere where we actually are not.

What is happening? is the starting point of any enquiry. It is the question which fosters and guides awareness, and this is necessary for any response to any challenge, particularly if that response is to be significant for the people involved.

What is happening? is the question which underlies any listening. This question is asked by both people in any interaction. It is also the basic question of any helping. Only when this question has been thoroughly asked can it be replaced by other questions; even then it is the question to come back to at any moment of difficulty, hesitation or new insight.

But *What is happening?* is not usually the first thing which most people ask when faced with a challenge. The need for a response is so deep-rooted that for most people the usual response to a challenge is 'What should I do?' or 'What is my duty?' or 'What is the best?' In other words, we think or feel that we have to give a practical response. That often means having to give the 'right' answer and saying the 'right' thing – that is, giving the answer which solves the problem or makes the situation better.

But *What is happening?* is essentially the question of awareness. Because the question asks for more, it is as if a space in time is thereby created when judgement is suspended. It is possible in this space to take a deep breath and look all round and take in what is going on. This means in the first instance to be aware of ourselves and our reactions and surroundings. Because more awareness is available, the subsequent course of events is likely to be more balanced and more creative. The awareness by itself is not yet going to change anything, either for better or for worse, but it is going to make any change more informed. The more this question is asked in the story of Elsie, for example, the more the people concerned will feel really involved and taken seriously and the fewer regrets there will be in the end.

What is happening? is perhaps the most important question we can ask of ourselves and others, but it is perhaps also the question asked least often. The reason is not difficult to see: the question asks for a 'story', and most of us are either too much in a hurry or too much concerned with ourselves to hear another's story. It would seem that this is a malaise which afflicts not just our everyday small relationships, but that difficulties in industry, politics and religion all seem to stem from the fact that we do not want, or appear not to have time, to listen to one another. We dare not ask the question *What is happening?* because we are afraid of the answers we might get. By deliberately asking *What is happening?*, a conscious shift of emphasis happens.

What is happening? takes in the facts as they are presented. The question considers feelings, emotions and pain of various sorts. It hears of good and bad memories and of dreams and aspirations. It stays with the things which often seem to be immovable forces and which make living so hard, such as laws and policies which are usually reasonable, but not in our particular case. It hears of traditions, cultures and mores which influence us subconsciously to such an extent that they can blind us to possibilities which might otherwise be perfectly obvious ways of moving forward. Most of all, it hears of the relationships between people: those involved in the present situation and those playing parts at one, two or three removes, but where they are still influential.

Sometimes we have to ask again and again, *What is* happening? What *is* happening? What is *happening?* – because some people are not used to being heard and therefore have never been able to tell their stories. They are not in touch with feelings or dare not ask the questions which torment them simply because they do not know how to relate them. If we can ask *What is happening?* and are concerned to hear the kernel or 'truth', then we will perhaps already have helped more than can ever be admitted. Perhaps the nurses in Elsie's story really do need to ask if tagging is an unsubtle way of cutting staff?

By asking *What is happening?* in as many ways as possible and as often as is necessary, we can get a picture of the situation which may be quite different from the one first presented. This may seem to make the picture more difficult because there are many more aspects involved. This is not necessarily the case, because the main issue will emerge more clearly.

By asking *What is happening?* we are staying with the problem and with the person concerned for as long as is necessary. Thus response ethics can be seen to be relevant at every level because it considers the psychological aspects of the people and events as much as the practical, theoretical and intellectual ones.

What is the meaning of it?

This is not Niebuhr's question, but mine. Niebuhr makes only a passing reference to meaning (1963: 64) when he discusses accountability. I am including this question here for two particular reasons: first, when we ask for an analysis of what is happening at any depth we arrive at a point of insight and this then usually leads to an understanding either of the meaning of this particular event, or of the events which have shaped our values which now apply. Secondly, we are really only willing to grapple with a problem or dilemma if we think that there will be something better at the end than there is now; that is, there must be a search for a meaning right from the start. I have therefore included this question in the general sequence of questions in the chapters which follow.

The search for meaning is central to philosophy and psychology. Different schools express this quest differently. Nietzsche, the teacher of the idea of 'superman', said that those who have a 'why?' to live for can bear almost any 'how?'.

Patients and clients will put up with a great deal of pain and discomfort from operations, injections and treatments so long as they know – or at least believe – that these will help them. The same can be said of people subjecting themselves to a process of unpacking and delving into the past in order to understand what is causing the present problems of an ethical nature.

Existentialism, another philosophical theory, denies objective universal values and advocates that people, being free agents, do, and need to, create their own values. They must take responsibility for the actions which follow from these values.

Frankl (1962), a psychotherapist, also constructed his Logotherapy on the premise that what people need most of all in life is meaning (*logos*). But he states that 'the meaning of our existence is not invented by ourselves, but rather detected' (p. 101). Frankl says that values have to be discovered. They do not 'push' us but 'pull' us. We are not driven to some action or behaviour; in each case we have the choice and decide how to behave; we respond to what is there. If we see meaning in something, then we go to it and with it by choice.

Rationalists consider that reason alone is the measure to make sense of the world around them and the foundation of certainty in knowledge.

Whichever approach is used from conviction or from inclination, most of us have our own value system which is, most likely, a synthesis of several theories which are used unconsciously but more or less effectively.

When we ask *What is happening?* we are looking in the first instance for facts. Some of these 'facts' are feelings, emotions, memories and also assumptions made. We are often not able to understand the hold of these elements upon us very well but they certainly guide the way we see the world and form our values. They will often have shaped our behaviour very early on. To see this now, perhaps when someone is helping us with a problem, is often very revealing and gives new meaning to life.

It may also be that the situation which calls for an ethical decision may itself reveal something which was completely unexpected. The insight gained gives new meaning not only to personal life but also to professional issues.

It is sometimes difficult to come to terms with such important insights. They may lead to changes of direction and almost always lead to restructuring of values held. If Niebuhr accepts that this is part of the process, I am saying that such insights need to be acknowledged specifically. This is why I am putting the question here. If we do not mark an insight it will not mark us – or rather, by marking the insight it will mark us.

We arrive at these insights through sheer hard work by staying with the problem, therefore we should allow ourselves the space to acknowledge them.

What has meaning for one person does not necessarily have meaning for another. It is therefore quite difficult to describe what might be meaningful in given situations. Anything significant, which makes sense, makes connections, shows helpful patterns, speaks to us at the moment, helps us to understand something or clarifies something, can be meaningful. Whatever the person concerned says it means, is what it does mean, and that should be good enough.

What is the fitting answer?

'What is the fitting response to what is happening?' asks Niebuhr (1963: 67). The response depends crucially on how we interpret what is happening.

The symbol of the 'answerer' – the person who responds to people, objects and events – is now the important element. We express our humanity mostly by responding to what is happening around us. A dialogue is created between us and people, objects and events.

Because Niebuhr places so much emphasis on relationships and being human through relating and responding, it is inevitable that he cannot conclude his questioning of *What is happening?* with an answer based on a theory of duty or achieving goals. Niebuhr looks for something much more 'holistic' and involving and encompassing the people concerned.

This does not mean that either duty or the search for good consequences is not considered; indeed it is, as are also all the other ethical guidelines, principles and theories. But they are not seen to be ends in themselves.

It is fair to say that a deontologist would always decide on the basis of duty and therefore would always make the same or similar decisions in similar circumstances. The teleologist would decide on the basis of achieving the best consequences and would therefore also make similar decisions in similar circumstances. This may mean that a deontologist – in any walk of life, not simply in medicine – would, for instance, see it as a duty to preserve life and therefore never take part in, condone or advise for abortions. Such a person would also consider tagging elderly people to be a duty by preventing harm happening to them. A teleologist, similarly, might welcome any advances in technology (regardless of their moral value) because they represent more opportunities, more jobs and more advances still. A teleologist might say that tagging would actually give elderly people more freedom of movement by not keeping them restricted to confined areas.

The *fitting answer* in response ethics to such situations will vary because it is made not on a blanket theory but is concerned with the people involved in each case. So it may be that someone having to decide if she should have an abortion would decide that it is *fitting* in this instance to have an abortion, but at the same time might be helping a friend who decides that an abortion is *not fitting* in her case; similarly, tagging might be advocated for one area but not for another. This is not seen as inconsistency, but as a very real involvement in the actual situation.

Equally, someone putting the ideals of response ethics into action might be very pleased that a piece of new medical technology might be able to help a large number of people, such as in heart transplants, but when it comes to his own case might decide that this is not what he needs most and might forgo a heart transplant himself because it would not be *fitting* for him and for the people around him.

Such decisions can only be made after having thoroughly considered *What is happening?* in every aspect, and having discovered a *meaning* in it all, this then feeds into the process of giving the *fitting answer*.

Such *fitting answers* will often be reached in discussions and reflections with others, in particular with the people concerned. The decision-making process is therefore not a lonely affair but one which very much involves people. In health care the protagonist is the patient or client, and this person has to be taken into consideration, even when that person may not be able to speak or take part in such deliberations. Too often doctors, in particular, have taken decisions on their own and have then had to carry the heavy burden of such lonely decisions. The idea of professional autonomy has often been stretched to lengths for which it was not intended, leaving the people concerned with anguish about their decision. When there is talk – responding, communicating and interpreting what was talked about – then there is not loneliness but relating, relationships and 'co-humanity' (Niebuhr) which results in joy because something has been achieved together and is now celebrated together.

The pattern of responsibility

Niebuhr saw that when the two essential questions are asked, a pattern emerges which is recognisable. He does not say that this is his theory (indeed, he appears to use expressions, such as 'social solidarity', first coined by other people) or that it represents a model, but he presents the pattern as a kind of summary of what takes place when the two questions are asked.

The pattern and the two questions have as their starting point a *challenge*: that which calls for an ethical response. The *challenge* may be a telephone call to do some more work, or it may be a diagnosis confirmed, a realisation that personal and professional values are incompatible, a request by a patient, the idea of tagging elderly patients, or something seen or heard which addresses one's conscience. In short, a *challenge* is that which makes us realise that we are called upon to respond in some fundamental way which involves the whole person.

The *response* depends on the challenge. It is significant that Niebuhr sees the initial response to be a bodily sensation, like a fast heartbeat or weak knees. Most theories of ethics do not get anywhere near so basic an element as bodily reactions. But because Niebuhr starts with this and considers it to be important, it is by itself a good reason for recommending this theory for use in health care.

Even if we have not experienced it ourselves, we all know how patients react to visits by and to doctors and to treatment rooms. The fear of being given a diagnosis or an injection can put up the heart rate, blood pressure and temperature, cause numerous trips to the toilet or make sweat glands overactive. And this is only the anticipation, not yet even the actual challenge.

These reactions are the physical signs of feelings: fear, anger, guilt, despair, hope and joy, to mention just a few of the most common feelings. They never happen in isolation, but only ever in response to a challenge. The feelings are certainly not wrong, and neither is it wrong to be aware of their physical aspects. It is simply that we often do not know how to deal with the feelings once we experience them, and therefore we are afraid of them.

When we ask *What is happening?* we are able to hear of feelings and emotions and of how much they influence what is going on. When these elements are not taken into consideration right from the start we may get a very distorted picture of the actual situation.

Some of the ethical theories are careful to say that we should not make decisions on the basis of feelings because feelings are irrational and unreliable. This is very sound advice, but it then tends to mean that feelings are not taken seriously at all, which is psychologically dangerous and even harmful. Feelings are irrational and unreliable, but they are *there* and they colour who we are and what we are. Therefore they have to be taken seriously. Only when they are acknowledged can they be understood and worked with.

There then follows an *interpretation* of what has so far been understood and unearthed in the given situation.

The response to the challenge is not simply instinctive, but is a reaction to an action upon us. When a grown man shows fear at the sight of a syringe it is most likely because he was given an injection as a child which he then experienced as an assault and as painful. The memory stayed with him subconsciously, and now his reaction is an interpreted reaction and the same fear is of the element which is visible. If this happens with relatively simple things like remembering pain, it is not surprising that when it comes with weighty ethical decisions, our interpretations of past events are powerful motivators.

We interpret events around us in the light of what we remember or have lived through in the past. The fact that two people can react in completely opposite ways to similar events shows that asking *What is happening?* is vital. Too often we assume that others think as we do, understand as we do and react as we do. Yet nothing could be further from the truth. We should ask and not assume, and not judge others for their different ways of being.

The fact that we have an ability to respond – a response-*a*bility – makes us essentially human. In order to remain human we have to respond to people, objects and events around us. Our respons*i*bility then becomes the application of the ability.

Niebuhr sees the next step in the pattern to be *accountability*. He explains that this word 'is frequently defined by recourse to legal thinking but [it] has a more definite meaning, when we understand it as referring to part of the response pattern of our self-conduct. Our actions are responsible not only insofar as they are reactions to interpreted actions upon us but also insofar as they are made in anticipation of answers to our answers' (1963: 64). We do not only remember, we also anticipate: what would happen if we said 'yes' to the request to stay on a few hours at work? What would happen if we said 'no'? Everything we say and do has consequences: our responsibility is therefore to be accountable.

Accountability has been stressed a great deal in health care in recent times. Fromer (1990) says that 'professional accountability can be divided into four more or less equal components: self, client, employing institution and society'. What matters is which of these components is the one claiming priority at any given moment.

Hunt (1991) makes the point that it is often only when accountability is absent that we become aware of it. 'Recent events have made many of us doubt the accountability of the police and the judiciary, bankers and financiers, the armed forces and the Government, doctors and researchers. We have good reason for this doubt, and we know exactly what is meant by demanding that these people be made accountable for their actions.' It is tempting to say that there is a difference between personal and professional accountability, and that what a person does in private has nothing to do with what is done in public. But that argument does not stretch very far before private and professional become completely intertwined.

Where we consider our accountability to lie will influence how we respond overall to a challenge. Any person's response will influence a wide circle. The way in which a manager acts will be felt by all whom she manages; the way in which a staff nurse responds to a telephone request to work extra hours will concern and influence his colleagues, any friends he may have put off, his patients and their relatives and friends, and future responses for similar requests. Our response-*ability* in every situation leads to *What is the fitting answer?* and the respons*ibility* which we consider ourselves to have, based on the interpretation and the accountability we recognise.

When we ask 'Who or what am I accountable to?' we inevitably match concepts of duties, goals and laws. Niebuhr does not deny this and does not belittle these concepts, but he considers that we should also ask, What else is happening? In this way we may become accustomed to look in more than one direction and take in the various aspects of accountability at once.

Accountability is that part of the pattern of responsibility which questions moral behaviour and analyses rules, laws and commandments. Accountability then becomes the sum of one's conscience, respecting ethical principles and using one's responsibility in the way that is most fitting. To do that, we have to listen much, hear and understand, and respond in a way which is both respecting of our own character and personality and that of patients, colleagues, institutions and society.

The last element in the pattern is *social solidarity*. If the *response* to the *challenge* is the *fitting* one, then the outcome will almost certainly be seen to be beneficial. The community of people concerned will have gained. But it is difficult to measure the sum of happiness in the community. This is surely why Niebuhr does not talk about accumulating happiness (as utilitarianism would) but searching for *solidarity*. Personal responsibility can only exist in relation to other people. One person's action is a response to another person, how each interprets the other's words and actions, and the expectation of each for a response from the other. This forms a continuing community of people responsive to one another. Through responding they become responsible.

Values underlie any ethical actions and responses. *Social solidarity* helps to shape better values. The thinking and searching within nursing at present about what constitutes 'caring' can be seen to be an outcome of more committed ethical reasoning and responding.

To care deeply for another person is to care ethically in a responsive way. This means listening carefully to the other person, but also asking the pertinent questions. When the questions and answers are *interpreted* they begin to have *meaning* for both '*answerers*', and their *responses* are *accountable* in the sense that a wider *solidarity* comes into being.

The following chapters show these points in action through the stories which form the basis for discussion.

Chapter 2
The principle of
the value of life (1)

Story

Alex, a woman of 22, and her boyfriend had been in a motorcycle accident. He was killed on the spot, but Alex was rescued by an ambulance crew. Her injuries were extensive, and even at the time there was doubt that she would survive. However, she even regained consciousness for a little while. Later, she managed to breathe on her own but she had to be fed via a nasogastric tube.

Her younger sister and parents were devastated and visited her frequently in hospital. They had high hopes that Alex would recover, and at first made themselves and everyone concerned believe that Alex would pull through. As the weeks turned into months though, the optimism faded, and when the anniversary of the accident approached, the strain on them all was visible. The nursing staff helped as much as they could by listening to them and talking with them. The sister, Tam, was particularly upset at the time and visited more often. She had been the most optimistic of the family, but now she often cried when she was with Alex.

Shortly after the date of the anniversary the social worker arranged a case conference with the nursing, medical and rehabilitation staff, and also invited the hospital chaplain to come along. The parents and Tam were informed of the meeting. A month or two after this meeting, the unit introduced primary nursing and Jenny was allocated to Alex as the primary nurse. She had been very close to the family, particularly to Tam, and she was chosen to explain to them what was discussed at the conference. The fact that Alex was beginning to be considered to be in a persistent vegetative state had been discussed, but that this could not yet be confirmed was also mentioned. The implications of this were clear for the staff, but Jenny had to choose her words well to explain to the family what this meant. They could not take it in very well right then, and Jenny spent much time with the family in the following weeks, going over the main points several times. She was happy to do this as she was a good communicator and had some counselling skills too.

Alex's condition changed very little, but despite good physiotherapy she became gradually more spastic.

Tam now visited three times a week and the parents twice a week. Tam's attitude changed from optimism to realism, and she emerged as the spokesperson for the immediate family, becoming very knowledgeable in medical terms about Alex and her condition. She asked Jenny if she could attend the next case conference. Jenny was hesitant at first, as she knew that if anybody's word would count legally, it would be more likely to be the parents'. Jenny spent some time discussing this with Tam and her parents, and also with colleagues who would attend the case conference. They agreed that this was the right thing in the circumstances.

At the next case conference persistent vegetative state (PVS) was declared to exist, though the doctors were still not prepared to say that this was the final diagnosis.

Another six months went by, and another meeting took place. It was now two years since the accident, and Alex was neither improving nor deteriorating. Her nursing care was excellent and she had no sores and had had only two or three difficulties with the urinary catheter, which had needed short-term antibiotics. Tam and the parents were no longer talking about hope, but were seriously beginning to wish that Alex might die. As far as they knew, Alex had never mentioned anything about what she would like to happen to her should she be in a state like this, but Tam felt close enough to her sister to be confident to speak on her behalf. Tam had read as much as she could about similar situations, and she had asked Jenny to call another case conference in which she wanted to make the point clear that she and her parents would like the life support stopped and that this should now happen speedily and not drag on.

The setting

In 1993 the case of Anthony Bland made headline news. He had been crushed in the Hillsborough football disaster nearly three years earlier. Tony's parents had asked for some time that the feeding tube should be removed and that Tony be allowed to die. In this they were supported by the medical and nursing team. The case went as far as the House of Lords, where the ruling was given that feeding was in this case considered to be 'medical treatment' and that this could now be stopped (House of Lords, 1993). A few days after this decision Tony died.

This was the first such case to be brought to public attention, but clearly there are many similar situations going on now and others will occur in the future. The advances in medical and nursing interventions have relieved untold miseries and restored health with ease and reduced suffering, but they have also given us dilemmas which we cannot yet tackle and which challenge our views and values in an unprecedented way. Technology has raced ahead of philosophy and even common sense – and society at large is faced with problems of life and death which it hardly knows how to address.

This is the setting for this scenario. The story of Alex is a dramatic one, and it is to be hoped that few health-care professionals will ever be in the situation described there. Ethics is not only about drastic life-and-death decisions, but also about everyday decisions. The point about this story – and all the others in this book – is that it can and should spark off critical analysis not only of similar situations but also of situations where only some elements may be the same.

According to Thiroux (1980: 130) the principle of the value of life 'is empirically prior to any other [ethical principle] because without human life there can be no goodness or badness, justice or injustice, honesty or dishonesty, freedom or lack of it. Life is a basic possession, the main possession of each individual human being'.

Thiroux (1980: 124) sums up this principle with the phrase: 'Human beings should revere life and accept death.' In order to think more clearly about medical technology as well as human mortality, Callahan (1993) says that 'we should begin backwards. Death should be seen as the necessary and inevitable end point of medical care.' Life and death belong together not only in philosophy and religion, but most particularly in medical care. Many aspects of life at present make it clear, however, that death is embarrassing. Death is avoided in the language we use about care and in the increasing rights which people believe they have, many of which they use in order to 'strive officiously to keep alive' at any cost. To 'accept death' is part of living, and it is important to keep this balance.

The principle of the value of life is the first principle according to Thiroux. Other systems or approaches might start differently, but life and the respect for it is intrinsic to any approach to ethics. The principle does not mean that life should be 'life at any cost', but that 'no life should be ended without very strong justification' (1980: 130). No ethical principles are absolutes, argues Thiroux (a Kantian view might not agree with this) – there must always be justifications for setting a principle aside – but principles should be near-absolutes. The principle of the value of life is a near-absolute because life is held both in common and uniquely by all human beings. Not to uphold this principle would therefore need a very strong justification. It is in these moments and situations of justification that ethical reasoning happens and ethical decisions are made.

When asking *What is happening?* in the situation of Alex, a great many aspects have to be taken into account to understand this and similar circumstances. Two of these aspects only – euthanasia and the right to die – will be examined now. Other aspects will be mentioned when relevant.

Euthanasia

The question of euthanasia is becoming ever more acute in our health care. As medicine advances in technology, it seems we are less and less able to deal with death. It sometimes seems as if the genie of technology has been let out of the bottle and we cannot get it back to where it belongs. Medical and nursing interventions have taken us down the road of prolonging life, but society at large has failed to face up to the consequences of these interventions (Wright, 1993). We have created the problem of euthanasia for ourselves but now find it difficult to solve it. Indeed, in the Tony Bland case medicine resorted to the law to solve the problem.

Euthanasia is no longer a question of applying the right definition, or arguing the distinctions between active and passive euthanasia, between voluntary and involuntary. In the past, says Castledine (1993), 'the only question to be answered was simply: "Morally may we do anything to put people mercifully out of hopeless misery?" Today, the question has expanded: "Morally may we omit to do any of the ingenious things we could do to prolong people's suffering?"' Euthanasia, a 'good death', should mean

> [a] death without that technological brinkmanship that knows no boundaries in the war against mortality. I would define a peaceful death in a public context as a death that, on the one hand, rejected a disproportionate share of resources which, through a kind of economic violence, threatened other societal goods such as education and housing; and, on the other hand, rejected euthanasia and assisted suicide as still other forms of violence, though medical and social rather than economic. (Callahan, 1993)

Death and dying have become inextricably linked with economics: can we afford to keep people alive? If we keep this person alive, it means that another person is denied medical care who might perhaps only need minor treatment to lead a fully 'useful' life again. The difficulty is that we are trying to solve a moral problem with economic measurements and language. If a dying person feels that there is a price on his or her head, he or she may feel obliged to give in to pressure and consent to be 'put out of misery'. The more dreaded scenario is that people simply are put out of their misery, if they want it or not, and that this would not be considered murder but economic expediency. The utilitarian argument of 'the greatest good for the greatest number' is a tempting one: the slowly dying, the emotionally dead and the unconscious take up resources which could be (better) used for those who will make a good recovery. Human beings should indeed accept death – not killing – but they should also first of all revere life.

The story of Alex does not reveal any discussions having taken place on the economics of the case. But it does not take long to work out that keeping a person 'alive' is very costly in terms of resources of equipment and people. We cannot undo technology, but the more agonising question for many people is how to use that technology morally, responsibly and compassionately.

Keeping someone alive is also costly for the family. One can put a price on the practicalities but not on the emotions, and emotions and feelings are what everyone involved is left with: anger, guilt and frustration at the inability to 'do' something. There may also be feelings of sadness of lives shattered which need not have happened, and impotence at being able to decide for oneself or fight the system effectively. The feelings which people are left with at the end of any important event help to shape their values, and these in turn influence many others. The emotional cost for society also has to be taken into the equation.

Castledine ends his article by saying that 'I have gained the most understanding of my life from those about to lose theirs'. It is only in sharing – in the widest possible sense – in the sufferings of others that we can understand suffering at all. This may be increasingly difficult in today's world where people will see tens of thousands of people 'killed' on TV by the special effects of techno-war.

> *I have been told of a 6-year-old boy who was given the news that his granny had died. His reaction was, 'Was she shot or poisoned?'*

Growing up (or into) a world where 'death' is so 'easy' at one level makes it very difficult to understand why it is so difficult at another level. It is only through personal understanding and sharing that our own values and those of society at large can be examined, acted upon and changed if necessary. Nurses have a vital role to play in society's understanding of life and death.

The right to die

The right to life will be considered in the next chapter, but here the right to die will be seen as a direct continuation of the debate about euthanasia. The right to die with dignity has become a more and more pressing issue, but was particularly highlighted in the United Kingdom by the Tony Bland case. A few weeks before another patient had made history: Mrs Lillian Boyes, aged 70, had been suffering from arthritis for many years and had repeatedly asked her consultant, Dr Nigel Cox, to help her out of her misery. Eventually he did, by giving her an injection of potassium chloride.

Those who commit suicide claim the right to die for themselves and involve nobody else in the decision. In Britain, suicide has been legal only since the 1960s, but it is interesting to note that in Germany suicide has been legal since the Middle Ages. Such cultural differences inevitably colour societal values.

The right to die means essentially that a person decides that now, or a given day, should be the day to die, because there has been enough living or dying. But that person does not want to die violently. When a person needs help with dying – because he or she is too ill, bed-bound, unconscious or mentally incompetent – a 'right' to die is inevitably questioned. Again in Germany, the concept of *Sterbehilfe* (helping to die) has found its way into the popular as well as the medical and nursing language. But how far the idea of helping to die has found its way into practice is less clear. Can one person ask another to help him or her to die? And in particular, can a doctor help anyone to die? Doctors are bound by tradition and professional practice to save life, not to destroy it. Newspapers and the media had been quick to condemn Dr Cox as 'Doctor Death', and asked their readers if they would be happy to be treated by him in view of the fact that he might give patients injections which might kill them and they would not know it. Can a patient ever trust such a doctor again?

The right to die as such exists only for people who are conscious and can express themselves; for those, like Alex and Tony Bland, who cannot speak for themselves, their families and carers have to invoke the right 'in the patient's best interest'. The question is, inevitably, what is in someone's best interest? To clarify this, and make the process easier, the idea of 'Living Wills' or 'Advance Directives' has gained in popularity. Had Alex, Tony Bland, or anyone else in such a situation had such a document, it is possible that they might not have lived for so long, but since such documents are not (yet) legal in Britain, the families would still have had to go to court to have the feeding stopped.

As a society we are more and more conscious of our rights, and the Patient's Charter (Department of Health, 1991) has made patients more aware of their rights. But these are essentially rights of etiquette and courtesy and do not touch the fundamental rights of living and dying. The right to die remains more an idea than something which can be demanded. Campaigns to have this changed have existed for a long time: the Voluntary Euthanasia Society was founded in 1935, and entitles one of its leaflets '*The Last Right*' (1989). The nurse who drew attention to what Dr Cox had done 'called for changes which would mean no nurse in future had to face the persecution she suffered' (Fleet, 1992). It might not be a change in the law which could solve the problem of how to die well, but a change in attitude. When 'human beings revere life and accept death', then the values for decisions of what is in a person's best interest will also change. This may look like Utopia, but then the hospice movement alone has changed attitudes to death and dying considerably, and pressures from many sources do eventually bring about change.

The right to die, the right to live, as well as most other such rights, are at bottom a plea to be respected as a person, to be heard and to be taken seriously. If, in order to achieve this, we have to proceed by establishing rights, then this too must be taken seriously and considered. Rights will be further discussed in Chapters 4 and 5.

What is happening?

Making ethical decisions oneself and helping others to make ethical decisions is always demanding. The questions of counselling and ethics outlined in the first chapter forms a framework for decision-making. This chapter considers the various aspects of the principle of the value of life through the story of Alex. In any decision, all the principles are involved, but clearly often one principle dominates. Making decisions around the issues of life and death can only be highlighted by just one case, given that every case is different.

What is happening? is the fundamental question of response ethics as put forward by Niebuhr (1963) and is *the* fundamental question for any kind of understanding and helping. *What is happening?* leads to awareness, without which no change is possible. And making decisions means making changes. *What is happening*, then, that in certain areas of living the value of that living is challenged, or needs to be challenged, by us and by others?

The question *What is happening?* needs to be asked by all the people involved in a situation which has become problematic and which needs a decision in order to resolve it. The question therefore is here asked of the family, of Alex, and of the staff involved in her care.

Living means taking risks, and therefore accidents happen. However much one can explain every accident and trace every illness to a source, one can never eliminate some unforeseen events or untested theory. The people who end up in hospital on life-support systems would surely not have chosen this state for themselves. However, since science, medicine and technology have made it possible that life can be supported mechanically, to trust ourselves to them is now another risk we take.

The story of Alex shows how all the people around Alex were very hopeful that she would recover, but that gradually this hope faded. The best technology can so far only support life, not restore it when a part of it has been irretrievably lost. The difficulty is that this support can go on for years. The question is, what sort of life is this person living? As soon as we start putting adjectives to this life, we see the difficulty: is it a good life or a bad life, a useful life or a useless life, a worthwhile life or a worthless life? When the Tony Bland case made news, there were letters in the press and on radio from parents of patients in similar circumstances who said that they would do the same as his parents, and from others who said that they would never do the same.

Alex's parents, and in particular her sister, came to the conclusion that she was not really 'living' in the sense in which she had lived before the accident. They decided that in a way her soul or spirit – that which characterised her as the unique person she was – had already 'died'.

In the months of watching and waiting by her bedside and in their discussions at home, the mother in particular must have pondered many aspects of life. What *is* life? What is the soul? How had she given life to Alex? Would it be better for Alex to die, or better to live as now? Does Alex live on when she dies? How alive is she now? Had a mother the right to refuse life to her child? Would she be able to live with such a decision? Can and should the family make a decision about Alex? How would such a decision affect their friends and relations and the staff caring for her? Would such a decision have wider implications? These and similar thoughts will have gone through the minds of the three family members most closely involved with Alex. They will also have heard of other people who, like Alex, were in a coma for a very long time and then had died, or indeed recovered. They will have heard of cases where the parents had to take drastic steps to stop the feeding. They will have imagined what they might do or not do, and some of their imaginings must have been more fanciful than realistic. Some well-meaning friends may have advised them to do this, and others advised them to do the opposite.

Perhaps the most difficult aspect of it all was that any decision taken to end Alex's life was going to be irreversible; they would have to live with the consequences of their decision for the rest of their lives. Would they be able to do this?

What was happening to the family therefore was first of all a stocktaking of their own values, strengths and weaknesses. We can hear of suffering and it never affects us, but when we suffer ourselves, our lives are changed. This family was suffering because of and through Alex, and in this way it was their suffering. They will often have said to themselves and their friends that they were glad that they had time to think about it and consider every aspect again and again. While this was a blessing to them, it was also adding to their grief in that once a decision was taken it took so long to see it carried out.

The issues of euthanasia and the right to die must have been very thoroughly discussed among themselves. They had to consider carefully what was in Alex's best interest; to understand that they often had to imagine themselves in her position, and think or feel what they would like done to them were it happening to themselves. But that had the drawback that a decision was not disinterested. They needed to learn to be 'objective' *vis-à-vis* Alex and decide what would be in *her* best interest, not what they imagined to be in her interest, or even what they would have wished for themselves. They will have begun to appreciate that this is in fact one of the reasons why families are often not the best advocates and why lawyers are asked to decide for patients in such circumstances.

The question *What is happening?* makes it clear that for the parents and the family a great many things are happening concerning their values, attitudes and beliefs about themselves and about Alex. But they also realise more and more that this is not just a personal problem but one which affects society as a whole.

What is happening? also needs to be asked of Alex herself. She is the protagonist, or main character, of this drama, even though she cannot speak her role. It is clear that all decisions have to be made in her best interest, and therefore on her behalf, but it can be easy to consider her now like a 'thing' or a means rather than an end in herself. When a person is in a persistent vegetative state it is assumed that hearing and sight are no longer functioning and the sense of touch is also lost. But the 'body' which is here is still the same body to which everyone related before PVS was declared. The parents and Tam still kiss Alex, stroke her and hold her: there is still a relationship with Alex, and that needs to be respected and taken into consideration. Even with a diseased and 'unlively' body, Alex still communicates: what she communicates to those around her are that feelings, relationships, principles, theories, laws, values and meaning all contribute to what 'life' is about.*

What is happening? needs to be asked also by and of those who care for Alex: the nurses and doctors, physiotherapists, the social worker and those who took part in the case conferences. What are they contributing to Alex as a person, to this particular situation, and to the wider care for patients and the debate about and the understanding of such cases? What are they gaining for themselves from this care?

Their work is done within the setting of health care in a particular place and time. They work with certain given elements which they cannot change, such as the technology available to them, and others which they can change, such as the personal care which they give. Each person

*The British Medical Association has published guidelines on 'Persistent Vegetative State' in 1993 which are available from The Medical Ethics Committee Secretariat, BMA House, Tavistock Square, London WC1H 9JR.

involved brings his and her own beliefs, attitudes and values of health, suffering, life and death, and they may all differ slightly. Some may feel the same as the parents and Tam; some may feel that Alex should be kept alive for as long as is possible. The differences in attitudes may sometimes be difficult to accommodate, but they contribute to the debate about what is fitting and help to shape the decision.

All the people involved have their professional standards to consider and to keep to. These include their codes of practice or conduct. For nurses this is the UKCC (1992) *Code of Professional Conduct*, and particularly the stipulations to safeguard and promote the interests and well-being of individual patients and clients (Clause 1).

Nurses may, and often do, find that their personal beliefs and values are opposed to those they find in their clients and patients and among their colleagues. Such concerns need to be acknowledged and not glossed over or dismissed, otherwise all parties are diminished in their care.

The ethical concerns around the principle of the value of life have been addressed already, but it must be clear that each situation has its own unique aspects, problems and question which cannot be foreseen.

The other principles are necessarily touched upon also. The principle of goodness or rightness is involved, in that 'good' people should do 'right' actions. Are the people involved here 'good', and in what way are they 'good'? Are their actions 'right', and why are they 'right'? What does 'good' and 'right' mean in this situation? Perhaps more fundamentally one would need to ask, what is 'good' and what is 'right' here?

All of the health-care personnel need to know that their care is right: right in the way they do it, and right in the way it is received. It needs to be given for the right reasons.

Doctors usually feel that they have a duty to preserve life; this is what the Hippocratic tradition demands of physicians and they see it as the right way to use their skills. An ethic of duty (deontology) is often closely allied with medicine for this reason. Nursing, on the other hand, has generally sided with utilitarianism, concerning itself with the wider context of the individual patient's care.

Nursing has therefore often defended different values from those applied by medicine. In the case of Alex, it is clear that it was nursing care which sustained her after medical care could do no more. It was the nurses who were in touch with the family, and it was to the nurse that Tam turned when asking if she could attend the case conference. It is therefore important that the nursing voice is heard clearly when issues of good and right are addressed.

The principle of justice or fairness has already been touched upon above when considering euthanasia. Justice has always been a difficult area in health care. The NHS rests upon the principle of equality; that is, everybody can get health care at the point of need. With an increasing emphasis on economy this no longer means that everybody has the right to equal care, but that everybody should have equal access to care. The idea of QALYs (Quality Adjusted Life Years, see Chapter 7) was put forward by health economists and has been used in the NHS to judge the economic situation of patients and to determine where scarce medical resources should be employed (Crisp, 1991).

Most people would say that they don't like to be a burden on others, be this in terms of care or of money. In purely economic terms Alex was not a great burden on resources (nursing care is on the whole cheaper than medical care), but she did block a bed for a long time. We will always need to balance economy with ethics; can one really put a price on another person's life?

The principle of justice will need to be considered very carefully in this case, otherwise a decision could be made for entirely the wrong reasons and the good and the right might be severely jeopardised.

The principle of truth telling or honesty is important precisely for this reason: what are the motives for deciding one way or the other in any given situation?

> In his well-argued and sometimes controversial book The End of Life, *Rachels (1986) tries to clarify the distinction between killing and letting die. For this argument he uses the example of 'Smith'.*
> *'Smith stands to gain a large inheritance if anything should happen to his 6-year-old cousin. One evening while the child is taking his bath, Smith sneaks into the bathroom and drowns the child, and then arranges things so that it will look like an accident. No one is the wiser, and Smith gets his inheritance.'*
> *Stories of this kind abound, some being more plausible than others. They do, however, show that not only do the motives have to be honest, but the truth has to be spoken, too.*

The question *What is happening?* is asked in order to collect as much data as possible concerning the problem, so that a fitting decision can be taken. In the search to collect these data, the present, the past and the future all play a role, and memories are particularly strong motivators. Past events which have left painful scars, can influence the present in ways which we are often not aware of or try to hide. Most of us, too, make so many assumptions that it can be difficult to know what are the spoken or unspoken parts of relationships, or the visible or hidden agendas. The question *What is happening?* may be the most reliable question for finding out the truth of a situation, or the truth about people's views and values and the truth underlying many motives and relationships. Asking *What is happening?* is not necessarily a digging into people's last areas of privacy, but a persistent asking of the question may be the most helpful way of arriving gradually at a position which clarifies issues which may have seemed impenetrable before.

The principle of individual freedom, also referred to as 'autonomy', is put as the first principle in some ethical frameworks because, unless we have freedom, we cannot express ourselves as persons. To be moral we have to be free. 'Freedom must be built into any moral system in order for such a system to function properly' (Thiroux, 1980: 137). But freedom does not mean that 'anything goes'; our behaviour as citizens is everywhere bounded by laws. For individuals to express themselves individually, they must be free 'to choose their own ways and means of being moral *within the framework of the first four basic principles*' (Thiroux, 1980: 128). The responsibility so much stressed by Niebuhr is only possible when there is the freedom to choose to be responsible. Freedom to act in a given situation must be possible for all the people involved. In the case of Alex it is necessary that all concerned are free to act in their own individual way. This may mean freedom to express themselves, freedom to care and freedom to relate to one another in individual ways – as long as this freedom does not compromise the other principles.

'Paternalism' has become almost a dirty word in health care. The concept of paternalism (and maternalism) implied that the expert knew best and literally ruled over the lives of others in a god-like manner. If the excesses of this concept have gone, the finer aspects of it are still very much alive and well. It was still possible for the team around Alex to hold a case conference and only afterwards tell the family that they had done so. Tam had still to ask to take part in such a case conference; she was not invited. One may want to ask what the team was afraid of. If one person is free to speak his or her mind, then all must be free to do so. The more they can speak, the more they can hear and learn from one another, and thus the process of decision-making is helped.

Alex's parents realised early on that they did not have the freedom to remove her nasogastric tube, or not to feed her any more themselves. They did not have the freedom to interfere in her life. They did not have to be told this, their own sense of morality told them, even though they may never have heard of a principle of individual freedom. In discussion with the caring team this may have come to light, but it is clear that people can make fully ethical decisions without knowing any particular theories. When staff have to help patients, clients or friends and relatives to make ethical decisions it is advantageous if they have the vocabulary in order to make any decision more informed. But the language used must also be such as to be understood by all, otherwise the whole exercise is indeed paternalistic. The parents and sister of Alex must not only have but be given the freedom to act ethically as they understand it, and decide as they see fit in their circumstances (after considering all relevant aspects, principles and theories). Only with this last principle of freedom considered can the other principles make sense.

What is the meaning of it?

The question *What is happening?* is asked with the aim of reaching a *fitting answer*. The reasons for which these questions have to be asked vary considerably: some may be technical (does a diagnosis of carcinomatosis in a person warrant a particular treatment?); and some may be emotional (does the relationship between mother and daughter influence the decision to withdraw life support?). Whatever answer is given in response to *What is happening?*, it will affect all the people concerned. After all is said and done, they are left with feelings and emotions which mark them. When asking such important questions we must be aware that there will always be more to the questions than mere words convey.

When we are faced with any kind of suffering we are faced with ourselves. If suffering is anything other than senseless, then it has to have some *meaning* for us. According to Frankl (1962), we do not invent the meaning of our existence, but we detect it (p. 101). He goes on to say that 'suffering ceases to be suffering in some way at the moment it finds a meaning, such as the meaning of a sacrifice' (p. 115).

When asking *What is happening?*, we are asking for self-awareness, and that may uncover much that we may never have considered about ourselves or dared to acknowledge. When Alex's mother asked herself the many questions about life, she may have realised that she might never have asked these questions – at least not in the same way – had she not been forced to by her circumstances. If anybody had asked her what was happening to her, she would probably have answered that she was trying to understand what was going on by asking herself dozens of questions.

To ask *What is happening?* is not simply a question of curiosity or a necessary first step in a process. By asking another person that question we commit ourselves to that person because we have to stay and listen to the answer. And listening *means* hearing deeply what is being said, and responding to it. The helping relationship is thus formed already. When we want to help someone, we have to listen in particular to the feelings expressed; they convey the *meaning* and need *meaning* to make them legitimate. Alex's mother may well have been angry with the boyfriend who presumably had a part to play in the accident which killed him and all but killed Alex. But she could not vent her anger on the boyfriend because he was not there. Some people might have internalised their anger in such a way that they would become angry personalities, or become physically or mentally ill. The meaning of their suffering might therefore be to perpetuate the suffering.

What is the meaning of it? – that is, of Alex's suffering – for Tam, her sister, was very different from the meaning for her mother. Tam grew to be the spokesperson for the family, the one who conveyed decisions and information. She saw in the situation in which she found herself a chance to develop a personality of confidence, of advocate and of go-between. Indeed, she went on to study law as a result of this experience.

When we ask *What is the meaning of it?* for Alex, the main person concerned, we cannot answer, but that very question was the one which sparked off the quest for understanding and the decision to ask that life support should be withdrawn. Until that decision could be made, to ask what the situation *meant* for Alex was the guiding force. In order to act in Alex's best interest, the meaning of that interest for her had to be gradually understood and also internalised not only by the immediate family but also by those caring for her.

When the health-care team asks *What is the meaning of it?*, they have to ask that question of themselves personally and collectively. What is the meaning of their care and of the kind of care they give? What *meaning* do they see in their responsibilities, in their duties, their policies, their involvement with the patient and her family and friends? It is possible to see this as an intellectual exercise to sharpen practice and make it more relevant and appropriate; but it is also possible to see in this question a deeper understanding, that of each person's own response to the situation. Why is each person in the job she or he is in? What satisfaction does each get from doing this work? Do they see it as a duty (in the sense of a religious 'vocation', perhaps) to humanity, or to fulfil their own inner needs, or as a kind of insurance policy (it may happen to me one day and I would like to have the same sort of care then as I give now)?

All the people who cared for Alex were touched by that care. No one who cares for another can be untouched: we are not islands, but 'a part of the maine', of society. Each person has to answer that question for himself or herself. It may not all happen at the same time and to the same degree, because each person has their own agenda to work to.

Meaning and *meanings* change throughout life. If this accident had not happened, none of the people involved would have had to relate to Alex in the way in which they were forced to. The suffering caused by this accident is unique, and therefore the meaning presented to each person by this suffering is also unique. The people who cared for Alex might feel more committed to the care of the dying, to changing policies regarding care, to euthanasia or opposition to euthanasia, or to something quite unrelated to this case but which suddenly presented itself as part of their work. The family, on the other hand, will always be marked by this tragedy. The father faded into the background, the mother sparked much discussion by her questioning of values, and Tam decided upon a career which would also mark her life. For each of them the *meaning* they had found in that situation brought consequences which marked them. But for each also, new *meanings* would present themselves at later stages of life.

What is the fitting answer?

The 'answer' to Alex's condition was a request to stop her life support. But it took well over a year until this answer was reached. In this case, this decision was seen to be fitting. It is not necessarily the right (deontology), the best (or good; teleology), the most useful or the most convenient answer; but it is the most fitting, because it alone fits into an interaction of response and anticipation of further responses.

In the 1960s, situation ethics was considered to be a major advance on the more law-centred approaches to medical ethics. Situation ethics (Fletcher, 1955) advocated a person-centred approach whose only obligation was love and whose implication was that each situation must make its own rules. This was a new idea and gave much freedom to some, but left many people very dissatisfied because it left them with little or no guidance on what 'love' meant when they most needed it.

The response ethics advocated here certainly has many elements in common with situation ethics, but it also differs in certain important ways: the idea of responding is central and means that there is dialogue with all those concerned; the pattern of responsibility is a simple but clear framework that has as its aim a *social solidarity* – that is, something must come out of a situation which leaves all the people involved with more understanding and more ability to respond to life in general than before the problem arose; and the notions of interpretation and accountability 'earth' the present situation in the person's past and future life.

The *fitting answer* is not arrived at arbitrarily. Those who give the fitting answer will have made their choice freely, having considered all the alternatives. But that choice is arrived at bounded by what is right and good, just and fair, truthful and honest and most contributing to the value of life. The people making the choice will have considered aspects of duty and ideas such as 'the greatest good for the greatest number'. When the response to all these aspects has been considered, and these aspects in turn have been 'heard' for the weight they have, then the *fitting answer* may be as Alex's family chose, or it may be the opposite, or yet some other possibility.

The *fitting answer* for Alex will have included considerations of what it means for her to have life support withdrawn; what this implies for the family; what the consequences are for other patients in similar situations; what the consequences are for medicine and nursing and for medical technology: in this case it may seem like a rejection of technology. The case may start a debate on the topic 'Just because we have the technology, does it mean that we have to use it?' This could be part of the *fitting answer* and it could also be part of the meaning. Thus we see that the process works not only in a linear direction forwards, but also backwards – or rather, circularly.

The pattern of responsibility

Niebuhr recognised the pattern of responsibility as 'a relatively precise instrument for self-understanding' which has realistic possibilities and limitations. Its possibilities are used here to summarise the main points of each chapter.

Response, the first element of the pattern, here indicated that all the parties involved had to learn to communicate with one another. The impact of the accident on Alex's family was considerable, and it was particularly the mother who sparked off discussions about living and dying by her diverse questions: her response to the situation was one of questioning, and this helped to clarify what was happening.

Interpretation meant that some of the questions asked by the family led to considerable self-awareness. It was not enough to ask the questions; they had to be answered, too. That meant interpreting past events in the light of the present, understanding how each deals with the situation in the light of what they had learned in the past, and seeing new meaning in behaviour, character and possible ways of fulfilling themselves. This was perhaps best shown by Tam's attitude and decisions.

The question *What is happening?* means what is happening *now*, but also, What has happened so far that brought us to where we are now? This question will have pointed to many areas of meaning of life, death, suffering, happiness and the many personal values held or changed by each person.

Interpretation here also meant looking at issues such as euthanasia, rights, theories and principles, and ideas such as duty, responsibility, utility, good, right, truth, justice and freedom. It was significant that the family took a long time to come to the final answer which was *fitting* for them, but nobody pushed them to make up their minds – at least, not the people concerned with Alex's care – and they knew they could cope with the feelings they were eventually left with. Had it been otherwise, the consequences might have been mental, physical and spiritual suffering, and this might have been just as demanding on the family and society as Alex's care was.

Accountability here means in effect asking, what would happen if . . .? What would happen if nothing were done? or if someone simply pulled out the tube? or poured some medicine down the tube? or stopped visiting? Can the family live with the decision – whatever it is? Does the family decide, or the medical team? And what should be the fitting response? If and when life support is withdrawn, what will the dying be like? Can the family cope with dying which may take some time? Should there not be other possible ways of dying than starvation? What could be done about that?

The past, the present and the future are all combining at this moment to find the fitting response to what has happened.

Social solidarity is a wider conclusion than that reached by simply asking what has happened? or by making an evaluation. Not only should all the people immediately involved in this situation feel that their effort in coming to the fitting answer was worthwhile, but they should also feel that their decision will have advanced society in its thinking and acting. The personal responsibility which each brought means that values are clearer, new meanings have emerged, persons have been affirmed through dialogue, and the interpretations made have formed a 'society' that is worthwhile. The interpretations constantly given to responses made on every side will have led the people involved to a more consistent way of acting and reacting – in other words, they are ethically more aware and capable.

All this will have happened around a person who was suffering and was allowed to die. It could then be said that her suffering and death was not in vain. Interpreting her life in hospital in this way could be giving it a meaning which might never have been visible before.

Alex's life did not make the headlines in the way that Tony Bland's did. His living and dying sparked off discussions, responses and interpretations of issues that might never have happened otherwise. His suffering, too, could be seen as not being in vain. Tony's suffering touched a whole nation; Alex's only a small part of it. It may not be the quantity which counts in the end, but the quality.

Chapter 3
The principle of
the value of life (2)

Story

Sarah and Daniel were both 32 and had been married for a few years but did not have any children. They decided that they would rather try every possible 'natural' way to conceive a child and would not consider in-vitro fertilisation. They kept to a healthy diet, they meditated and they had both also had hypnotherapy. When Sarah did finally get pregnant, they were overjoyed.

Sarah and Daniel had discussed every aspect of her pregnancy with the midwife, including the fact that there might be a small risk of the baby being handicapped. They declined scans and invasive tests; they had done it the 'natural' way so far, and they wanted to continue in this way, fully aware of any risks they were taking.

Samuel was a little late and rather heavy on his arrival. He did not cry immediately and there was a silence which seemed to last for ever just after he was born. Sarah was aware of this and did wonder what was going on. Finally Samuel did start to cry – or rather to whimper, and he was handed to Sarah to hold: the moment she had been waiting for had arrived. She cried as she held her son in her arms.

The midwife who had been with Sarah throughout her pregnancy and labour seemed rather embarrassed. She would have to tell Sarah that Samuel had distinct Down's syndrome features. This was not the first time she had had to do this, and she did it as well and as gently as she could. The midwife asked for the consultant to come and she was there within the hour and could only confirm what the midwife had already said.

The next few hours revealed what was feared: that Samuel also had oesophageal atresia and a severe heart defect. A few tests and X-rays all confirmed the diagnosis of Down's syndrome. Sarah and Daniel were not really prepared for this although they had known that it might happen. Actually seeing it was so shocking that they could not really take it in. They were silent together for a long time while Samuel tried ineffectually to suck at Sarah's breast.

The consultant and the midwife talked with each other about what their next move would be. They felt that they needed to tell the parents exactly what were the possibilities and the probabilities of Samuel leading anything like a normal life. His multiple abnormalities would require many operations, and the severity of the syndrome meant that he would have a very poor quality of life. The choice was between operating within a very short space of time, or not operating and letting the child die. They also agreed that the parents should have a little time to think about it, and perhaps to sleep on it. The consultant would give the main explanations, but the midwife would be there as long and as often as the parents needed to talk. She would try not to coerce them into making a decision which they might regret.

This was put to the parents and they were pleased to have this arrangement. Daniel was offered a bed in the same room as Sarah so that they could stay and talk together.

After much talking, crying, thinking, hugging and also laughing, Sarah and Daniel decided that they had wanted this baby so much that they would like it to have as much of a life as possible. They had not wanted any tests which might have led to an abortion, and they felt now that they could not act in any other way than the one they had chosen in the first instance. Samuel was theirs, and his life was as precious as theirs. This decision would completely alter their life together. Despite the first shock, they loved him dearly already – they had indeed loved him since the moment he was conceived.

Two days later Samuel had the first operation to release the atresia. In his first year he had four operations, but by then he was beginning to feel and seem more like a normal child.

Later on, other handicaps came to light, and Samuel died when he was 7 years old. Sarah and Daniel never felt that they had made the wrong decision, although they often found it very hard to live with.

The setting

In 1981 the paediatrician Dr Leonard Arthur made history by prescribing 'nursing care only' and dihydrocodeine for a newborn infant with Down's syndrome. On learning of the diagnosis, the baby's mother had totally rejected him and Dr Arthur did not challenge her feelings or reasoning. He was tried for attempted murder but was acquitted.

Since scans, amniocentesis and other tests of pregnancy have been available, it has been routine to offer them to any woman who might be at all at risk. If there is any risk of a positive test, the woman is automatically offered an abortion. To decline to have the tests might be considered to be folly. It takes courage to say 'no' and to stick to one's convictions. Some of the 'no'-sayers may be justified, if some recent studies are considered (McTaggart, 1993). Sarah did not decide on the basis of any statistics, but only on that of her own beliefs and convictions. The fact that the technology is available does not yet mean that it has to be used. The 'right to say no' (Dickson, 1982: 32) (as well as 'yes') may need to be taken as seriously as the other rights promulgated in the area of health care.

Amniocentesis may seem positively old-fashioned when compared to the range of genetic tests which are and may shortly be available. Sex selection is possible and has been advocated for hereditary diseases such as Huntington's disease, and may be available to eliminate Alzheimer's disease and determine the sexual orientation of a person. It seems as if it is only a very short step to having a designer baby: eye and hair colour of one's choice, height set at a particular level, this and that disease ruled out, and presumably dying when it is most convenient. While this may sound fanciful, the possibility of its becoming reality is distinctly there. The summary of the principle of the value of life, 'Human beings should revere life and accept death', could be an encouraging dictum here, rather than a frightening one of what technology might do next.

We cannot escape the debate about economy in this story either: is it fair that a handicapped child should have many operations and treatments when it is reasonably certain that he is either not going to live long, or not be able to lead a life which could in any way be described as 'normal'? Should Sarah and David subject their child to all these operations? Having not wanted any tests during pregnancy, should they now be consistent with their views of wanting everything done 'naturally' and let the child die naturally?

These are some of the questions which might be asked, and perhaps should be asked, in order to understand the problem from every possible position. The question underlying this is, however, a much deeper one: what is a person? This is a philosophical question about which volumes have been written. To get the question in perspective, just a few aspects of this debate should be mentioned here.

What is a 'person'?

Pettifer (in Campbell, 1987: 204) states that, since Descartes, the starting point for thinking about human beings was 'to see the defining character of the person as being rationality'. He is quick to point out that this is a false starting point, since 'to focus on rationality alone is to separate thinking from emotion and from the springs of action'.

A person can be defined as an individual or as a self, but neither gives a total picture. 'We become persons through our relations with other persons, that is, through our participation in community.' It could be said that we are individuals, have a self and become persons. In philosophical terms, it is important not to confuse the term 'person' with notions of 'human being' or even with 'human life'.

Warren (1973, in Johnstone, 1989: 240) gives a list of five criteria which must be satisfied for an entity to be a person:

1 consciousness (of objects and events external and/or internal to the being), and in particular the capacity to feel pain;
2 reasoning (the *developed* capacity to solve new and relatively complex problems);
3 self-motivated activity (activity which is relatively independent of either genetic or direct external control);
4 the capacity to communicate, by whatever means, messages of an indefinite variety of types – that is, not just with an indefinite number of possible contents, but on indefinitely many possible topics;
5 the presence of self-concepts, and self-awareness, either individual or racial, or both.

The definition of 'person' is important, as this determines how we think about abortion, euthanasia, the mentally handicapped or ill, and the medical treatments or interventions which we consider appropriate or not. This simple outline does not really do justice to the massive literature on the subject, but merely indicates that it is a central issue in this and other ethical concerns at the beginning and end of life.

The concept of 'respect for the person' has usually been seen as the basic principle of morality, since other issues, such as justice, truth and freedom, are based on the fact that people are beings who can think, decide and act morally.

The next step is to consider the 'right to life', as this concerns those people whose status as 'persons' is questioned.

The right to life

The doctrine of the sanctity of life has held that all human life is of equal worth.

> All human lives must be regarded as having an equal claim to preservation simply because life is an irreducible value. Therefore the value of a particular life, over and above the value of life itself, may not be taken into account. (Kadish, 1977, in Kuhse and Singer, 1985)

The debate about the 'right to life' challenges this view.

In his book *The End of Life* (1986), Rachels bases his arguments on a distinction he makes between 'having a life' and merely 'being alive'. 'Being alive, in the biological sense, is relatively unimportant. One's *life*, by contrast, is immensely important; it is the sum of one's aspirations, decisions, activities, projects, and human relationships' (p. 5).

He cites the case of a couple who had been married for over thirty years when the wife began to show signs of Alzheimer's disease. She deteriorated to the point where she was reduced to screaming 'fire' and 'pain' all day. Her husband could not bear this any longer and shot her.

Rachels does not condone killing, but he could not condemn this man for the action he took. The wife was alive in the biological sense but not in the biographical: she could not any longer live any of her aspirations, make decisions, pursue activities and projects and maintain human relationships. Was her husband therefore not right to judge as he had done? To kill someone in cold blood is very different from killing in this and similar situations.

Rachels is concerned to 'debunk' (his word) irrelevant distinctions in traditional doctrines. One of them concerns the criteria applied to new-born infants with Down's syndrome. He says that 'duodenal atresia is not part of Down's syndrome; it is only a condition that sometimes *accompanies* it. When duodenal atresia is present, a decision might be made to let the baby die. But when there is no intestinal blockage (or other similar defect requiring surgery), other Down's babies live on. Let us focus on this fact: *some Down's infants, with duodenal atresia, die, while other Down's infants, without duodenal atresia, live.* This, I wish to suggest, is irrational' (1986: 110). Helga Kuhse and Peter Singer, two philosophers who made history all over the German-speaking part of Europe in 1989 with their lecture tour on 'Practical ethics', also point out a similar situation. They say that 'in accepting abortion, as so many Western nations have now done, we have already taken a major step away from the traditional principle of the sanctity of human life. We have, however, come to place great weight on a boundary line – the moment of birth – that, while clear and precise, is not really crucial from the point of view of the fetus' or infant's moral status. The move to a less precise, but more significant boundary – the point at which there is self-awareness and a sense of the future – is therefore not as big a step as one might at first think.' Kuhse and Singer were accused of being the Nazis of the 1980s, and their lectures were cancelled in many towns amid huge protests. Their criteria for 'humanhood' are similar to Rachels', and include 'self-awareness, self-control, a sense of the future, a sense of the past, the capacity to relate to others, concern for others, communication and curiosity'. A baby with Down's syndrome – or other serious handicap – will most likely not be able to fulfil all of these criteria. Should such a baby, therefore, have the same right to life as one who can fulfil them?

The notion of the 'potential' is also argued here. A normal infant has the potential to fulfil the above criteria, but a handicapped infant may not. 'Is it not this potential that distinguishes the normal infant from the severely handicapped infant, and gives the former, at least, a right to life?' ask Kuhse and Singer.

All this is easy to argue in the abstract and in philosophical terms. Parents and health-care professionals, however, are there when such decisions have to be taken. Doyle (1992) describes one mother's 'unhappy story'. She and her husband believed 'that more account should have been taken of the quality of Dominic's life, and of their parental request 'for no further intervention' . . . . However difficult and traumatic it is to decide to stop treatment, nothing can compare with the anguish that dominates the lives of parents with a severely handicapped child.' The potential of a handicapped child is not only for that child's life, but concerns also the lives of those around him or her. Perhaps the parents do indeed know better than any doctrines or philosophers, what the *fitting answer* is in any given situation?

Another point about the right to life is made by Meilaender (1993), who makes a distinction between 'someone who' and 'someone which': 'To have a life is to be. . . a living body whose natural history has a trajectory. It is to be a someone who has a history, not a someone with certain capacities or characteristics.' He questions Rachels, who never explains, for example, why 'one's period of decline is not part of one's personal history, one's biography'. He would point out that Alex's biography (in the story in Chapter 2) did not end when she had the accident, but that it continued for another two years and more. That was part of the tragedy of her life. Thus Samuel in this story is 'someone who' has a life, and a biography – albeit one which he may not be aware of or tell others about; he is not simply 'someone with' Down's syndrome. Meilaender makes his point because he believes that 'personhood defined in terms of the right autonomously to determine one's future [is in danger of giving] way to personhood defined in terms of the present possession of certain capacities'. In the case of Samuel, it is his parents and those who care for him who determine his future, rather than he himself, but the point stressed by Meilaender is that the *body* itself matters, not just what the body can or cannot do.

Many of these doctrines and views are shaped by religion and culture. Ethics today is trying to be 'general' and not bound by particular views. However, religion and culture are in the 'collective unconscious' as much as in the individual consciousness, and colour our behaviour significantly. It is often pointed out that in ancient Greece, infanticide was not only practised but also advocated for children born deformed or handicapped. Sarah and Daniel, as their names might suggest, were Jewish, and that may have been influential in their decision to let Samuel live. In a transcultural study of ethical behaviour among nurses, Norberg *et al.* (1994) found, for example, that nurses in Israel were more likely to feed severely demented patients than would nurses in Sweden. They justified this by expressly citing the principle of the sanctity of life.

This chapter stands under the heading of the principle of the *value* of life. The sanctity of life, argues Thiroux (1980), is too closely bound up with religious doctrines and the sometimes dogmatic views associated with them. To refer to this principle as the *value* of life, therefore, may take in all the points raised above, and consider them in the effort of finding the fitting answer.

There are injunctions against killing in all the known systems of ethics. But throughout history – and religious history in particular – one people has looked down on another, one nation has considered a neighbour inferior to itself, with slavery perhaps the most obvious example. Killing the 'other' was never considered to be as serious as killing one's own kin. We may need to be clear what we mean by a 'right to life', as many aspects influence our thinking and acting.

What is happening?

This question stands logically at the beginning of the ethical decision-making process. Without it, we are inclined to rush into other people's lives where angels fear to tread because it is none of their business.

What is happening to the parents, the child and the staff involved here? A short outline of the main possibilities may help. The *parents* had been longing for a child and, by following their own values of naturalness, did not want any tests. The most appropriate test might have been amniocentesis, which might have revealed that the fetus would be born with Down's syndrome. But even the best test cannot be totally accurate, and theirs might also have been the one exception where the result might have been negative. The fact is that Samuel *was* born with severe Down's syndrome, including other physical defects. They are now faced with the decision as to whether he should be allowed to die, or be allowed to live. If any tests might have been positive, they might have had to make a similar decision earlier. They might still have made the same decision as now.

As well as rationalising what might have been, feelings of guilt play a very strong part at this early moment: guilt at not having wanted to have the tests; having followed their own values rather than those of everybody else who saw tests as the norm; at being different and wanting to be different; wanting to pursue their values now rather than conform; and making a child live when everybody said it would not have much of a life. These thoughts may be in the minds of the parents, the midwives and the friends and family around them – or if they are not, they may soon be put there. Such pressures can be strong but very subtle. When considering *What is happening?* these points, too, must be looked at if they are present. If they are not present, it may have to be stated that they are not present, because assumptions are usually made by all concerned, but rarely voiced.

The parents are at a crucial stage in their lives when a long-awaited child is born; this will alter their relationship with each other in any case. Having now to make a decision of such magnitude will mark them for life. If they are close and communicate well, then they will think very similarly and come to a unanimous decision fairly easily. They will know what aspects they have to discuss, and they will do it without much help.

It is more likely that they are too shocked even to begin to think. This is when they will need, and probably appreciate, help from the midwife, the consultant, or anyone else who is significant at that moment. Although a decision is needed, it does not have to be taken in five minutes. Whoever helps them to decide will need to know how much time is available, and in this way they can all work together.

What is happening? has to be asked also of the child, Samuel, himself. He is not able to answer for himself, and therefore the deliberations about him have to be all the more careful. What rights does he have? What is in his best interest? This is the area where the feelings and thoughts of the mother are of particular importance; she has formed a relationship with him during her pregnancy, and her reactions at his birth are of paramount importance. Sarah and Daniel had both said that they had loved Samuel from before his birth. Despite the moment of fear, or perhaps because of it, they now felt that they loved him still, whatever he looked like or might turn out to be. But in their discussions they will have to consider the points made above about the right to life.

The staff, the midwives and doctors who care for Sarah and Daniel, however briefly, also need to be considered in the question *What is happening?* They have their own feelings and opinions, which they need to express. The birth of any child, let alone a handicapped child, affects them too. By helping the parents, in whatever way they can, to come to a decision, their presence and professional care (in this instance, also the ability to help in ethical decision-making) are perhaps more important than many of them might admit. Their professional responsibility is their response-*ability* at this time and in these circumstances.

In the question *What is happening?* are included all the points made above about the ethics of living and dying, and letting live and letting die. Every situation will bring to the surface many more aspects and questions than could even be mentioned here. Some of these points are so deeply embedded in the cultural psyche that it takes a great deal of discussing and searching even to notice them, let alone challenge them. The principle of the value of life is particularly questioned here. The summary of the principle, 'Human beings should revere life and accept death', may be a good starting point. Those who help others to make ethical decisions need to have that essential quality of all helpers: a non-judgemental attitude;

revering life, but not at all costs, and accepting death, but not blithely, means starting from a non-judgemental basis. No ethical theory is value-free so that it could be applied whatever the circumstances. We can only use the best possible model for helping and whatever communication skills are available to be with another person at a decisive moment.

This story is here considered under the principle of the value of life rather than any other principle. The main point of the story is about life and how to regard it and treat it. When we are responsible for the lives of others at a crucial moment, then we do need to be aware of our feelings, values, beliefs, attitudes and ways of thinking. We need to have at least some ideas about the discussions around the issues involved.

The midwife and the consultant considered together what they would do and say. This is one way in which they had already asked *What is happening between us?* If they communicate well, then there is no fear in taking a stance, but they do not impose it. Their own self-awareness will mean that they are each able to respect the lives of others in such a way that they can help in an individual way but also in a common way.

The principle of goodness or rightness must be in the mind of everybody who is concerned with this case. What is the right thing to do here? What is the best thing to do? These questions are not excluded in response ethics, even though they might not be regarded as the best questions, since they stem from systems which may be rather limiting. But if people are 'good' and their actions 'right', then these questions are also on their minds.

It is 'right' to ask these questions as part of *What is happening?* because they help to shape the final question, *What is the fitting answer?*

With the principle of justice or fairness we are back again into the topic of health-care economics. Is it right that a baby like Samuel should be allowed to live, possibly for only a few years, and have many operations and spend much time in hospital, being cared for by people other than his parents?

In 1993 there were some heated debates in the media and in medical journals, sparked off by the case of a patient who was refused a coronary bypass operation on the premise that he was a heavy smoker. The use and misuse of scarce resources in health care suddenly made headlines. *The Independent* carried an editorial with the headline 'Only saints need apply for NHS treatment', and said that 'the through-put of hospitals could be reduced to a fraction of the present levels if all those suffering from self-inflicted illnesses or injuries were refused treatment'. Justice is more than simply economics, but whenever the topic is discussed today, money is not far away. The argument might therefore be that because Sarah and Daniel had chosen this 'selfish' or un-saintly path, they should be denied the further care for Samuel which the NHS would be obliged to give if they decided that Samuel should live.

When considering the principle of truth-telling or honesty in this case we see that there are no problems here, at least not obvious ones. All concerned acted with integrity. A difficulty might arise if Sarah and Daniel decided to let Samuel live because they had been made to feel guilty or were otherwise put under pressures which might make them decide against their instincts or better judgements. If at that stage they were not able to be truthful with each other and with the staff, then their decision might indeed not be fitting. Not only would they then regret the decision, but as they have to live with it, one can only imagine what sort of consequences this might have on their personal lives and on those around them.

This principle is the one which many people simplistically feel to be the most straightforward – truth is truth and anything less is not acceptable – but this is far from the case. Truth comes in many shades and is easily compromised. Our dealings with one another are delicate. If we want to maintain relationships, then we have to negotiate between revealing and concealing ourselves and our thoughts. Truth is not always 'the whole truth and nothing but the truth', but truth gradually comes to light and is then accepted or rejected according to what someone can manage. Whatever truth has come to light should be accepted along with the person concerned.

The principle of individual freedom is perhaps the most visible principle after the main one of the value of life. Sarah and Daniel had chosen the way in which they wanted to manage the pregnancy, and their decision now demonstrates their freedom to choose for Samuel in their way, despite any pressures or 'oughts' put upon them. The story shows that Samuel died when he was only 7 years old, and the lives of Sarah and Daniel had been very different while Samuel was alive from what they had envisaged before his birth. This, too, was part of their choice. They may often have sighed with the burden of that choice. But when they looked back over their years with Samuel, they said that they would choose the same way again. Something within them made them choose in that way, and they had to respect that 'something'. Some people may call that 'something' God, the soul, or the self – whatever name we give it, it is that to which we respond and which ultimately gives meaning to our lives and thus has to be obeyed.

What is the meaning of it? _____

Making ethical decisions is not only about ethics. It is about being human and expressing that humanity. When helping others to come to a decision we need to have some basic helping or counselling skills. By starting with the basic question, *What is happening?*, we are also starting with the basic question of counselling. Unless we hear the story we cannot help.

Rogers (1975) outlined the three basic elements of counselling as congruence, warmth and empathy. By congruence he means an honesty which makes people relate to each other openly. Warmth points to a liking of each other which shows itself in interest and acceptance, and empathy takes this a step further and shows a 'way of living' which responds to the other at a level which fosters the person.

At some time during the process of finding out what is happening, most people will be asking something about the sense of the ethical challenge. Why did this happen? Why did it happen to me? Such questions rarely have an answer which satisfies. It is only when we actually discover a meaning in it that an event can be accepted and used in the sense of enhancing rather than destroying life. When congruence, warmth and empathy are present when someone is helped to make an ethical decision, then the many questions which inevitably arise can be considered carefully, one by one. Helping others to make ethical decisions is not simply a technical process, but is often a way of getting to know oneself differently. Being under pressure in a situation can concentrate the mind for some, but scatter it for others. The use of the twin skills of ethical decision making and counselling can then help a person to more effective living.

Sarah and Daniel were given the opportunity to have time together soon after Samuel was born and to talk with each other and also with the consultant. Naturally, they were shocked when Samuel was born handicapped. They may also have been very tired, but the new situation made them face themselves in new ways. Once they had said to each other that they had always loved Samuel, they could not reject him and let him die. Perhaps in their discussions they had never asked themselves the actual question, *What is the meaning of it?*, but the question was there anyway and their discussion turned around it. The *meaning*, as much as one can guess, was for them what life – and, in particular *their* life – was about. Their life was being challenged by the life of Samuel. He was their question, so to speak, and they answered that question by their own lives.

In the months and years of Samuel's short life they may have needed to discover that *meaning* again and again; or it may have presented itself differently to them at different times. But for them to have lived out their first commitment to Samuel, they will have had to have a good sense of some *meaning*, otherwise they might have given up their care and love for him. In the hours after his birth they may have had only a small glimmer of a sense of *meaning*, but that was enough then. Their 'gut instinct' to let Samuel live must have come already out of a deep sense of *meaning* of and for something; hence the importance of accepting such instincts.

What is the fitting answer?

All the foregoing discussion shows that the fitting answer for Sarah and Daniel was the only one they could make if they wanted to be true to themselves and their beliefs and values. Another couple might have decided the opposite. Indeed, this was the case in the situation in which Dr Arthur had found himself. Because he respected the mother's gut reaction he had got into trouble. For him too, the *fitting answer* was respecting the mother and her feelings rather than persuading her otherwise. The principle of the value of life means that we revere life – respect the person – and accept death. Others may indeed question our actions, but individual freedom gives us the right to act as we see fit *so long as that freedom is bounded by all the other principles*. We cannot be responsible *for* someone else, but we must be responsible *to* others, and our ability to respond humanely and effectively is seen in our responsibility.

The pattern of responsibility

The *response* in the pattern is, first of all, a physical and emotional response. The first response to a handicapped child might indeed be a rejection, as had happened in the Arthur case. The story here relates that there was a moment's silence after Samuel's birth, and Sarah must have experienced fear: what is wrong? The response at seeing a deformed child is likely to be a strong and very basic one: either revulsion or compassion, perhaps born out of the fear that the worst might come true.

When it is one's own child, an additional feeling may also be revulsion at one's own body for producing such a child. The physical response is instinctive rather than rational, but it comes out of deep emotions and is finally expressed in feelings. Fear is one of the feelings which must always be considered, as it drives people more strongly than many imagine or admit.

The *interpretation* aspect of the pattern highlights the awareness which follows the first response. A gut reaction has to be interpreted by the mind in order to be understood and accepted. Interpreting a person's feelings and reactions, and the pattern which, over a lifetime, has shaped them, is the starting point for further responses. As one person responds to another, so each one's response is based on interpretations made of the earlier response.

The diversity of individuals becomes visible here. Each person responds differently and this enhances any argument. The total understanding of a particular situation comes to light in dialogue; but it is also often the downfall of relationships: we don't think and act like anyone else. When others think and act differently from ourselves, we are often quick to condemn. When we ask *What is happening?* we may also have to take into account our own prejudices, blind spots and emotional shortcomings.

The question about the future life of the child touches on the *accountability* mentioned in the pattern. Having considered their thoughts and feelings and interpreted them, all concerned now look forward, anticipating 'objections, confirmations and corrections' (Niebuhr, 1963: 64). They 'take into account' what might be their actions, attitudes and values of tomorrow. In any ethical decision making, these will affect other people, and in this case it is the child, Samuel, who will live out the consequences of his parents' choice. The way in which all concerned feel about the future and convey these feelings and thoughts to one another will also shape it. If a future is envisaged in which the child is able to develop, he probably will. Otherwise, prophecies of difficulties and doom may become self-fulfilling. The consequences of fear can be powerful motivators for good or ill.

The *social solidarity* which Niebuhr describes is more than just a simple evaluation; it means that the whole process of deciding should leave the people involved with more insight and more ability to cope and decide ethically. In this way, everyone should have gained. The process of asking *What is happening?* should be helping all concerned, and this in turn should pervade society. This is clearly an ideal – but ethics is also about ideals and how to achieve them eventually.

When asking *What is happening?* we are engaging in dialogue, or responding to each other, and this may not always be easy. In talking about an ethical situation we lay ourselves open to misunderstandings and misinterpretations. Many of our views and values may not be clearly formed; most of them are open to be challenged and changed. Many people feel that professionals have or should have clear views and that they can help and advise people because of such views. But professionals are not superhumans – thank goodness. Stories of nurses and midwives crying with patients and clients are not rare any more. When we can be human with those who are human with us, and vulnerable with those who are vulnerable, then we have already achieved one kind of *social solidarity*: that of *co-humanity*, which Niebuhr describes as the basis of his response ethics.

Chapter 4
The principle of
goodness or rightness (1)

Story

Rose is a staff midwife in a large city hospital. She has been in the
same job for many years, for a while working part-time. She has
four young children to whom she is very devoted and who she was
keen should 'turn out well'. Her values about life, family and work
are based on a deep Christian commitment, nurtured in her large
family of West Indian origin. Her mother lives nearby, and her
children are always welcome there when Rose is at work.

Living in this large town means that Rose cares for many young
single mothers. When she asks these 'children' (as she sees them)
what is happening to the baby, some of them seem detached and
say that they are giving the baby away for adoption. In her concern
and as part of her care, Rose always asks the mothers if they have
really thought this option through well enough. In conversation,
Rose often hears that in fact there is a family – parents, aunts – who
would be willing to have the baby, but the mothers would not
consider this option. They are young and want to be free and not
be encumbered with a baby. They also feel that it would reduce
their marriage prospects.

Rose always feels in a quandary in these situations: her own
background is very similar to that of these mothers, and she knows
how much she has benefited from it. She wants to help by making
the mothers see that they have a duty to their babies and that they
should keep them. Later in life they might bitterly regret having

given their child away. But she also knows that she cannot impose her ideas; if she tried, she would be rebuffed. Her life experience is valuable to her and she wants to use it, but the values of society and her profession ask for information, not persuasion. She has learned from life what is right and what is not and what is a person's duty. She herself feels that it is her duty to point out to her clients what she considers to be the right thing to do. Rose feels more and more unhappy at her situation. How can she keep her integrity as a person and a professional and yet help her clients effectively while respecting their views?

The setting

This principle attempts to define what is good and what is right. This is what ethics is about. Having started with the point that life is what we all have in common, we now have to decide how to live that life so that 'a spirit of brotherhood' (United Nations, 1948) is created and maintained.

This principle starts with a philosophical basis and ends in a practical way. It asks, What is the moral basis of or for an action? Why should people be moral? Why should they act morally? It has taken centuries to think about this, and many boooks have been written about it, so it must be clear that these pages are at best only touching the subject in a very small way.

The basic idea of the principle of goodness or rightness is that if people are to live together they should be 'good' and act 'rightly'; or conversely, that people should not be 'bad' and should not act 'wrongly'. This means generally that people establish or follow a system of morality which finds its expression in some code of behaviour. This usually has a religious basis. Thus the Jewish expression is that of a covenant between God and the chosen people, enshrined in the Ten Commandments. The Christian expression takes this basis and adds loving one's neighbour as oneself. The Muslim expression is in living life according to God's will (Muslim) and in submission (Islam) to God. 'The Islamic code of conduct is founded upon the bedrock of the testimony of faith.' And Buddhism recognises the Four Noble Truths of life, expressed in the Noble Eightfold Path which comprises

Right knowledge
Right attitude

Right speech
Right action
Right living
Right effort
Right mindfulness
Right composure. (*The World's Religions*, 1982)

The philosopher Immanuel Kant (1724–1804) developed his theory of duty ethics on the argument that he could not prove the existence of a God who established laws. He believed that it must be 'possible to set up valid absolute moral rules by reasoning alone, not by reference to any supernatural being or by empirical evidence' (Thiroux, 1980: 59). Kant was concerned with absolute moral rules; that is, rules which must apply to all people at all times and therefore cannot be negotiable. He summed up his theory in the *categorical imperative*, which states that the rule which authorises an act must be able to be made into a rule for all human beings to follow. This means, in effect, that 'every time people are about to make a moral decision they must . . . ask first, "What is the rule authorising this act I am about to perform?" and, secondly, "Can it become a universal rule for all human beings to follow?"' (Thiroux, 1980: 61). Following this, Kant established the *practical imperative*, which can be translated as 'treat every human being, including yourself, always as an end and never as a mere means'.

Kant believed that obeying such rules was done out of a sense of duty. Only people who so acted could be described as moral. This could be illustrated by describing a warden at a home for elderly people who dislikes old people but who, because her own mother is in such a home (or for some other compelling reason), makes herself do the job out of a sense of duty to her mother and humanity.

This theory of ethics is known as deontology, or duty ethics (also known as non-consequentialism). The action itself counts and has to be right, regardless of any consequences. If the action is right, then probably the consequences of the action will be right anyway.

The other well-known theory, teleology, states more or less the opposite: an action is only right if the consequences of the action are right. Hence this theory is known as consequentialism. Its best known version, utilitarianism, was conceived by Jeremy Bentham (1748–1832), and developed by John Stuart Mill (1806–73) in the middle of the Industrial Revolution. Mill established the 'greatest happiness principle', which says that actions are right when they promote happiness and wrong when they produce the opposite. Mill then needed to elaborate on what happiness consisted of, and so he declared that the pleasures of the mind are superior to those of the body.

'The greatest good for the greatest number' sums up his theory, and in its day led to many of the 'reforms in conditions of employment, the prison system, public health provision, parliamentary representation and the status of women' (Campbell, 1984: 45).

Against this background of duties and goals to be achieved it is clear that Niebuhr's theory starts from a very different angle. Niebuhr starts from the idea that in order to be and remain human, people respond to one another. As one responds, so the other is interpreting this response, and further interpretation to that response also happens. When we respond to one another in a responsible way, we enhance our own personal humanity and that of people and societies around us. Niebuhr, as a professor of theology, started with a Christian background, not making either dogma or faith a prerequisite of his theory, but rather stressing the common humanity of all people. Because of this, he is close to feminists and other modern thinkers (for example, Callahan, 1993), who put a strong emphasis on the body (as opposed to seeing ethics only as a mental and rational function). The idea of response-*a*bility leading to respons*i*bility is attractive for Niebuhr and is certainly a good basis for ethical decision making.

The story of Rose and her problem of saying what is right can now be seen in the light of these various theories. Her rights and responsibilities cannot be separated. This chapter considers these aspects from a personal point of view, the next chapter from a social point of view. But first a little detour back into ethical theory is called for.

Beneficence and non-maleficence

One of the basics of the principle of goodness or rightness is that people 'attempt to do three things: (1) promote goodness over badness, (2) cause no harm or badness, and (3) prevent badness or wrongness' (Thiroux, 1980: 125). Beneficence (doing good) has always been a cornerstone of medical ethics, going back to the Hippocratic oath which states, 'I will prescribe regimen for the good of my patients according to my ability and my judgement and never do harm to anyone' (Duncan *et al.* 1981: 210). Like all the principles of ethics, doing good cannot be absolute because in order to do good one has sometimes to do harm first: in most treatments there is an element of harm. An operation may restore health, but it also has risks; a course of medication may cure, but any medication has side-effects. It is enough that we 'attempt' to do good, because that is all that we can do. As with so much else in ethics, the intention counts as much as the outcome.

Non-maleficence (doing no harm) is the other half of doing good. It has been called 'arguably an *absolute* moral duty' (Hanford, 1993: emphasis added), though in the light of the above paragraph, that is perhaps an over-statement, at least in medicine. Nevertheless, deliberately causing harm can be seen as 'bad'. The concept usually relates to humans, but most people would also want to include animals in this injunction. Increasingly, this is also extended to the environment and indeed to all living things, of which the earth is merely a part. Perhaps, after all, doing no harm should be an 'absolute' moral duty?

Personal rights and responsibilities

One person's rights are another person's responsibilities. The principle of goodness and rightness tries to consider what is good and how people act rightly. Apart from establishing laws, defining good and right can also be done through codes and declarations. The Universal Declaration of Human Rights (United Nations, 1948) grew out of the Nuremberg trials in 1947, where twenty-three German defendants, mostly physicians, were accused of crimes involving experiments on human subjects. The Preamble of the Declaration cites as one of its reasons for drawing up the thirty Articles the 'disregard and contempt for human rights [which] have resulted in barbarous acts which have outraged the conscience of mankind'. Its aim is therefore 'a world in which human beings shall enjoy freedom of speech and belief and freedom from fear and want [which has] been proclaimed as the highest aspiration of the common people'. Such a declaration of intent does not yet, however, guarantee that it will also be carried out.

The publication of the Declaration of Human Rights started the movement for rights: the right to die and the right to live examined in the two previous chapters; the right to make mistakes (Dickson, 1982: 32); the right to equal opportunities – to mention just a few. This movement has been much strengthened in Britain with the publication of the Citizen's Charter and the charters covering various aspects of the life of the nation, such as those of patients, parents, passengers, council tenants, job seekers, court users and so on (HM Government, 1992). Codes and charters regulate what is good and right, thus effectively taking away from individuals the need to decide for themselves what is good and right, but also giving to individuals the rights which they could never claim for themselves if they lived in conditions of abuse.

If a person is to have personal and social rights, this presupposes that another person or persons act rightly in the first instance. Thus the legislature – Parliament and statutory bodies – have invested in them the power to decide what is good and to make laws on behalf of their citizens. This is well and good when there are no difficulties, but we have all seen in recent times how vulnerable such positions are and how little credibility politicians and legislators are left with. The famous phrase by Margaret Thatcher, that there is no such thing as society, only individuals, therefore takes on an even more ominous air than it already has: the individual needs to rely more and more on his or her own wits and sense of morality. Is this right? And is it good?

The story of Rose shows that she has a well-developed sense of what is right. Her way of seeing life and the family is very clear-cut and based on a clear model. Because she feels she is right, she also feels that other people should think like her. She also feels that she has a duty to put her viewpoint across. This is where the difficulty arises.

People with strong religious, political or personal views tend to be people with a mission: they want to get their points heard. But other people tend to label them as fanatics and avoid them. And yet the freedom of speech and belief is the first right mentioned in the Universal Declaration of Human Rights. This surely shows that the moment we set up a right we have to qualify it. Indeed, it shows that each of the ethical principles mentioned here has to be bounded by all the others. The principle of individual freedom has to be bounded by the principle of goodness and rightness, and vice versa.

What is good and right for one person is not necessarily so for another. Rose was very much aware of this from the response she got from the young mothers to her remarks, and also from her professional injunction not to persuade. But this clashed with what she saw as her duty as a person, as a Christian, and as an experienced midwife.

One of the standards which have always been used to make moral decisions is *conscience*. This has been defined as 'a mode of thought about one's acts and their rightness or wrongness, goodness or badness' (Beauchamp and Childress, 1983: 270). Chadwick and Tadd (1992: 30) relate conscience to guilt as the outcome of an action where conscience is not obeyed. Johnstone (1989: 327) sees conscience as moral reasoning, moral feelings, and a mixture of these two. She believes that it is this last category, the mixture of moral reasoning and moral feelings, which is most responsive to moral triggers. Reliance on the mutually guiding and instructive forces of moral sensibilities and moral reasoning leads neither to blind emotive obedience nor blind devotion to reason. For most people, conscience is an inner guide which they ignore at their peril, but which can also weaken and lose its authority if constantly forced to be violated (Johnstone, 1989: 332), as was so clearly shown in the Nazi atrocities – and indeed in the many violations of human rights the world over.

Rose tried to square her conscience with her work and found it more and more difficult. When this happens, positions become hardened, and creative ways of responding are abandoned. What usually happens is that positions become entrenched and there is an over-emphasis on the personal mission or duty.

One friend has referred to this as 'the hardening of the oughteries'.

Chadwick and Tadd (1992: 31) suggest that 'reflecting on one's moral actions with a view to finding morally acceptable alternatives is a more positive approach to determining future behaviour than either subjecting oneself to pangs of guilt or to setting standards which will be impossible to reach'. With this admonition they are close to Niebuhr's idea that responsibility leads to *social solidarity*; that is, something greater and more complete than existed before an ethical decision was made.

This, then, suggests that to have any right – be this of freedom of speech or of 'saying no' – we also have a personal responsibility to use that right effectively and responsibly. Niebuhr sees this response first of all to be to the self, in self-awareness and self-knowledge, to identify, compare, analyse and relate events 'so that they come to us not as brute actions, but as understood and as having meaning' (1963: 61).

All professionals have a legal responsibility to their clients, but they also have a personal and moral responsibility. Some of these aspects are captured in codes, but the personal and moral aspects can hardly be prescribed. Yet, as any consumer of any services knows, we notice when they are absent. A person who does not feel morally responsible in any situation or job can at best show a grudging legal responsibility.

Responsibility is the response from one *person* to another *person*, not just from a professional to a client. Responsibility means listening to the other person, 'getting involved', challenging oneself and one's views as well as those of the other person. It means interpreting what the other says in the light of all that is known and understood. It does not mean being responsible *for*, but being responsible *to*. When we are responsible *for* someone we take over, but when we are responsible *to* someone we do indeed respond to the person. This is perhaps the dilemma for Rose – as it is for many professionals.

Conscientious objection

Practising nurses and midwives have only one possibility in British law where they can object to take part in treatment on the basis of conscience, and that is for abortion. The Abortion Act 1967 has a 'conscience clause' on which objection can be officially based. In the view of the Act, abortion is not a 'treatment', whereas nurses cannot object to any treatments of patients and clients on the grounds of conscience.

Conscientious objection to abortion is usually on religious, but certainly on personal, grounds. Once they practise professionally, nurses' personal rights and responsibilities are few. The dilemmas which therefore arise for many nurses are often quite severe and accepted with resignation. With an increasing awareness of personal rights it is hoped that this will change, but it is difficult to see how such rights can be accommodated. When AIDS was first seen in hospitals, some nurses objected to treating patients with this disease, partly out of fear of contagion, but partly out of homophobia. Professionals cannot pick and choose whom to treat or not to treat on spurious personal whims. However, the UKCC *Code of Professional Conduct* (1992) provides in Clause 8 the opportunity to report any conscientious objection 'which may be relevant to your professional practice'. This is encouraging, as it implies that dialogue is possible, and that both parties might be committed to 'finding morally acceptable alternatives' (Chadwick and Tadd, 1992: 31) which may be more positive than either pangs of guilt or silent suffering that can too easily lead to stress and distress.

What is happening?

The issues outlined in the headings above colour the society in which we live and become part of the 'collective unconscious' as a basis for our values. This, therefore, needs to be taken into account when asking *What is* happening? We need to ask this question of Rose and of her clients, and also of the communities in which they all function.

The case of Rose is the classical one of a health-care worker having a set of values which she considers 'right', and trying to persuade her clients that they should hold the same values. This is indeed a very common situation. Any expert has more experience than a client, any professional more than a lay person and any older person more than a younger one. But more than that, the institutions in which we work also shape our values. Nurses (perhaps more than midwives) are coloured by values which see health by and large from the standpoint of illness. Being surrounded by disease and by mechanical and technical ways of dealing with it, we acquire tunnel vision about health.

The problem for Rose is not that she sees childbirth as 'illness', but that she believes that a child needs a family, and possibly a big family, to grow up well. This is a very laudable view, and one which religions and teachers of all walks of life uphold and foster, not only those with 'Victorian values'. There is nothing wrong with her views. But they are not those of her clients. Can she, an older woman, a professional and an experienced mother, impose her views and values on young, inexperienced women (whom Rose refers to as 'children') who may have more pressing priorities than caring for the child they possibly did not want in the first place?

What is happening here is that Rose believes and trusts her values, and feels that her clients have not got the same experience as she has and are therefore to be 'taught' what is right. She presupposes that her values are right, or at least better than those of her clients. Personally and professionally, she has a right – and indeed a duty – to live by and defend her values. Her clients might not have thought much about the consequences of their decisions to give the babies away – but they might also have thought about it a great deal. Just because they are young does not mean that they are immature or incapable of moral reasoning. For sure, they are the children of a different society: one in which personal rights are fostered and personal responsibilities perhaps not much considered. This does not give Rose a 'right' to teach them a lesson.

Any person in hospital or in the care of others is vulnerable to exploitation. Is Rose taking advantage of this vulnerability of her clients to get her views across? Her account does not give this impression, but when asking *What is happening?* we also have to consider any possible hidden agendas. This is not meant to encourage a 'witch hunt', but rather, by discussing all the aspects fostered by this question, to stimulate the self-awareness and self-knowledge which are crucial in this decision-making process.

Taking advantage of people's vulnerable and possibly helpless position must be seen as not right. The idea of *paternalism* grew out of the position of superior–inferior and professional–lay person, but while it is still around, this position is no longer tenable in health care today.

Rose is rightly aware that her profession asks her to inform, not to impose. This still leaves her with the question, how does she reconcile her personal beliefs and values with the requirements of her profession, as they seem to be contradicting each other? When considering *What is happening?*, it is often useful to state the obvious problem and to spell it out in black-and-white. A problem which is not stated – however simple or however obvious it is – may not be perceived as a problem and may therefore be overlooked or assumed not to be important. Rose has one life experience and her clients have another: is there a *fitting answer* to the dilemma?

Rose is consciously or subconsciously aware of wanting or having to do good as part of her personal and professional life. She has a strong sense of duty; but who is the duty to? Is it only to her clients? Is the duty to herself? To her parents, perhaps, to her church, her convictions? It may not be possible to be very clear about all these people and ideas which claim a duty from Rose. A person is a 'whole' in the sense that all these aspects should be integrated, and not neatly compartmentalised. Her answer to these questions may therefore be 'yes' to each aspect. This is neither wrong nor bad, but asking the question will have raised her self-awareness and self-knowledge, and that may be the important element as it will help her in her decisions either for a goal or for a *fitting answer*.

Rose has a clear right to have her opinions and to stand by them and make them known to her clients. This does not mean that she has the right to impose them on anybody. Nor does it mean that anybody has to accept them as their own. Rose has a right to be heard by those to whom she talks, in the same way as she has a responsibility to listen to others' opinions and ideas.

Rose also has a right to change her opinion, should she want to, and she has a right to live according to her conscience. Ideally, this should mean that she should not be troubled about conflict between her conscience and her professional practice, but this cannot be seen as a right as such. However, concern by her colleagues and use of their counselling skills should help Rose to work towards a resolution of her dilemma.

Rose has a responsibility to her clients which consists of legal, moral and personal aspects. Her legal responsibilities are those of providing the best care and treatment as a professional. This includes helping her clients to adapt to their new role as mothers, and as Rose is aware, informing them but not imposing her views on them. If they ask her about that role, Rose has a professional responsibility to listen to them, help them and inform them – with the proviso that this be done in a 'professional' (read: detached) way.

This is the crux: Rose is not simply a professional; she is also a person, a mother, a human being, and she relates to her clients not just in a professional way, but in a personal one too. If she were simply a professional, she would be detached. But she has something in common with her clients – the big family, the children – and this gives her an empathy which she values and believes to be of help to them. At the moment her conscience pushes her in one way, and her professional commitment in another. This makes for emotional discomfort, and is the main reason why theories which appeal for professional objectivity (such as logical positivity) came into being.

When we consider *What is happening?* to her clients, we begin to see a very different picture. Rose is mainly concerned with very young women, possibly teenagers, and those who may not have thought much about the responsibilities of motherhood. They are a minority of clients, but a significant enough minority for Rose to be concerned about. A typical client may thus be about 15 or 16 years of age, still at school, and come from a West Indian family which has a tradition of caring well for their own. These mothers had not planned a pregnancy; had possibly not realised that they were pregnant, otherwise they might have had an abortion; have no wish to live with the father; and are generally not willing to be tied to caring for the child. They may see the whole thing as a bad moment in their lives, and the sooner it is over, the better. Adoption is therefore the easiest way out of an embarrassing situation.

Rose thinks that these mothers have not thought much about the implications of giving their babies away. Do the mothers think the same? Could they in fact know what they are doing? Have they thought that in later years they might really regret having given away a child so easily?

Teleology would here say that the consequences of the action matter: if the mother gives the child away, is she therefore going to be happier, and will the child be happier because of this action?

Deontology insists that the action itself has to be right and the action has to be performed out of a sense of duty. Rose would here say that it is the mother's duty to keep the child. The mother herself may say that she has a duty to herself first of all, and this means that she cannot care for a child right now. She defines 'good' as that which brings most happiness and pleasure (a concept known as hedonism), and looking after a child now would bring neither happiness nor pleasure.

Response ethics starts not with an answer, but with a question: *What is happening?* Thus the emphasis is placed on the *people*, almost taking a step sideways. The emphasis is not on an abstract right or good, but on the *people* who have to make the choice. When they have had time and opportunity to consider the various positions they occupy, then the *fitting answer* may suggest itself almost naturally.

The young mothers will probably not have considered the finer details of ethical theories. They will have made a choice on a basis of convenience and of a possible future as they see it now, in a restricted and limited way.

A likely scenario is then that such a mother is not able to accept the responsibility for her pregnancy but feels a victim of an accident, or of a boy's greed or lust, of society which expects young girls to have sexual experiences early, of her school or parents for not teaching her about sex, or indeed of her classmates who might have goaded her into sleeping with a particular boy. When one can blame someone or something, one feels less responsible.

When Rose noticed that some of the mothers were rather detached from childbirth, this is what she may have thought. Such a mother may then feel that if the child is given away, any feelings of unease or even guilt may go away with the child. Rose, on the other hand, is pointing in the opposite direction with her questions, and is saying in effect that they will feel even more guilty later and regret that they cannot then come to terms with their feelings and deeds in a psychologically healthy way. It was pointed out above that people in hospital are vulnerable, and this is the young mothers' vulnerable point and time. Rose now reinforces this by uncovering their weak argument. No wonder they give her a dusty answer or a cold shoulder. The young mothers have a right to be listened to if they voice disquiet or worry, and Rose, like all professionals, is obliged to hear them and help them as best as she can.

One of the essential counselling skills and attitudes is being non-judgemental. This means that we accept what the person says as being her view, her story, her truth. It does not mean that we cannot hold the opposite view – we can, but we put it aside for the moment until we have heard the other. When we ask *What is happening?* in a counselling framework, we see as a starting point that Rose is judgemental. She sees her intervention as 'helping these young mothers see sense', but in fact she is saying, 'You are wrong and you must change'. We do not have the right to challenge others until we are able to challenge our own attitudes, and anyone wanting to help Rose must also be aware of this proviso. We cannot ask others to change either; we can only change ourselves.

> *One way of asking* What is happening? *is asking* What is happening to you? *and* What is happening to me? *The person I have called Rose told me her story, and asked me what she could do to keep her integrity as a person and as a professional. In this way I am laying before you, the reader, what is happening to me. Perhaps as you read on, you might ask yourself what is happening to you as you read this and imagine what answers you would give and what actions you would take.*

What is the meaning of it?

When Rose wondered how she could keep her integrity as a person and a professional and yet help her clients effectively, she was asking for a solution. She had a 'solution' to the situation of her clients – to do the right thing and keep the babies – and in the same way she was asking for a solution for herself. Most health-care workers like to have solutions to problems because they are practical people. To ask them *What is the meaning of it?* may not be what they expect to hear, but it may eventually be more helpful than to propose a solution.

In the discussion so far several points have been highlighted which, after having asked *What is happening?*, have led deeper than simple statements of facts: the mirroring of Rose's need for a solution to the dilemma she presented her clients with; her judgemental approach at a time when her clients are vulnerable; her drive to do her duty; her sense that she has to 'help' when this could be seen as meddling; and finally, her pain at wanting to keep her integrity in the face of conflicting values.

Ethical decisions are not just about the big issues of the day – abortion, euthanasia and whether gene therapy is good or not – but are made in a thousand daily instances when it matters that right and wrong are seen for what they are.

It is interesting that H. Richard Niebuhr's brother, Reinhold, was the man who wrote the famous 'prayer', 'Grant me the serenity to accept the things I cannot change, courage to change the things I can, and wisdom to know the difference.'

With the question *What is the meaning of it?*, we go to the cause of a problem and to the psychological possibility of seeing the problem. Rose could go on telling her clients that they should keep their babies and go on getting the same dismissive answer. She could say her piece with ever increasing vehemence because she is so convinced of her rightness and their wrongness. Eventually, her conscience would not question any more that there is a problem between her stance and that of her clients: she is convinced of her rightness. If this scenario is extended only a little, it is clear that this is the beginning of any dispute and eventually of war. If we ask *What is the meaning of it?* we change the emphasis.

What is the meaning for Rose in this situation? It is possible that she had been brought up to know her mind and to speak it; it is possible that as she was one of several children, she had to have a mind of her own or else she would never be heard; that she actually feels insecure and compensates for this by putting her finger on other people's insecure spots; she may have a dominant husband or mother and, rather than stand up to them, she dominates others in turn. There may be a hundred and one reasons. But we are talking about ethics, not about psychoanalysis. Yet ethics affects people and relationships. It is therefore not possible to take ethical decisions in isolation; other people are inevitably affected by one person's decisions. If we know the motives out of which we act, then our actions are more self-confident, more 'true' and 'better'.

The question *What is happening?*, if asked well enough, will lead to insights, and these insights must then be addressed in order to use them effectively. The question *What is the meaning of it?* is therefore not so far-fetched as it might appear. Indeed, it is the logical next question. When an insight has been gained, then the process of making a responsible decision can be considerably advanced.

What is the fitting answer?

What answer does Rose herself give to her problem of how to keep her integrity in her work with young mothers? What is a more fitting answer to the mothers than the one Rose gives at present?

Having gone through the process of ethical decision making based on response ethics, Rose will need to feel at the end of it that she is not diminished in her views and that her values are not belittled and that she does not have a conflict of conscience any more.

Having looked at her situation, gained insight and stated her goal, it is possible to see that Rose

- is judgemental because she feels insecure as a person;
- feels that she has a duty to 'help' or 'put them right'.

The *fitting answer* which Rose gives herself may therefore be that she learns first of all how to listen more to her clients. She says that she listens – and indeed she does, otherwise she would not hear that they want to give their babies away – but she listens selectively; she hears what she wants to hear. She may want to learn to listen with a non-judgemental attitude.

The *fitting answer* to being an insecure person is probably to learn self-awareness and find where and when and how she is insecure. Once she is more aware, she will gain insights which could lead her to some goal which might include self-assertion. She may not find this difficult, as she has some skills in assertion, although they are not used in the most effective way.

The *fitting answer* to her sense of duty may be that she needs to examine the idea of 'duty' further. Her understanding of the term at the moment seems rather simplistic. She may need to look at the word and concept of duty in the way it is understood in ethics, philosophy and religion, as well as in terms of her professional code of practice. She may find that in doing this, she comes to a different understanding.

Having done all this, what, finally, is the *fitting answer* to her clients, so that they are really helped and Rose keeps her moral integrity?

Having gone through this process of questioning, Rose may suggest to her clients, if they voice a problem to her, that she might help them to come to their own conclusions using the same framework as she had done. This would be the most fitting in terms of counselling skills.

But Rose may not want to wait until her clients approach her to help them. From her past experience, she may ask the mothers outright what they are going to do with the baby once they leave hospital. If they say that they are going to give the child away, Rose may ask herself *What is happening* here? – in other words, What is happening to me as I ask this question? Do I have a right to ask this question? If so, what is it? Do I have a responsibility to ask this question? If so, what is it? When she can answer these questions fittingly, she will have answered well.

The pattern of responsibility

The pattern implies that first of all there is a *challenge* which evokes an ethical question. In this case, the challenge was in two stages: first, there were the replies by the mothers that they would be giving their babies away; and secondly, there grew in Rose a sense of unease at the demand by her profession only to give information and not to question practice, leading to unhappiness about not being able to be herself with her clients. This was finally framed as 'how to keep personal and professional integrity'.

The *response*, according to Niebuhr, is first of all a physical and an emotional one.

The problem here is not an urgent one which needs quick action or decision; it is a problem which has gradually emerged and at some stage has become conscious enough to be expressed as painful. Once Rose became conscious that her integrity was compromised, she may have felt a sinking sort of feeling in her body – the sort of feeling which people describe when they feel let down; everything in the body goes 'down': the shoulders, the gut, the heart – and in her mood. One feels bad, defeated and deflated.

These physical feelings stem from the emotional responses of an earlier similar situation. The memory is a reliable function, but often not a very conscious one, and the memory has in the meantime become overlaid with interpretations and meanings which were possibly not there at the time.

Rose's *response* is now one of paralysis and defeat: I can't get it right. Her discomfort from this situation grew until one day she mentioned it to a colleague. When she did talk about it she was looking for a quick answer, as that would have relieved her discomfort. This is a usual response. Nurses (and midwives) are very used to the analogy with medicine: if it hurts, take an aspirin and in a few minutes you feel better. If this doesn't work, take something else. Moral pain, however, usually needs more than a quick fix.

The *interpretation* looks at the memories which now come into play. What has happened in the past which makes us give this particular response? The various possible reasons why Rose dealt with her situations in this particular way were traced back to her upbringing. She may never have been in exactly the same situation before, but similar ones can be very helpful. In what other situations is she judgemental? Where else does she feel she has a duty? It has something to do with children and their education: Rose wanted her own children to 'turn out well' and this is perhaps something which she heard said in her childhood. It is certainly what she feels towards her clients; she is concerned that they also 'turn out well' and so she has to educate them, but her 'education' fails.

Her sense of duty – what she 'ought' to do – is very strong. This is not quite the same as responsibility, which relates to responding and interpreting what she hears in response to what she says. Indeed, her response-*a*bility is reduced in the face of what she perceives as her duty.

The *accountability* in the pattern looks forward to what might be possible. Thus, Rose asks herself what she could do to feel better about herself, yet still keep her integrity. If she approached the problem differently, would it help? If she said something different, would she be heard? If she were more dutiful, could she claim some professional sanction? Would her profession still trust her if she claimed a Christian duty? What would need to change for it all to be better? For change there has to be – she cannot continue as things are. The question is what that change is.

Thus under the heading of *accountability* we see the process of moving through an analysis of the situation, of what meaning there might be in it, and what possible goals there could be. The pattern is not the process itself, but an outline of what is in fact taking place.

The last part of the pattern is *social solidarity*. The goals which Rose had set herself of listening more, trying to be less judgemental, more assertive, and studying the concept of duty in various aspects, must surely all help her to feel more at ease. Once she feels easier in herself – those around her, in particular, her clients – will also feel more at ease. The *social solidarity* will then consist of more harmonious professional relationships, but also in Rose's own sense of herself. She will not feel torn any longer, and when she is happier, she will be more relaxed and more true to herself.

Chapter 5
The principle of
goodness or rightness (2)

Doug was a lecturer at a well-known college of nursing. He was a competent and empathic teacher and also good-looking. He managed to dress in a way which enhanced his figure and looks, and was aware that he had quite a following among his students.

Moira was one of these students. She was 28 when she started her nursing training, having been a dog-breeder before. She and Doug got on well with each other, each aware that the other had qualities which enhanced their respective personalities.

They began to meet occasionally in the pub across from the college. There was nothing unusual about this – most lecturers used the pub for tutorials when the need arose. Moira was by then into her second year of studies. She was not a brilliant student, but her easy manner and good contact with her patients and clients made her a popular student. Doug made it clear to her that she needed to concentrate more on her studies as otherwise she might not get through her exams. He was willing to help her in any way he could.

Moira did go to him a few times for help, but each time she found that Doug did not talk about her academic problems, but wanted to talk about their personal lives. This was interesting but did not get her anywhere. She began to look for help among her fellow-students. One or two of them were rather offhand with her,

66

saying that she could go to Doug – he had always wanted to help her.

Indeed, Doug began pressing her to go to him for help. He began to make regular appointments for her with him. They were mostly outside his working hours and Moira was very concerned about this: she knew she needed help, but perhaps not this kind of help. She saw Doug a few more times, unable to find a way out of the appointments made. Although she had at first gone along with the easy, friendly relationship, she was far from happy now. Doug had become increasingly close physically, and she wondered how far he would need to go before it could be called sexual harassment. She worried that if she continued to see him, he might believe that she enjoyed these advances and take them further still.

She decided to seek help from the occupational health department. They asked her if she would like to see a psychiatrist, but she declined. Rather at her wits' end, she went to see her union steward, Frank. It did not take long before Moira heard that two other students had complained about Doug. Moira was relieved that she was not just imagining the whole thing, but was now faced with the problem of whether and how to take the matter further.

The setting

The setting for this chapter is a story of sexual harassment. It might also be a story of 'granny-bashing' – over a quarter of disciplinary hearings now involve nurses working in the care of the elderly (Eaton, 1993) – or having blacklists of people not to be employed in particular areas or districts. The situation is of one person taking advantage of another, one person considering himself (or herself) better than another, and what to do about it. Any situation where one person diminishes another person must be considered unethical.

The issue of sexual harassment reaches into all areas of life. Nurses – at least in Britain – have long had a 'sexy' image. They have been the butt of dubious and insalubrious jokes. And while this may have been true of female nurses, male nurses have been suffering from sexual harassment too, perhaps more from their colleagues than from patients.

From the viewpoint of the principle of goodness or rightness, it is never good or right to discriminate. This principle stands to enhance any ways in which people can live together harmoniously, and discrimination gives one party an advantage over another party, person, nation or race. The fact that we need to spell this out so simply means that discrimination is, however, a very ingrained idea.

> *In my counselling practice I have yet to come across one person who doesn't say something to the effect that parents had made it clear to their child that their family was different from other people. Most children also feel that they are different from others, often believing that they are misunderstood. This leaves them with a mixture of arrogance and self-loathing which can lead to serious psychological problems later in life.*

Therefore, when we look at the principle of goodness or rightness, we may find it difficult to be clear about what is good or right, simply because our upbringing has left us with confused messages. Perhaps it is therefore reasonable that each generation has to find its own level of responses to these fundamental questions.

Ours seems to be the age of charters, declarations, codes and all manner of statements of equal rights, equal opportunities and equal responsibilities.

The issue of sexual harassment has been brought into the open by the women's movement. When women became bolder about being equal people and citizens, they were no longer inclined to be the objects of jokes and degrading attitudes. As so often happens in such situations, the pendulum swings wildly at first, before coming to rest somewhere in the middle. The point about looking at this ethical principle of goodness or rightness is that it should help to provide a *fitting answer* in particular situations, and that must mean a balanced answer.

Because ethics has become a household word in health care, nurses, midwives and health visitors in Britain should by now be familiar with the UKCC *Code of Professional Conduct* (1992). It attempts to sum up what is good practice for professionals. With the Code, the UKCC has published *The Scope of Professional Practice* (1992), which is a position statement by the Council about what it expects from its practitioners. While it concentrates on actual professional practice, it is clear that nurses must also be involved on a personal level: nurses have to be 'good' people before they can perform 'right' actions. Paragraph 1 refers to 'sensitive' practice, and Paragraph 2 mentions the 'personal experience, education and skill(s)' of nurses, midwives and health visitors. Practitioners are not robots, but if they are to give 'holistic nursing care' (Paragraph 13) then they have first of all to be 'holistic' people. The story of Rose in Chapter 4 shows what can happen when a person is no longer able to be 'holistic' herself: her practice becomes questionable and she suffers as a person. The story of Moira shows what can happen when colleagues take advantage of each other.

Loyalty to family, institution or nation often makes people blind to some of their less good aspects: 'He wouldn't do that' or 'It couldn't happen here' may not be said so much as assumed. Thus we may tolerate certain practices far beyond reason, turning blind eyes, making excuses and being economical with the truth to absurd lengths. Acting rightly, from good motives, is far from easy, and if it is not easy on a personal level, how much more difficult is it on a global level.

Like most of us, Moira was presumably brought up to respect authority. Therefore when she saw that the authority of her teachers was not what she had expected, it was doubly difficult to act rightly. Having gone into nursing with considerable life experience, she probably entered the profession with realism at one level, but also with an idealism which she may have wanted to preserve. The remarks of her fellow-students about Doug did not open her eyes to what was happening. Being good and doing right is not something we are born with. For most of us it would be much easier just to look after 'Number One', do exactly how, what and when we please. The problem for teachers is not only how to teach the three Rs to children, but also how to educate them to be responsible, moral beings.

> As I write this, the trial is going on of two boys who abducted and killed a 2-year-old child. This has to be done without using names, because it is held that 11-year-olds are not yet capable of moral reasoning. But they were capable of the worst crime of all. So when and how do we become 'moral' beings?

This is not a question which has a clear answer. The codes of ethics and practice to which professionals are required to adhere guide those people to a common, basic way of being professional *vis-à-vis* their clients, their colleagues, their profession and society at large. Having a code does not make a professional moral, but he or she can be judged against this code in a case of less than moral behaviour.

This chapter concentrates on the social rights and responsibilities of people seen from the point of view of the principle of goodness or rightness.

Social rights and responsibilities _____

Personal and social rights and responsibilities constantly overlap because not one of us is 'an island entire of itself'. Ethical problems arise and are decided between and among people; between and among individuals as well as nations.

Decisions are constantly made about us which affect us, but over which we have very little control. Examples are, how much tax we pay, how many police officers a locality has, which sectors of public life will be privatised and how many beds are available to NHS patients. We have to trust the decision makers to be good and honest people who have the interests of society at heart. We may disagree with their decisions, write to our MP, take part in a demonstration and sign petitions, but in the end an individual has a very small voice. This is very disconcerting for many people, and so they decide that they prefer not to do anything anyway.

Because nursing has for so long been women's work, and women were 'the weaker sex', nursing has not had a political voice and therefore has not had the prestige and weight of the medical profession. All this is changing, but quite painfully. While doctors have often been in the limelight for unprofessional behaviour, nurses have only recently acquired this reputation, and it has seemed all the more shocking coming from 'angels'.

Nurses have been highly rated for their tender loving care, and in recent years this aspect of care has been given new emphasis. But this care has not often been understood to be also political, ethical and managerial. Even now 'holistic' care is understood to include complementary therapies such as reflexology and nutrition, but not politics. Yet if we are to give whole (holistic) care, we have to consider all the aspects of a person's life, the client's as well as the nurse's.

As nurses we, in turn, control other people's lives – patients' and clients' – and we must be aware that by our control we render others impotent or weak. Advocacy (see Chapter 6) is also changing this aspect, but here, too, we must be aware that all too often we are still guided by tradition rather than enlightened holism.

Perhaps the first and most fundamental right – though not one written in any code – which we have as human beings is the right to be heard. In our society, in which 'time is money', to be listened to is often a luxury which many people never experience. But this is the basic need of the model of response ethics: in order to be responded to in a responsible and human way we have first of all to be heard. And if we claim this as a right, then it has also to be a responsibility. We should treat others as we want them to treat us, exhorts the Bible (Matthew 7:12) and also 'To retort without first listening is both foolish and embarrassing' (Proverbs 18:13). This difficulty of listening, or rather not listening to and not hearing what the other person is saying, is the root cause of most of our problems. We call it communication, and again and again we hear that all kinds of traumas could have been avoided if people had listened and been listened to: if Moira, in this chapter's story, had been listened to by Doug, by her colleagues, and by the occupational health department, she might not have got into the same trouble.

If a nurse complains about being short of staff and then a drug error happens on her ward, the error might have been prevented if the nurse had been listened to. If a prison inmate had been heard he might not have been driven to suicide. If union leaders listened to their members and their needs and ideas, money and emotional lives might be saved.

When people are involved in making decisions about their work, they are prepared to work harder and take a personal interest. They also suffer less from stress and burnout.

Listening and hearing does not happen automatically; we have to make it happen. The social rights and responsibilities of people in general stem from their personal values and how they apply them. What we consider valuable to us we normally extend to others also, but what we do not value we find it harder to understand if and when others value it. But we do not have a right to condemn it; we have a right to question it, and a responsibility to acknowledge it.

The legal responsibilities of British nurses are enshrined in the UKCC *Code of Professional Conduct* (1992). It is interesting to look at the sixteen clauses of the Code and at the first word of each clause: 'act', 'ensure' (twice), 'maintain', 'acknowledge', 'work' (twice), 'recognise', 'report' (four times), 'avoid', 'protect', 'assist', 'refuse'. The fourfold exhortation to 'report to an appropriate person or authority' is conspicuous in this Code. It is perhaps useful to reflect that this Code was re-issued in the third edition at a time when there was much concern within nursing about 'whistleblowing'. Among the nursing hierarchy there may have been a fear that speaking out would get out of hand, and that it was better to restrict nurses in this way. What nurses did speak out about, as might be expected, was the fact that such appropriate persons or authorities were not listening and could therefore not be trusted. As it stands, the Code presumes, perhaps naïvely, that relationships between staff and management are always good and always trusting. One would hope that this is so, but simply because the Code implies that it is, does not yet make it so. The 'it wouldn't happen here' idea is rather artless in a climate of fierce competition.

On the other hand, the Code's first clause is a masterpiece of the pen:

> As a registered nurse, midwife or health visitor, you are personally account-able for your practice and, in the exercise of your professional accountability, must:
> 1. act always in such a manner as to promote and safeguard the interests and well-being of patients and clients.

This sentence sums up the whole Code, and it seems that all the other clauses are merely an elaboration of this one sentence. How this, and the Code as a whole, is interpreted in practice does, however, remain the responsibility of each practitioner. The Code is a code of *ethics*, not a law, and it leaves each person free to explore what it would mean in his or her practice. Perhaps in the story of Doug and Moira, Doug had not con-sidered that Moira was his 'client' according to this Code and that he should 'promote and safeguard [her] interests and well-being'.

Whistleblowing

The Universal Declaration of Human Rights of 1948 (United Nations) states in Article 19 that 'everyone has the right to freedom of opinion and expression; this right includes freedom to hold opinions without inter-ference and to seek, receive and impart information and ideas through the media and regardless of frontiers'. Like all such freedoms, freedom of speech is a good idea, but not when it hurts those in authority – or so it seems. As soon as an authority is attacked, it fights back and tries to put a stop to the freedom.

When such a freedom is not an absolute right, those who expose the restrictions and injunctions against the freedom are seen to be subversives, troublemakers and whistleblowers, rather than people doing a legitimate job or carrying out a service.

The first edition of the UKCC *Code of Professional Conduct*, published in 1983, asked nurses, midwives and health visitors in Clause 7 to 'have regard to the environment of care (physical, psychological and social) and to available resources, and make known to the appropriate authority if these endanger safe standards of practice'. This was enlarged in the second edition, in 1984, into '... have regard to the environment of care and its physical, psychological and social effects on patients/clients, and also to the adequacy of resources, and make known to appropriate persons or authorities any circumstances which could place patients/clients in jeopardy or which militate against safe standards of practice'. This was gradually being heard by nurses as a legitimate way of squaring their conscience with the practice they saw around them.

In 1987, Reg Pyne, then Director of Professional Conduct at the UKCC, wrote an article entitled 'A professional duty to shout', in which he stated that 'many practitioners now understand that it is respectable to challenge and complain where that is necessary and to accept that to do so is an intrinsic part of proper professional behaviour'.

However, in 1991, Tadd published an article with the title 'Where are the whistleblowers?', in which he found that 'individuals are too often punished, rather than rewarded, for their moral conscience'. He bases this on the fact that 'many students are reluctant to question or criticise care practices in case they then receive an unsatisfactory ward report. . . . After three years of making such compromises it is hardly surprising if students learn the value of order rather too well.'

There can be few British nurses who have not heard of Graham Pink, the nurse who spoke out about the conditions in the hospital where he worked on night duty. The various 'persons or authorities' to whom he addressed his complaints did not act in a way which was satisfactory to Pink, and so he took his case to a national newspaper. Having complained about inadequate staffing, Pink was finally sacked from his post for breaching patient confidentiality. If this can happen to one nurse, it can happen to many. Once someone is labelled 'difficult' or a 'troublemaker', the whole machinery swings into action against that person.

Most people who complain do so about practice; that is, staffing levels, equipment or working conditions. Blowing the whistle on a colleague seems to be more difficult, more dangerous and even immoral. It seems to be linked with a failure of the nurse who is blowing the whistle to deal with the situation himself or herself. Yet all three editions of the UKCC *Code of Professional Conduct* make it clear that it is the psychological and social as well as the physical effects on patients and clients which are covered by these clauses. In the story of this chapter, Moira was clearly covered by this part of the Code.

The activities of whistleblowers and the treatment they received once they had done so has sparked a lively debate both in government and in the media. The NHS Management Executive published *Guidance for Staff on*

Relations with the Public and the Media in June 1993, and in July MSF (the Manufacturing, Science, Finance Union) published its *Freedom of Speech in the NHS*, which is a 'Guide for MSF negotiators'. This latter document contains the *Guidance* but in a *Charter of Staff Values* clearly challenges the *Guidance*.

The *Guidance* states (Paragraph 6) that 'under no circumstances are employees who express their views about health service issues in accordance with this guidance to be penalised in any way for doing so', but in Paragraph 27 implies that anyone taking a case to the local Member of Parliament 'unjustifiably' could be liable to disciplinary action. The NHS Chief Executive had to circulate a letter later in the year informing management that this was not the intention of the *Guidance* (Hunt, 1994).

The MSF *Charter of Staff Values* resembles the UKCC *Code of Professional Conduct* in many respects, but Clause 9 states that

> you have *a duty and a right* [emphasis added] to report to a competent person any instruction, policy or practice which you believe would result in inadequate or unsafe conditions likely either to harm the safety, health or well-being of patients/clients or colleagues, or be contrary to law, or be to the detriment of the health service and public confidence in its operation.

Clauses 10–14 all deal with these aspects of duties and rights which are believed to harm others, counteracting also the so-called 'gagging clause' of the NHS *Guidance*.

Charters of all kinds are sometimes seen to be a smoke-screen for tackling the real issues, but one can also say, 'If you can't beat them, join them', by making effective charters which are seen as workable and having an impact.

In November 1992 a pressure group called 'Freedom to Care' was launched at the House of Commons. This is a network of employees in the health and social services and other public services which assists whistle-blowers and campaigns for changes in management culture, administrative procedures and the law (Freedom to Care, PO Box 125, West Molesey, Surrey KT8 1YE).

What is happening?

It is time to apply these considerations to the story of Doug and Moira, and how Frank helped Moira.

Frank was the person who listened to Moira and heard her story, and he also had some information which dramatically changed the situation. With or without this, Frank was the one who, in order to help Moira, was most likely to ask Moira *What is happening?*

Deontology would here ask 'What is my duty?' In other words, Frank should ask Moira what she considers to be her duty, given all the facts. This theory places emphasis on the action itself: whatever Moira *does* has to be right in itself.

Teleology would ask 'What will be the goal or the consequences?' 'What should Moira do which will have the best consequences?' This theory also takes into consideration that the consequences should serve the greatest number of people for good.

Response ethics starts not with duties or consequences, but with *What is happening?* What is the given situation? What has happened that has led to the present situation? *What is happening* to all the people involved?

It is likely that Frank heard the factual outline of the story and realised that this was very similar to two other accounts which he had heard. As far as he is concerned, he may consider that there are two main options: Moira takes the situation further, or he does. Since Moira brought the problem to him he does not tell her this but asks her to tell him more of the story: *What is happening?*

It is easy to say that all who are in any way sexually attacked, harassed or raped bear some responsibility for it; that they were too provocative; that they didn't know how to say 'no' or defend themselves. Frank needed to listen without prejudices or assumptions.

Frank will have heard of Moira's initial good relationship with Doug; of her need to acknowledge and even trust authority; of her realisation that she was not brilliant academically but that she knew she was nevertheless a good nurse and that some help was not only welcome but also needed. He will have heard of her hesitation to talk about what was happening to anyone; of her fellow-students who dismissed her; and of her earlier attempt to talk with the Occupational Health Department. All these are the given facts.

As Frank asks further, not yet looking for any answers or solutions, we will discover that Moira has pondered for a long time over what would be the right thing to do. She will have looked at the *Code of Professional Conduct* and wondered if this applied to her. Should she report the matter to 'an appropriate person or authority', and who might this be? The situation was not harming patients or clients, but it was harming the psychological environment.

As they talked together they will have looked at the aspects discussed above: good and right, beneficence and non-maleficence, personal and social rights and responsibilities and whistleblowing.

They will have talked about how all this affected Moira personally, and what finally led to her seeking help. This was, perhaps, as in the story of Rose in the previous chapter, a growing unease that two standards could no longer be held together side by side.

They will also have considered *What was happening* to Doug. On the face of it, Doug was concerned about Moira's academic achievements. As a lecturer, this is his duty and thus he can be seen to be doing his duty. It is not known if he was as caring with all his students, but it is fair to assume that he was. Presumably, he has not been in difficulty before with his female students and so it should be asked why this is happening now. This is not a question which Moira and Frank may be able to answer, but taking the stance of asking *What is happening?* to you and *What is happening?* to me, it is possible to consider both sides as observers in order to learn.

Doug has clearly overstepped the mark with Moira and with two other students. He has acted from selfish motives and not considered his professional responsibilities. Most likely it is something in his personal life which prompted him to this: a sense of personal inadequacy, the knowledge that he may be getting older and losing out on life, difficulties with friends and family, or a thousand other reasons.

Doug has acted selfishly, and this infringes the principle of goodness or rightness because it disregards any harm which may thus be caused to others. Acting selfishly means in effect, 'I am better than you' or 'I have more rights than you', and thus the principle of the value of life is also affected as well as the other principles: justice, in that this is not equitable; truth, in that this behaviour is dishonest; freedom, in that this restricts someone else's freedom. Doug has not acted rightly in a personal and also in a social way in that he abused other people. His ability to respond to a particular situation – that of Moira's need – was not responsible.

If Doug had been aware of what he was doing (and he should have considered his professional accountability), he would either not have embarked on this road, or stopped it when he realised what he was doing. But this demands the constitution of a saint, and most people are not paragons of virtue, nor do we demand this of them. We make mistakes and we have a right to make mistakes, says Dickson (1982: 32). She points out that 'it is important to see that you can *do* something stupid without implying that in essence you *are* stupid or unintelligent. You can behave incorrectly, make a wrong move or do a bad job without it indicating some intrinsic flaw in your character'. If Frank and Moira considered these things, then they are on the way to a *fitting answer*.

Before they get there, they will need to consider what this answer might be. Having considered all the events and emotions which might have led to the possible situation now where Moira is asking for help, they will need to consider the future: what would happen if . . .?

What would happen if Moira did nothing? Would she be able to live with her conscience after this? Could she confront Doug on her own and tell him that she does not want to see him any longer? This would not solve the problem of harassment of the other two students. But is Moira responsible for them as well as for herself? Would this not betray a trust of confidentiality to them?

Should Moira let Frank take over? What does Moira consider that he should do? Should Frank take the matter to the Principal Lecturer of the College, the General Manager of the Health Authority, or to the police? Should Frank get the three people concerned together and should they act as one? Would this not betray confidences?

What might be the consequences of any of these actions in terms of procedures? What might be the consequences for the personal and professional lives of Moira, Frank, Doug and the two other students? This is perhaps the biggest question, and the one least foreseeable. How can Moira and Frank ensure that no one is going to be hurt who is not involved, such as families and friends? How long would any procedures take? Should Frank act alone, or should he involve a solicitor at this stage?

Are there any guidelines or policies which must be followed? If there are no guidelines available, is it possible that this case could lead to their being formulated, and if so, would this be a good thing? What would any of the people involved gain from making the matter public, or from keeping it in-house?

These and any other relevant questions need to be considered and perhaps written down somewhere, so that they can be used as bases for further discussions, or as proof in any investigations.

What is the meaning of it?

When the factual story has been told – and perhaps retold on another occasion – then certain elements will have emerged which will have led to greater self-awareness and self-knowledge. These will have led to insights which might change the whole problem. It is possible that Moira might have seen that her easy manner could also be a defence; that she has a need to be helped by authority; that she is not clear enough about what is right and wrong, or many other points. These insights are only helpful if they help the person to change and become more whole or integrated. The *meaning* might therefore be that this problem is helping Moira to lead a more purposeful life; or see herself as a champion of others who are sexually harassed; or as daring to blow the whistle. It is only when something like this has been grasped that it is no longer a sense of hurt or being a victim which drives people, but a real understanding of motives, values and attitudes.

This process will need help from someone with counselling skills, but it must be stressed that this does not need to be a trained counsellor. The questions given in this book as a framework are adequate to help another person – with the proviso that at every stage there is effective and responsive listening.

What is the fitting answer?

When these two basic questions have been considered well enough, the *fitting answer* may emerge.

The answer will contain elements of duty, consequences, fostering of humanity, of avoiding harm and acting as rightly as possible but also as fittingly as possible in this particular circumstance. This may mean that in other similar situations there might be a different answer or conclusion to a very similar problem.

Response ethics is more flexible in its approach and outcomes than the other two ethical theories considered, in that it does not keep strictly to one basic idea, but this does not make it any less rigorous in its approach. On the contrary, it is perhaps more deeply involving of the whole person, and of all those concerned, in making ethical decisions which are not just right or dutiful, but *fitting* in the widest sense of the word.

It took Moira and Frank several meetings of discussions, listening, debating and pondering the whole issue. Moira began to realise that the problem was bigger than she might at first have imagined, particularly as she was not the only person involved. This fact was decisive.

The answer which was in the end the most fitting for this situation was that Frank and Moira requested a meeting with the General Manager of the Health Authority in which they put their problem before her informally.

The other two students had declined to be part of any discussions at this stage but were kept fully informed (this is one of the points made in the MSF *Guide*). Frank and Moira wanted to discuss the situation with a view to some disciplinary procedure for Doug. From their discussions they had realised that Doug was under great stress at work and also had a problem with a mentally handicapped daughter, and therefore they considered that he might best be helped with personal attention. This was their perception, but it meant that they did not want to press for any heavy-handed intervention. They were concerned about his emotional well-being as well as their own. This was their recommendation; it still depended on the outcome of the discussion with the General Manager and on what Doug would agree to.

Doug was indeed only too pleased to receive personal counselling, as he had realised that he had a problem but did not know how to handle it. He felt very grateful to Moira for taking the matter seriously but also for not blowing it up out of proportion. He wrote her a letter to this effect, not quite having the courage to face her directly. He himself had in the meantime quietly arranged that Moira be allocated a different tutor, which pleased Moira.

The pattern of responsibility

The pattern of responsibility provides a good framework for a summary of this chapter.

The *challenge* in this story is that Doug's relationship with Moira became increasingly more personal and intimate and less professional. At some stage Moira realised that this was not right and that she had a responsibility to do something about it.

Her *response* to the problem was one of increasing awareness. Perhaps at one of the meetings Doug became physically too close, and Moira felt in her body a sense of intrusion or revulsion at having her personal space invaded. This may have been the trigger for her to realise that she must act. There is a difference between knowing something instinctively and knowing it to the point of acting on it. The realisation that she needed to act might have grown over a space of time, but Moira might have been able to trace it back to a particular moment of recognition.

Such a response is mostly realised in the body first, as a physical sensation. It is very important to notice this, and be aware of it, as it is often a very accurate sign of what may lie at the root of the problem. Moira was an attractive person, but also insecure in her attractiveness. Any invasion into her territory would therefore reinforce this insecurity.

As Moira later *interpreted* what was happening, with the help of Frank, she began to make sense of these feelings and insights. She had never seen herself as an insecure person. Her outer appearance and behaviour camouflaged her real self. This incident triggered an insight which she might not have gained in any other than this painful way. The truth about ourselves is often only revealed in such moments of pain and suffering. Learning to interpret these moments of truth is therefore most valuable in shaping the personality.

The interpretation leads eventually to the formulation of meaning, but it does often take quite some time 'unpacking' a great deal of emotional and value baggage before we get there. Our actions and ways of thinking until this moment may all be questioned by the challenge.

The challenge is only a challenge because it is an unknown event, or perhaps an event which we might prefer had not happened.

Moira had come to the insight that she was insecure as a person, and thus she began to see other areas of her life in which she was insecure. In particular, her deference to authority made her go along with situations which she should have been more assertive about and challenged long before rather than tolerating. Although Doug had clearly overstepped the mark, she began to see that she too was involved. But this insight has to come to the person from within; to be told it – as an accusation – would only be damaging and would not be helpful.

Once Moira had seen these things in her conversations with Frank, she was more clearly able to see a way forward.

Her *accountability* was now first of all to herself and the insights she had gained. This was a moral kind of accountability in the first instance, but one which gradually led to managerial and professional accountability. Niebuhr also uses the word 'accountability' in a way which relates to the future. The pattern shows that the challenge, response and interpretation form one big movement which culminates in this sense of responding to the given situation in a fitting way. The response-*a*bility leads to the responsibility which characterises this theory of ethics. The fact that response ethics is first of all concerned with being human with one another makes it clear that there must be an element of accountability. We respond to one another, but in such a way that we enhance one another as persons, not only to uphold a theory or principle – though these are never dismissed as unnecessary.

The *social solidarity* which Niebuhr sees as resulting from this process is clearly visible in this story of Moira, Doug and Frank. As Moira and Frank talked through the problem, they began to see that any outcome had to be good (beneficent), do as little harm as possible (non-maleficent) and yet be *fitting* in this particular case. Moira had felt that, as she had gained so much from the process of personal help, Doug might also benefit in the same way, and she was proved right. By her actions she had avoided a possible crisis, but what is more, she had actually helped to make something greater take place: all the people involved gained from the process. Each one could in the end respond more adequately to the situation in which they had originally found themselves and feel and know that their response to the situation had been well interpreted.

The story does not relate what happened to the two other students involved, but it must be assumed that they were also included in this *social solidarity* of having gained from the process.

Chapter 6
The principle of
justice or fairness (1)

Story

Pam was in hospital recovering from a lumpectomy for a
carcinoma of the breast. It had all happened so quickly that she was
as much recovering from the mental as the physical shock of it. On
the second night she had talked with Richard, the staff nurse on
night duty, and had found him a very good listener.

The next day the consultant came round and told Pam that a
course of chemotherapy was planned and that she would have to
come in regularly for two days a month for at least six months. She
had known that chemotherapy was one of the possibilities, but she
had not realised that it would go on for so long or that she might
have to be admitted for this. When this dawned on her, she turned
quite pale and said to the consultant, 'But this is my whole life,
how can I do this?' He simply nodded, and said, 'There is no
choice.' 'Oh yes there is,' Pam said to herself, quite loudly.

When Richard came on duty she asked him if she could have a
word with him. He assured her that he would come along as soon
as he could, but that might not be for another hour at least. Pam
was willing to wait. When Richard came, Pam told him what had
happened during the day. At the hand-over he had heard that Pam
would probably be going home the next day and then attend for
chemotherapy as an outpatient.

Pam asked Richard to tell her as much as he could about the
chemotherapy which she was going to have. She also asked him if
he knew what her other options were. Richard was well versed in

the complementary therapies, having taken some courses in reflexology which he sometimes used to help patients, and he put some of these possibilities to her. Pam had also read about some of them. In particular, she had met another mother at her daughter's school who had had cancer and had followed a very strict diet for a long time but was convinced that she was cured of her cancer by this. Richard had heard about this diet, but did not know exactly what was involved, so did not actually recommend it. But he encouraged Pam to find out more about it. If she felt that something would help her, then he agreed with her that it would; and conversely, if she felt that chemotherapy was not going to help her, then it probably would not.

Pam felt a new confidence and had a more restful night than previously.

When Richard came round in the morning she asked him if he thought that she could talk with the house officer before leaving for home and tell him that she was not willing to have chemotherapy – at least not yet. Richard assured her that this was her right and was perfectly possible. But Pam felt that she might not have enough courage when the moment came. Would Richard be with her and lend her moral support? Richard agreed, saying that he would be willing to stay on for a while.

The house officer appeared early on the ward, and Richard asked him if he could spend a few minutes with Pam. He went with him, and Pam told him that she was not willing to have chemotherapy, at least not just yet. She wanted to try a particular diet first. The house officer was quite appalled, saying that this was irresponsible, and then Richard spoke up. He said that Pam and he had discussed her options at some length the previous night and that he supported Pam in her decision. At this the house officer got quite angry, saying that this was *his* job, not Richard's. Pam felt in two minds: perhaps she had decided too quickly, but perhaps also she wanted to follow her instinct and this time stand up for her convictions. The latter thought got the better of her, and she was pleased that Richard was there to speak for her. The fact that he was there gave her courage.

Pam thanked the house officer for what his team had done and said that she would keep her three-months appointment in out-patients. She followed the diet to the letter, and a year later was doing very well.

Richard was called to the manager's office. The manager had received a letter from the consultant complaining that he had overstepped his professional boundaries. The house officer had evidently considered Richard's stance inappropriate and had taken the matter further.

The setting

This chapter concentrates on the issues of justice and fairness from a personal point of view. Justice can be an abstract idea which can be talked about; but justice is also present in most practical dealings between people.

By justice here is meant *moral* justice, not *legal* justice. Thiroux (1980: 125) points out that it is not enough that good and right are done; they have to be seen to be done: 'there must be some attempt made to distribute the benefits from being good and doing right'. The story of Pam will be used to illustrate some of these points.

Despite the fact that deontology stresses that an action itself matters, not the consequences, every action does have consequences. Ethical decisions are made with people, and so, if one strives to act ethically, one affects other people.

Aristotle had quite a lot to say about justice, particularly as Greek uses the same word for justice, fairness, equity and righteousness. Equality of justice, argued Aristotle, 'had to be understood as meaning fair or proportionate treatment' (Gillon, 1986: 87). Thus he could say that 'equals should be treated equally and unequals in proportion to the relevant inequalities'. This must be understood as meaning that those who are unequal (the poor, the sick, the deprived or the minorities of any society) should be given more or helped more than those who do not need such help. The question, however, is: on what basis does one make a decision to deem someone worthy of 'unequal' treatment? Would one consider Pam to be one of those who need or deserve 'unequal' treatment?

In an attempt to answer this question we need to consider what underlies justice, what motivates people and what they want to achieve by being just.

In his study *After Virtue*, MacIntyre (1985: 134) looks at 'virtues' through the centuries. When considering the Greek word for justice he finds that in Greece in the fifth century BC there were certain virtues commonly acceptable: 'friendship, courage, self-restraint, wisdom, justice'. He points out that later studies distinguished between 'cooperative' and 'competitive' virtues, and that justice was one of those over which there was disagreement. This disagreement can now serve as the starting point for looking at both aspects; the 'cooperative' side of nursing will be discussed in this chapter, and the 'competitive' side in Chapter 7.

Today we talk perhaps less about virtues and more about values. The two main values to have emerged in nursing are caring and advocacy. They are by no means the only ones, but they are the only ones to be considered here. Both stress the 'cooperative' character of values by seeing them as necessary to the helping relationship.

Values of nursing ethics: caring

Caring as a concept has recently been receiving more attention, largely encouraged by feminist thinking and writing. It is therefore right that caring as a particular value in nursing should be considered.

A very consistent and comprehensive set of values of caring for the health professions has been developed by Roach (1987). She sees caring to be 'the human mode of being' (p. ix); in other words, to be human is to care – to care is to be human. Roach considers that 'caring' has five aspects, each also beginning with the letter 'c': compassion, competence, confidence, conscience, commitment. She considers that 'comportment' could be another aspect, but does not include it in her list of 'Five Cs'.

Compassion as a value in nursing and health care is gaining momentum (Fox *et al.*, 1993, and see their references; also Pence, 1983). Care which is not given 'with passion' (compassion) is not beneficent care.

According to *Chambers' Dictionary* (1993), compassion is 'a feeling of sorrow or pity for the suffering of another, usually with a desire to alleviate it'. Pence (1983) considers that 'compassion is characteristically focused on a particular person or situation', whereas 'pity can be aroused by suffering, but may contain condescension and interpersonal distance absent in compassion'. What is most necessary for compassion is imagination – a rich and powerful imagination 'to understand and feel the suffering of people of different backgrounds, values and needs'. Pence makes an important statement about this when he says that

> part of the reason why this imaginative understanding is an achievement (and also why compassion differs from concern for social justice) is that this understanding presupposes an *intimacy* between people through which the sufferer reveals personal details to the listener. Such intimacy (is) almost always built on related moral qualities between listener and sufferer of trust, honesty, and the time and willingness to listen.

The use of the word 'intimacy' makes it clear that compassion is something very human, involving the body and its senses.

The story of Pam shows that she and Richard had built up a very good relationship very quickly – an intimacy had been created between them. Pam felt that she could trust this relationship, and this gave her the courage (one of the Greek virtues) to follow her intuition and thus trust herself. Richard showed that he had listened to Pam, and heard her for herself; he used imagination to understand another person and respond to her at the level which she needed and wanted.

Competence, in this set of values, means in particular professional competence or that which distinguishes the expert from the novice (Benner, 1984). Professionals have to be competent in their practice, but they also have to be given the freedom to practise their expertise in a personalised way. Certain practices have to be standardised and thus carried out correctly, but beyond that the care given has to be individual.

It is very likely that Richard would not have given exactly the same information to another patient. Not only did Pam's questions draw from him his own answers, but because he tried to hear what she was saying, he responded in a personal and a professional way. He gave her information and he discussed issues of treatment and outlook with her which were within his professional scope. He did not advise her what she *must* do but what she *might* do, and indeed this shows in that she herself decided what she would do. She then simply asked him to accompany her in her resolve and be a moral support.

Confidence fosters trusting relationships. Relationships, particularly professional helping relationships, are firmly based on trust and honesty. This is all too clearly evident when, for one reason or another, trust has been lost. Patients and clients need to be sure that they can trust the professionals who care for them, that they give them the right medications and treatments and that they do not misuse the trust placed in them. But the professionals also need to trust their patients, that they do not misuse them and their expertise.

Pam and Richard had such a trusting relationship and, by each exercising it, both were helped and satisfied, having done the fitting thing in the circumstances. This backfired later for Richard, but rather through the professional insecurity of a colleague than through his own incompetence.

Conscience is 'a state of moral awareness' (Roach, 1987: 64), the 'caring person [is] attuned to the moral nature of things. . . and grows out of experience, out of a process of valuing self and others'.

In the *intimacy* between Pam and Richard, a bond of 'moral qualities' was created which fostered trust and honesty and that 'moral awareness' which guided them both in their discussions and decisions.

Commitment is a certain 'stickability'. We are committed to patients and clients not just for the duration of certain treatments, but for the duration of their stay in hospital or community care. This is well recognised in the idea of the named nurse and primary carer. It is also an 'inner' commitment in the sense that this does not only mean doing things for that person, but 'being with' him or her on a human and personal level. Only in this way can a helping relationship develop and flourish. Such commitment was often frowned upon as 'getting involved'; but unless we do get involved we cannot really be human, let alone 'become' human. There is little job satisfaction in simply carrying out treatments, making beds and writing reports unless we do these things with, for and to people; the satisfaction is in knowing that *this person* has been helped with this treatment and *that person* feels better in a well-made bed.

The commitment in the story of Pam is clear: Richard listened to her and took time to listen and be with her. But then the commitment went further: he stayed on for a while in the morning to be with her when she wanted to speak to the house officer. Had he not done this after Pam asked him to, she could not have faulted him because his time was legitimately up. But Pam would have been disappointed, and so would Richard. He would have known – his conscience would have told him – that he had let Pam down. He had taken on the role of advocate, and he needed to fulfil that role.

Values of nursing ethics: advocacy

The story of Pam reveals that advocacy is a regular and vital part of nursing care. It is also a vital part of the principle of justice or fairness when considering equity. If justice means that unequals should be treated unequally, then someone needs to be concerned about the unequals.

Curtin (1983) makes this point graphically when she tells of a case 'involving a nurse who refuses to participate in the implantation of a cardiac pacemaker because the patient, an elderly, acutely confused woman, refused consent. A second nurse, recognizing that the refusal may be a direct result of the confusion, caused by a reduction in cardiac output, agrees to assist in the procedure and the woman is restored to health and the bosom of her family.' Only a few situations may be as dramatic and 'simple' as this one, where it is likely that one nurse was just more experienced than the other. The point, however, is that the more experienced nurse knew what to do and took a risk in doing it. The patient had, after all, refused to give consent for the operation. The first nurse had, strictly speaking, acted correctly, neither compromising the patient's integrity nor her professional future for taking part in a procedure for which there was no consent. Advocacy, therefore, happens at the interface between the strictly correct and the personally possible.

Advocacy rests on the need for information and the ability to assimilate this information and act on it. 'As patients become increasingly ill, their personal control over their own destinies may give way to intensified dependence on their physicians, and this dependence may result in poorer attention to, interest in, and recall for information about consent' (Morrison, 1991). Morrison makes the point that the dependence on doctors and nurses can also be explained in psychological terms. Patients revert to childhood patterns of behaviour and let the authority figures of 'father' or 'mother' take over. It is easy for doctors and nurses to assume the roles given them by patients in such circumstances and exploit them. With paternalism (and maternalism) now being seen as unhealthy, the emphasis has to shift from 'taking over' to pleading or interceding 'on behalf of'. This presupposes that the patient has information and the ability to act, but needs someone as an ally; or that the patient is not able to speak or act due to illness and needs someone to defend him or her on certain aspects of care.

Sawyer (1988) says that 'sadly, it seems one of the main reasons for patient advocacy by a nurse is the existence of unequal doctor–patient relationships. This is leading nurses to speak on behalf of their patients when there is a conflict with the medical staff'. Not only is there an unequal doctor–patient relationship, but there is also an unequal doctor–nurse relationship, generally resulting in poor communication. It could therefore be argued that the nurses' role as advocate is not so much based on real needs of care as on inadequate means of and ways for solving problems of communication. Perhaps the first issue to be considered is indeed equality – justice – between people: patients, professionals of all grades, those who 'know' and those who 'don't know', those who 'can' and those who 'cannot'. Justice or fairness begins very far back.

Many nurses feel that the advocate's role is unique to nursing and belongs to nurses almost by right. It is perhaps not surprising, therefore, that others feel that they can exploit that role. A Health Education

Authority report *The Smoking Epidemic: a Prescription for Change*, asks nurses to use their 'key position' and the 'special empathy' which many practice nurses have with their patients, to help them to give up smoking. This would reduce the cost to the health service in treating patients with smoking-related health problems (*Nursing Standard*, 1993). This sounds very reasonable, but it does undermine the nurse–patient relationship when nurses are asked to persuade patients to change their ways by a government which has consistently refused to ban cigarette advertising.

The role of nurse advocate is a delicate one and needs to be undertaken with care and thought. There are many grey areas in advocacy, the best-known possibilities being in palliative care, where patients ask to have their lives ended but have neither the means nor the strength to do it themselves. Or what of the alcoholic patient who begs to have the bottle of whisky, taken from him at admission, given back to him? Nurses who do take on an advocacy role may all too easily be considered to be whistleblowers or troublemakers. It is 'not enough to intervene on a patient's behalf; unless we can fully accept advocacy as part of our role, and ensure that provision is made to encourage nurses to undertake that role knowledgeably and professionally, we will flounder to the ultimate detriment of patient welfare' (Morrison, 1991). Nurses and the nursing profession will have to think much more carefully what this role involves and how it may best be developed as part of the 'cooperative' values of nursing.

What is happening?

If an ethic of nursing is to exist as something recognisable, it has to be understandable by every nurse, not just those with academic or philosophical leanings. It has to be understood and make sense in the practical situation, and indeed start from there. Only when we can see *what is happening* – ethically – here in this case, with these people and these circumstances, can we understand what ethics is all about.

The story of Pam is about a more and more common situation. Doctors examine and prescribe care, but nurses 'translate' and explain and make sense of it from day to day. (The issue of informed consent will be considered in detail in Chapter 8.) Sawyer (1988) points out that 'this may be interpreted as nurse and patient colluding against the medical profession, whereas it should be seen that the nurse is performing a function for the patient which, for a number of reasons, he [*sic*] cannot perform himself'.

What is happening to Pam is that, like many patients, she is overtaken by events. She will have heard and read much about breast cancer and its treatment and will probably have met people who have had chemotherapy. She will have known that this usually means a long course of regular outpatient appointments and injections. But knowing about it and experiencing it for oneself are not necessarily the same thing. She had coped well physically and emotionally with her operation, but when she heard the word 'chemotherapy' she could not accept what she was hearing. One can almost imagine Pam sitting on her bed, a small figure, with doctors towering over her and throwing facts and words at her, not asking her about them, but just dumping them in her lap. She raises her arms as if to hide and protect herself and she just manages to growl 'no'. She is extremely vulnerable, and in this state she turns to the only person whom she instinctively feels she can trust because the night before he had listened to her. She trusts this ability now.

Whatever it is that makes patients and clients trust nurses, it is a strong motivator and bond. The recipients of this trust are most likely not aware of this quality in them but when they are, they can use it even more effectively. It is that which makes a nurse–patient relationship so enriching for both parties. The two people relate to each other as persons, not simply as giver and taker, but as human beings who share something and who are committed to each other at an important level.

It is not only seriously ill people who have difficulties with attention to, interest in, or recall of information given them. Anyone under stress has difficulties of concentration. They hear what they can emotionally bear or want to hear. Thus it is likely that Pam was indeed asked if she were willing to have chemotherapy. She may have been spoken to very politely; she may have been given some explanations – but all this she neither recalls nor pays attention to. What stopped her from doing this may be the crucial question and that which eventually gives meaning to her decision.

When asking *What is happening?* to Pam we must consider several clearly defined areas; these are her physical illness, the way in which this is usually treated, and her place in the continuum of the treatment plan; her emotional reactions and responses to the illness and its treatment; the influence on her of other people's experiences of breast cancer; her family and their needs, influences and fears. The influence of the family has deliberately been minimised in the story in order to concentrate on the relationship between Pam and Richard, which was such a strong and important one. Pam's family were, in fact, very supportive of any decisions she took but did not try to influence or persuade her in any way.

What is happening to Pam is indeed what is happening to many patients: faced with a personal crisis, their world changes dramatically. Values held for all their lives suddenly collapse, and new and unknown values present themselves and have to be coped with. For Pam, these can be summed up as: having to face the fact of a malignant illness; probably a shortened life expectancy; deciding for herself what she can cope with in the way of treatment; making up her own mind independently of expert advice and expectations; considering alternative ways of treatment; treating herself rather than relying on other people's help; saying 'no' to authority; having decided what she wants, going through with the decision and not buckling under pressure to change her mind – in other words, seeing herself as an independent person with views of her own which are valid, which don't have to be changed because someone else, who seems more important, says so; speaking up for herself and being assertive. It appears, therefore, that Pam was not assertive but dutiful and submissive before her operation, always doing what others wanted her to do. This may sound somewhat unreal, but is in fact all too often the case when people are under pressure.

These things may not have been spoken of between Pam and Richard, but Richard must have been aware of them, or at least known of their possibility, because the help which he gave to Pam was appropriate: he put facts to her, he encouraged her in her own views and supported her in pursuing these views, and finally he stood by her when she had to speak for herself. He didn't do it for her, but he confirmed what she had decided and he took responsibility for his part in the shaping of the decision.

It is at this level that it becomes clear that Niebuhr's way of dealing with ethical challenges is not just an intellectual exercise but a way of seeing the whole of life as being governed by ethical behaviour, and also that ethical principles reach into every aspect of living, and caring in particular. The idea that unequals need to be treated unequally is clearly evident in the story of Pam: she needed help, there and then, to deal with a major decision in her life; she asked a professional for help, and that person responded in a professional way. Aristotle did not specify exactly who the 'unequals' are, and even if he had done so, this does not preclude anyone from deciding that a person needs his or her attention or help at a particular moment. Most people in need do in fact need only a small amount of help at any one time, and when that help is given, they can then cope better and more effectively than before.

What is happening to Richard in this story? He was there, he gave his help, and he was punished for it.

Richard was an empathic carer; his listening and helping skills were evident to his patients and they responded to this and trusted him. He was clear in his boundaries, having told Pam when he would be free to speak with her, and then he made it clear that he was not in the business of turning her against her doctors or any treatment. He was aware that Pam hesitated in accepting the proposed treatment and, as she was sceptical of its efficacy, he supported her view that something else might help her more if she believed that it would.

Stories of miracles and easy cures can be very attractive, particularly when one has known the person who told of the miracle. Most people would like to avoid long and debilitating treatments, and complementary therapies are certainly less often seen as 'cranky' nowadays. There may therefore have been an element of avoidance on the part of Pam which Richard played along with, but this was tempered by Pam's decision not to have chemotherapy – yet. She was not entirely against it, but wanted to try her own way first. Richard considered this not only feasible but also right and so he supported Pam.

When Pam asked Richard to be with her when she told the house officer, Richard agreed again. He needed to follow through with his professional commitment to Pam; not doing this would have indicated to Pam that he was not wholly supportive and she would have hesitated and wavered in her resolve, and this might have been emotionally damaging to Pam to an extent which she might not have fully realised at the moment. As time went on, she could well have lost trust in any health-care professional.

Richard went beyond the call of duty when he stayed on a while to see Pam through the hurdle of talking with the house officer. This is the only thing which might be held against Richard when looked at from a strictly procedural or contractual point of view. But part of the 'competence' outlined above is that professionals can and do make decisions of this kind and must be given the freedom to make such decisions. Nurses who are not versed in any ethical vocabulary would nevertheless make such decisions because they see them as 'right', 'just' and 'fitting'.

Richard might well have had to make such decisions before, and helped patients in similar circumstances. This background of experience and knowledge will have shaped his approach and conviction in dealing with Pam. Had he been disciplined before this event, he might have dealt with it in a more cautious and perhaps less honest way.

Most of this reasoning and considering was probably absent in the talks between Richard and Pam. Theirs was a straightforward helping conversation, each person saying what seemed necessary to be said, considered and decided. But without a background awareness of these elements, there would not have been a fitting conclusion. Had there been any need on the part of Richard to go more deeply into the matter of decision making with Pam, he would have had to draw on these considerations.

What is the meaning of it?

Two elements in this story of Pam and Richard need to be looked at under this heading: Pam, who protested to the consultant 'Oh yes, there is', when he told her that there was no choice except to have the chemotherapy; Richard, who was accused of overstepping his professional boundary.

It is likely that the ideas of ethics, *meaning*, process, decisions, outcomes, good, right, justice and so on were never mentioned in the three conversations between Richard and Pam, but they were implied.

Being able to talk with Richard about her, perhaps, unexpected needs and feelings, Pam was helped to take those needs and feelings seriously and work with them rather than discount them and later perhaps regret having discounted them.

Pam was in a crisis which she had perhaps not realised fully. The shock of the operation and the proposed treatment brought her up sharply to face herself and her future. As she indicated, this was the first time in her life that she had taken such an action and made such an important and far-reaching decision. She suddenly realised that her life might be foreshortened and that she was not going to have doctors and treatments as the directors and masters of the rest of her life. If she was going to be in charge of her life, then she had to be consistent and act as from *now*. She was not used to this, and she needed someone to stand by her. She was not used to assertion, but she instinctively knew where to look for help: the person whom she had trusted from a short conversation the night before.

This dramatic change in the direction of her life will only be understood gradually by Pam. This one decision will affect all other decisions she takes from now on, because she will have changed her whole way of thinking and behaving, literally overnight. This would not have been possible had she not subconsciously been prepared for this. Ideas of a 'cancer personality', of not expressing but hiding feelings and living one's life through other people who take charge over one can all be seen to make sense in this case. Many patients say that cancer was not a 'disaster' for them but rather an eye-opener and even a blessing. It may be that in the year in which Pam followed the diet with such good effect, she, too, came to hold these views.

Why was Pam not assertive, not able to speak and decide for herself before she got cancer? She may have been brought up in an authoritarian household; some event from early childhood may have lodged itself in her childish reasoning which later determined how she should behave; she may have had to learn early that anger was not appropriate for a girl – such insights may eventually come to her as she looks back but will probably not have been available to her at the time of the conversation with Richard. But had Richard not talked with her, all this might have been going on just under the surface and later had catastrophic sequelae, with further physical illness and certainly emotional wounds of perhaps self-loathing, anger and inappropriate despising of authority figures. The principle of justice was therefore well served here by Richard spending a little time with Pam. His values of caring were well applied.

Richard might not have given the whole incident much further thought had not the letter from the consultant made him question his attitudes and values. Like Pam, he was faced with the fact that others thought that they were right and he was wrong. Like Pam, Richard should then have had someone with whom he could talk about his situation. That someone should then have helped Richard to look at exactly the same questions as are asked here, namely, *What is happening?* and *What is the fitting answer?* In asking these questions Richard would have been able to see clearly what he had done right or wrong, and what would be his response after noting his interpretation of, and accountability in, the matter.

What is the fitting answer?

When we ask this question of Pam it is clear that, having taken the decision not to have chemotherapy but to follow the diet she had heard of, she needed to tell the medical team of this decision. This will have been much the hardest step for her as she was not used to standing up for herself nor to telling anyone that she was not going to accept their well-meant advice.

It could be argued that in the unfolding of her decision it was only logical that she had to come to this point. But she could equally well have argued that she could go so far and no further. She could have decided that she would just go home and not turn up for the chemotherapy appointment; that she would ask Richard or her husband to tell the doctor; or that it might be easier over the phone in a few days' time. But none of these possibilities was good enough. She had taken the first step on the road of self-determination and assertiveness, and she knew that she had to go the whole way. Richard will probably have helped her to come to this decision by not offering to speak for her or suggesting that she might take the easy way out, but by asking her to formulate a goal and consider how to put it into practice. When Pam did decide that she herself must speak with the house officer, she knew that this was the *fitting answer* in her situation. She was more than right to ask Richard to stand by her and support her.

The *fitting answer* for Richard to the question of whether he would stand by Pam then was clearly 'yes'. His compassion, competence, confidence, conscience and commitment all pointed in that direction. Good and right do not only have to be done but they also have to be seen to be done.

The pattern of responsibility

The pattern which emerges when ethical decisions are taken is always the same; Niebuhr has highlighted this by naming the various aspects of the pattern, and these can now be used to summarise the events in this story.

The *challenge* – that which sparks an ethical enquiry or debate – was the statement that Pam would have to have chemotherapy. Given that she knew that she had cancer, this should not have been totally unexpected, but to Pam it was. The word shot into her more sharply than any injection might have done, and disturbed her more than any drug would have. It hit her so hard that she knew she would never be the same afterwards.

The *response*, then, was first of all this physical feeling of complete lack of acceptance and rejection of the whole idea. This was so strong that it elicited a whole string of reactions and further responses. This initial feeling or instinct was almost stronger than Pam herself. Even if she had not trusted her instincts so far, this time she could not do anything but trust them.

The physical response is conditioned by the underlying emotions, which in this case seem to have been an accumulation of feelings of repression, humiliation, being put down, used as a doormat and giving in to any request by anybody – in short, being treated as an object rather than as a person. Clearly, Pam had allowed this to happen, but until she could acknowledge this she experienced it as being done to her. The word 'chemotherapy' was now literally the straw that broke the camel's back. Her refusal to accept chemotherapy was like the floodgates being thrown open after years of being forced shut.

By *interpreting* these feelings and responses, it could therefore be seen that Pam's refusal of chemotherapy might simply be seen as an irrational act, given her past conditioning. Any 'good' nurse would therefore say to her, 'Don't act on your feelings, think of your family, it won't be as bad as you imagine'. But this is just the point: nurses and helpers who are skilled in listening and counselling will not make Pam's interpretations for her but help her to make her own interpretations. 'Good' nurses are not necessarily skilled nurses. Pam herself has been 'good' all her life, and where did it get her? She needed someone who could ask *What is happening?* of her and not give her a ready-made answer.

Under the heading of *interpretation* Pam will have learned gradually to make sense of her unexpected and unusual response. She will eventually have come to insights into why she had let herself be the doormat she experienced herself to be. She will perhaps also have learned that the 'doormat' is not the whole of her life and that there are many other aspects to her life and person which do not conform to this image. Her memories will play a large role in the way in which she interprets her response and makes sense of it.

The part of the pattern described as *accountability* gauges how a decision would affect the life of the person concerned and those around them. Here, too, Pam hardly had time to weigh up, speculate, consider and anticipate. She had gone from challenge to decision almost in one leap. The fact that she made this leap with the help and support of Richard is significant, because he will have provided a kind of balance. The fact that he was prepared to support her also shows that her decision was not wild or irrational but, on the contrary, based on an instinct which could be trusted.

Many ethicists would say that real ethical decisions are rational and logical decisions, based on certain theories or principles, such as deontology or utilitarianism. Decisions like Pam's would therefore not be considered ethical decisions as such, but medical decisions, or decisions of psychological importance. Yet it is clear that Pam's decision affected not only her own life, but also that of her family and friends. The person who had originally told Pam of the diet which she was now willing to follow had exercised a great deal of influence (no doubt, quite innocently), and Pam's decision may in turn influence other people. Besides this, if the diet was not successful, her family might be without her even sooner than if she had had the chemotherapy. The diet would be expensive and time consuming – would they be able to afford this? Pam will not have had time to consider all these points. What mattered to her was her own being and well-being. Thus she could now be called selfish. Gradually we see the ethical dilemma in this story: whichever way she acts, Pam is going to be described as 'someone with' (Meilaender, 1993) a problem, or a disease, or attributes which others judge from their point of view. If Pam wants to be 'someone who' has a history, who is a person in her own right, then her

> life is a story and has narrative quality – a plot to be lived out. That story begins before we are conscious of it, and, for many of us, continues after we have lost consciousness of it. Yet, each narrative is the story of 'someone who' – someone who, as a living body, has a history. (Meilaender, 1993)

It is this history which Pam began to be conscious of and live for the first time in her life, and, like Frank Sinatra, she did it 'my way'. It must be debatable if this is egoism or a good person doing a right action, in that she will inevitably be a more fulfilled person who will be living life much more fully and helping others to do the same.

When a *fitting answer* has been arrived at, even though this may not be the answer which was expected, then the *social solidarity* gained will be seen and felt. Pam's decision not to have chemotherapy will therefore be seen to be the right one when the family can go along with her decision, support her and themselves benefit from the decision in that Pam is fulfilled as a person and their family life is strengthened. It is difficult to measure this in any kind of way, but 'happiness' is one of those things which crop up again and again in ethical literature as a goal or end to be achieved. As far as we know, this was the case for Pam.

It was clearly not the outcome as far as Richard was concerned. He was at the receiving end of a colleague's sense of inferiority and perhaps also jealousy. If Richard was helped to go through the process as he had helped Pam, then there could have been a good outcome for him too. This is to be hoped, because such incidents are essentially very harmful. When learning is possible, then that in itself can also lead to integration and social solidarity.

I shall end with a quotation from Hubert (1993):

> It has been found that patients gain more confidence by having someone by their side and are more often able to say what they do or do not want. Although nurses often act as the patient's advocate when they see a patient feeling pressured or uncomfortable, or unable to stress a point of importance, it has also been found that they are unable to act as full advocates without going against other health-care professionals or their personal and professional views and beliefs.

The story of Pam and Richard is an example of both the negative and the positive points made.

Chapter 7
The principle of
justice or fairness (2)

Story

Bernie was the Practice Nurse in a large fund-holding GP practice.
There were two older partners, and two younger ones who had
joined this group about six months earlier. There had been some
initial difficulties in making contact with all the patients of the two
new partners, and in particular, to get all the elderly people to
come for their annual health checks.

Mrs Fox was a patient of one of the new partners, Hugh
Mathews, and she had been sent a letter to explain the changes and
also to say that she was due soon for another check-up. She was 74,
widowed and in reasonably good health. She had smoked ever
since she had met her future husband, when he was about to go in
the army. Since her husband died, some fifteen years ago, she had
also had her 'wee dram' every night, but Dr Mathews suspected
that this was rather a large dram.

At the beginning of the winter Mrs Fox turned up in the surgery,
coughing very badly and looking ill. Bernie checked her notes and,
rather puzzled, asked Mrs Fox if she hadn't had her flu injection.
She had never heard of a flu injection. Had she not been sent a
letter, asked Bernie, to come to the surgery for this? Certainly not,
insisted Mrs Fox.

That week there were several other elderly patients of the
younger partners who presented with bad colds. None of them had
been invited to have the flu injections either. Bernie began to

wonder what had happened to the system of automatic mailing, and asked Hugh, Mrs Fox's GP. He said that surely Bernie knew that there was a shortage of flu vaccine this year. Yes, she knew, but the other partners all had enough. Hugh said that he considered it his duty to allocate his scarce resources in the medically most sensible way. He had not thought that Mrs Fox was one of the people who would most benefit from the vaccine because of her life-style. He had asked that several of his patients should be removed from the list of people who would be sent mail shots about the vaccine. If they remembered it by themselves he would not withhold a prescription. There was, however, no guarantee that there would in fact be any vaccine available.

Bernie had to quiz Hugh to get this information, and she made it very clear to him that she did not agree with this practice. She pointed out that her own practice was compromised by his action, which she considered to be one-sided and judgemental.

The setting

Good and right do not only have to be done; they have to be seen to be done – only thus can justice be understood.

However, Husted and Husted (1991: 41) consider justice to be an 'undefined term' and therefore neither a principle nor a standard. They exclude justice from their model of bio-ethical standards, considering justice, which is related to issues of resource allocation and health care, to be a political issue or problem.

The idea of 'fairness' is often deeply ingrained in children, and many of them grow up with a very strong sense that 'fair play' is the only play. Indeed, there are plenty of proverbs and sayings which stress the idea of fairness: 'What is good for the goose is good for the gander' and 'Outward be fair, however foul within' (Charles Churchill, 1731–64) are but two. Fairness in health care is an ideal which is stressed again and again, often to make the point that, if it were applied, life would be better. In this sense the words 'justice', 'equity' and 'fairness' can indeed be used interchangeably.

With this in mind, it is interesting to look at any nursing journal and see how many news items refer to issues of justice, or injustice. For instance, *Nursing Times* (1993a) mentioned in the week 10–16 November:

- More than 50 teaching jobs and 75 student places are to be cut at three northern colleges.
- People who have meters pay more for their water than those who have no meters. This affects large (and often poor) households more than small (and often well-off) households. The incidence of dysentery has risen in 1992, and health visitors are claiming that it is due to metered households saving on water.
- The number of nurses working in the health service fell by nearly 6,000 between 1990 and 1991, while the number of senior and general managers increased by nearly 4,000.
- Strong links between mental illness and social deprivation have been picked up by new research.
- Medium-secure units in inner cities are in crisis, swamped by waves of new patients diverted from prisons and discharged to care in the community without adequate back-up.
- Parents in ground-floor flats near the Elephant and Castle junction in London are afraid to open their windows in case car fumes seep in and cause asthma attacks.
- British women have the worst breast cancer mortality in the world.

The reaction to all of these news items could be 'It isn't fair'. Somewhere, justice is not being done. But perhaps Husted and Husted (1991) are right in saying that this is not a *biomedical* problem, but a political one. A great many decisions made in health care these days are political problems. Operations are cancelled because budgets are running short, not because the patients don't need them. People with mental handicaps find themselves sleeping rough, not because this is their choice but because a policy has closed their hospital. Fewer nurses are caring for more patients, not because nurses have decided that they would like to care for more patients, but because reorganisations at district and area levels have caused changes which affect care. A unit is working as a surgical ward for ten months of the year and as a medical ward for the remaining two, not because this seemed a good idea in itself, but because it was the only 'political' solution which would keep the unit open. It is not possible to keep politics out of the discussion about justice in health care; the 'competitive' side of justice has also to be considered. For health care workers to be 'just' may mean that they have to be 'political': not party-political, but cooperatively and competitively concerned that equity in health care is firmly on the agenda when economy, effectiveness and efficiency tend to be the only standards applied.

The idea of personal and social rights (see Chapters 5 and 6) is based on justice and fairness. The claim is that everybody should have the same rights, and those who are deprived, or left out, claim a right in order to be equal with those who are not deprived or left out. This shows not only that society is inherently made up of unequals, but also that society is constantly striving to overcome this. It is important here to be aware that this is *moral* justice (morally, we all have the same rights) and not *legal* justice, because, legally, we certainly do not all have the same rights.

Justice in health care has traditionally been applied to issues of equity: if ten patients need kidney dialysis and only one machine is available, which of the ten people gets it? Is a decision made on the patient's worth, ability or need? Thiroux (1980: 127) argues that a fairly conducted lottery is the most equitable measure. But nowadays both patients and health-care personnel look for something a little more sophisticated than drawing the short matchstick when it comes to life-saving treatments – even if it feels that this is what is happening.

Who deserves care?

Who gets treated and who does not get treated? Medical decisions have always been made in a mixture of morality and economics. Before the word 'paternalism' existed, and the concept was not questioned, nobody gave it any serious thought. With people being more and more aware of their rights, the tables have completely turned. But with rights go responsibilities, and it is these which have yet to be considered as widely as rights.

One effort to set priorities in health care was made in Oregon, USA, in 1984 (Crawshaw, 1991). A total of 75 ordinary citizens of Oregon, briefly trained 'in the world of bio-ethics', held some 300 community meetings involving 5,000 fellow-citizens. They concluded that their issues were about

- autonomy and dignity
- prevention of disease
- access and justice
- cost control
- allocation of fairness.

These people were 'alive to the responsibility of relieving human suffering in a world so complex we sometimes feel abandoned and lost'. They realised that the values they had listed were the 'missing ingredients in health policy'. Out of these original meetings has now grown the Oregon Health Services Commission, which is mandated by the legislature. The Commission has defined categories for health care, and Crawshaw (1991) believes that this has freed doctors

> from the odious burden of pretending that with a few more dollars and a smattering of volunteer work the medical profession can care for the poor. Today we have a way of emerging from the quagmire of managed care which converts physicians into gatekeepers . . . . As physicians acknowledge and work through a civic approach to health care we can regain our ethical stance.

On the other hand, Fuchs (1983: 64) quotes from a letter by a physician, who writes:

> Fully 80 percent of illness is functional, and can be effectively treated by any talented healer who displays warmth, interest and compassion regardless of whether he has finished grammar school. Another 10 percent of illness is wholly incurable. That leaves only 10 percent in which scientific medicine – at considerable cost – has any value at all.

This sounds rather cynical, but there is probably more than a grain of truth in it. How much influence do nurses and health care workers have in any decisions of who gets care and what sort of care they get? Generally speaking, very little, but nurses may partly be blamed for this by not making themselves available enough when treatment decisions are made.

In the 'value for money' drive so beloved of the current NHS managers, there have been several widely publicised cases of patients who did not get the expected treatment because they represented a bad risk. Besides smokers, who might be discriminated against in a cash-restricted health service, Dimond (1993) mentions also:

- attempted suicides because they might try again, along with drug and drink abusers and the obese who only have themselves to blame;
- sports injuries, e.g. from skiing, motor/cycle/horse racing, climbing, boxing, pot holing as they knew the risks of injury and voluntarily took them on;
- AIDS/HIV patients, apart from haemophiliacs and children, as they also only have themselves to blame;
- elderly over 70 years as major surgery is hardly justified considering the life expectancy at that age. (Ambulances are sometimes instructed to take coronary cases over 70 to the geriatric ward and not to coronary care.)

- severely mentally infirm as they do not appreciate the benefits of health care and treatment;
- sex change, as this can never be justified. (Had God wanted a person to be a woman rather than a man he would have made him that way.)
- reckless drivers, as they caused their injuries by their crimes.
- those dependent on social security, as how can they fund the food, heating, housing and support necessary in convalescence and to prevent recurrence of their health problem? Is there likely to be a significant health gain if the underlying social and economic conditions remain?

It has become clear to most people in recent times that health is not something we have by right; that health care is very expensive and is becoming increasingly more expensive; and that resources are restricted. Medicine, or perhaps rather science and technology, have given us the possibility of long life with good health and, when health breaks down, the further possibility of being fixed with more and more imaginative 'spare-part surgery'. Can we say 'no' to using the equipment when it is there? And on what grounds do we decide not to use it? And who makes the decision not to use it? The newly emerging discipline of health economics will shape all our lives more and more in the future.

Quality Adjusted Life Years (QALYs)

QALYs are a 'measure of quality of life which combines length of survival with an attempt to measure the quality of that survival' (Harris, 1987). According to Williams (1985), the 'architect' of QALYs, this means that

> The essence of a QALY is that it takes a year of healthy life expectancy to be worth 1, but regards a year of unhealthy life expectancy as worth less than 1. Its precise value is lower the worse the quality of life of the unhealthy person (which is what the 'quality adjusted' bit is all about). If being dead is worth zero, it is, in principle, possible for a QALY to be negative, i.e. for the quality of someone's life to be judged worse than being dead.

Crisp (1991) has tried to make this clear with an example:

> Consider a patient who is expected, other things being equal, to live in perfect health for ten years after a heart transplant. The gain in QALYs is $10 \times 1 = 10$. A patient undergoing treatment for leukaemia may also live for 10 years, but her quality of life may be diminished by the illness. If we assume that her

quality of life is only half as good as it would be were she in full health, we can calculate the QALYs produced by treating her as 10 × 0.5 = 5. But this, of course, does not mean that we should allocate funds to heart transplantation and not to treating leukaemia. For cost must be considered. Let us suppose that a transplant costs £100,000; a course of chemotherapy £20,000. We can now work out costs-per-QALY. For heart transplants, this will be £100,000/10 = £10,000; for leukaemia treatment, £20,000/5 = £4,000. If we assume these figures to be correct (they are not, in fact), then treating leukaemia is a more efficient use of funds than transplanting hearts.

The debate of quality of life versus quantity of life is never far away. It often seems as if there is a straight division between doctors concerned with quantity and nurses with quality and the patient is in the middle, between a battle of wills.

Harris (1987) argued that, as a measure for available resources, QALYs favour the young and is 'the practice of valuing life-units (life-years) rather than people's lives'. Both he and Crisp (1991) make the point that QALYs further the many 'isms' which already exist in society: ageism, sexism and racism. Crisp adds another one – 'defectism' – meaning discrimination against people on the ground that they are mentally defective in some way.

> So an administrator might say: 'Well, we can save either these 10 non-defective people, or those 10 defective people. Other things being equal, the non-defective people are likely to live lives of higher quality, so we must sacrifice the defective people.'

> *In discussions, workshops and lectures I have again and again raised the question of QALYs. Most health-care workers have not heard of this term, but all of them condemned it as unfair and not right. When asked if they thought that some measure like QALYs was being used in their institution, they usually thought it was, but that they were guessing. When further asked what might be a fairer way to decide how resources might be allocated, they were not able to give an answer.*

Perhaps one of the difficulties with QALYs is that it seems remote, leaving out a personal element. 'They' decide what is happening, what chances a person has of getting the best or the most appropriate treatment. A criterion which is often applied in such situations is this: 'Would I like it to happen to me (or my wife, husband or mother)?' The fear then is that everybody would say 'no', and that everybody only wants the best, the most expensive, and they want it now. This would ruin health care altogether, and therefore checks and balances have to be built into the system. But probably people are not as unreasonable as that. Not everybody wants or needs the most expensive treatment; indeed, many people feel that less would be more, but that they are not given the chance to voice their opinion. They feel that they are on a treadmill of investigations and treatments and cannot get off. If they could be heard, they would be happier, and so would the providers.

In one area of life this is now slowly happening. The introduction of 'living wills' (see p. 21) is an area where people are making their preferences known, almost in spite of measures such as QALYs, though this is as yet also an imperfect measure.

Resource constraints

Right through this discussion of justice and fairness in health-care settings runs the theme of constraints on resources of money, people and goods. QALYs is only one way of tackling the problem. Perhaps because it is so far the only published way of managing resources, it is receiving a great deal of negative criticism. But perhaps it is also because 'one of the major choices any society must make is how far to go in equalizing the access of individuals to goods and services. Insofar as this is a question of social choice, one cannot look to economics for an answer' (Fuchs, 1983: 22), and QALYs is trying to be an economic answer to individuals' access to care.

One of the changes in health care in Britain which has been largely hidden or overlooked by the general public is the shift from 'health care for all' in the NHS to 'access to care for all'. When district general hospitals were truly 'general', patients received all their inpatient care conveniently close to home. With the market economy, care is being centralised and competition for patients is fierce. Care is not given any more where it is most convenient for the patient, but according to the trust, centre or consultant specialising in that particular aspect of care. Care may no longer be available for all regardless of need, but access to care when necessary is assured. This means that resources can be pooled and are therefore cheaper to administer – but it is not cheaper for patients and their families if they have to travel to receive them.

Fuchs (1983), who writes about health, economics and social choice, states that 'economics is the science of means, not of ends' (p. 29) and goes on to say that economics 'can explain how market prices are determined, but not how basic values are formed; it can tell us the consequences of various alternatives, but it cannot make the choice for us. These limitations will be with us always, for economics can never replace morals or ethics.' This is a timely warning, because it feels all too often as if nowadays the people in decision-making positions believe that economics ('value for money') is the answer to all problems, and they seem to be surprised when this turns out not to be the case. To have an economic answer to a problem is clearly easier than to search for the ethically fitting one.

In any setting where justice, fairness and equity are not upheld as principles or ends in themselves, inequalities are created which can be very damaging. The erosion of justice usually begins slowly, but when asked to compromise again and again, people become apathetic and demoralised. If they are 'constantly forced to abandon their reasoned moral judgments and consciences in favour of preserving the paragons of law and convention' (Johnstone, 1989: 332), then not only are those individuals disillusioned, but inevitably, also, care suffers.

Most people accept that countries and governments do not have bottom-less purses, and in Britain we are well enough used to the annual debate over the allotment of money to government departments in the yearly budget. It often seems to be a question of robbing Peter to pay Paul. But many people also feel that the distribution of the sums used for health care is not fair. It seems that those who shout most loudly get the biggest share and that those whose voice is less powerful, such as the elderly, the mentally handicapped and ill and people with 'unsocial' diseases or habits get less. The 'unequals' do not get treated 'unequally'.

But it is not only treatments which are hit in this way. If the linen supplies are inadequate and patients are only given sandwiches for supper, that is another form of cost-cutting which affects the unequals: the patients who cannot afford to supplement their food from the hospital shop; and the nursing aides and assistants who often make the beds. Many nurses find that in such circumstances they can be neither advocates nor whistle-blowers – because there is nothing intrinsically wrong – and that they are truly trapped in situations in which they cannot function properly either as persons or professionals. This then leads either to frustration or indiffer-ence, but it cannot leave people untouched. If and when people are involved in decision making over issues concerning their sphere of influ-ence, they are less likely to be demoralised – but this calls for ethical as well as political awareness on the part of those who hold the purse-strings.

What is happening?

The story of Bernie and Mrs Fox may seem positively simple in this minefield of ethical and political debate. It takes only one example to show up the whole system, and there must be many 'Mrs Foxes' who for one reason or another are not offered or given adequate health care. The word 'short-termism' has crept into the language, and it certainly applies in this case.

What is happening to Mrs Fox? We are not given the exact reasons why her GP decided not to invite her for a flu injection, but it is easy enough to imagine the assumptions made: a 74-year-old woman, a smoker and drinker (to some degree), living alone and basically in good health. Flu vaccine is in short supply because everybody is expecting a bad strain of flu to hit the country in the coming winter. If rationing has to happen, then those who don't actually suffer from respiratory diseases must be considered as less needy. The underlying assumption here is also that Mrs Fox has had her 'three score years and ten', has no dependants and is abusing her body already with cigarettes and alcohol. In other words, her life is less worthwhile than that of someone younger, not a smoker or drinker and with dependants, or at least a family who could care for him or her and for whom she or he cares.

These are the given facts. The other facts are that a flu injection costs around £5 and a course of antibiotics about £3. Given the calculations made above for QALYs, it is possible to see that not giving the injection is indeed a saving. But is it just and fair to measure health in this way? Those who are concerned with economics would presumably say 'Yes, because we have to establish some basis on which to judge'.

If Mrs Fox herself had been asked what she wanted for herself, she might indeed have said that she didn't want the injection. She had never had one before and had survived as long as she had. She might not like injections. But she would probably not have calculated that her health was worth £5 or £3. Had Mrs Fox known these costs and these reasons for giving or not giving the injection – had she been able to make an informed decision – she might have made quite a different decision.

What is happening? points here to the fact that even in small matters, patients are rarely able to make a completely informed decision. Indeed, should people like Mrs Fox even be asked to decide? She is of the generation which accepted what someone in authority said, and she might be quite unwilling and unable to decide what is best for herself. But should we, the health-care professionals, make all these assumptions? If ethics is about how to be 'good' and do 'right', then we must seriously begin to ask patients and clients the basic question *What is happening* to you? and must not make assumptions.

What is happening to Bernie? As the Practice Nurse, she meets the patients before anyone else and she deals entirely with many of them, or at least before they get to see the doctor. She is also particularly concerned about screening programmes and health checks.

Bernie is a partner with the GPs, but with a *different* role, not an inferior one. When she saw that Hugh had changed one of the policies in the practice unilaterally, she felt rightly aggrieved and not taken seriously because she had not been consulted. If she was to do her work to the standard which she expected of herself and which her colleagues and her profession expected of her, then her work should not be interfered with by her colleagues. She pointed out to Hugh that he had done wrong by Mrs Fox and by her, not only by his action but also by his omission to tell her of his action.

Bernie took on the role of patient advocate when she went to Hugh to ask what had happened when Mrs Fox didn't get a letter to invite her for the injection. In Chapter 7 the point was made that advocacy may be necessary mostly because of communication difficulties between patients and doctors – and this is just such an example. The patient is inevitably in the middle, and, if she knows what is happening, she may also feel very uncomfortable about it. Bernie might have dealt with the situation differently, but clearly she had to do something. Asking Hugh for an explanation was the most correct one from any angle.

What is happening to Hugh? He had decided that some of his patients should not be sent letters to come for the flu injection. He had taken a unilateral decision in this matter which presumably the Practice Secretary had not questioned. But why had he taken such a decision? The given facts are that a flu epidemic was anticipated and that therefore the vaccine was in short supply.

Did Hugh want to impress his partners by his economy? Did he think that this was the best way of economising? Why did he not discuss this with his colleagues? The impression is that he is young and perhaps not so sure yet of his standing in the practice and has to show that he can decide on his own. He is also somewhat chauvinistic in that he seems to consider his job better than Bernie's – what *he* does counts; what *she* does matters less. When she asks him his reason for acting in this way, she does not get a clear answer but has to interrogate him; he is cagey and defensive. All these are classical reasons for patient advocacy to exist – but they are not the best reasons for it to be effective.

With his action, Hugh has damaged every one of the five principles of ethics: the value of life, in that by taking a superior stance he did not respect either Mrs Fox's, Bernie's or his other colleagues' intrinsic life; goodness or rightness in that such an action came out of a false sense of duty (from the point of view of deontology) and would have unhelpful and even disastrous consequences (from that of teleology) not only in the broken trust between Hugh and his patients and colleagues but also in the possible medical consequences of severe illness; it has damaged the principle of justice or fairness in that choosing some people on a random and unequal basis does not help anybody and makes the public's cry for justice in health care even louder and possibly more neurotic – but with reason; truth telling or honesty in that he did not consult with his colleagues and was most reluctant to admit what he had done when it was discovered; individual freedom in that the kind of freedom he used was egoistical and not ethical. When one principle is compromised, then all of them are, as is usually only too easy to see.

What of all that was said above about deserving care, QALYs and resource constraints? Does the NHS really stand or fall on one £5 injection? Are those weighty matters applicable to one patient?

Justice seems to demand that what is done for one is done for all, and vice versa. Policies and guidelines exist so that there is some order and uniformity in care and not just chaos; that it is not simply that those who are strongest do not get the most, but that those who are weakest also get what they need.

What is the meaning of it?

The story of Bernie is a tale of the uncovering of ethical wrongdoing. It is therefore more a story of the uncovering and managing of what has happened and preventing the same or worse from happening in the future. It is not a question of having to make a difficult choice. The element of meaning is therefore not as central, but it is still vital.

We may assume that Bernie had never been in such a situation before. She might therefore never have had to challenge a colleague before on his practice. This might be quite daunting for her. In her actions and decisions are shown the values which she stands by. Bernie was clearly upset that a mistake had been made and that, because of his action, Mrs Fox did not get what she should rightly have had for her health care. But Bernie was also upset because she was treated in a derogatory manner – or if not she personally, then at least her practice. In every way, justice was not done by her colleague. Her values of professional care were therefore questioned, and she had to look at what these were for her and perhaps refashion them or re-interpret them.

In an ethics of nursing, relationships matter just as much as any principles. Nursing ethics is characterised by the kind of relationships it keeps and fosters. These have to have a basis in justice or equity. This is shown in that Bernie was concerned about the relationship between Hugh and Mrs Fox and between Hugh and herself. Both were damaged; both are essential to good patient care. When Bernie later reflected on what had happened, it may have been that these were her main issues. They would also have been her reasons for later efforts to discuss policies in the practice and establish good working relationships again for the sake of their patients and themselves.

What is the fitting answer?

Once Bernie had discovered the details and the truth of the missing letter, she needed to follow through what this revealed to her. By asking Hugh exactly what had happened, she was trying to get to the bottom of what was beginning to become clear. Perhaps at that stage, getting to the bottom of it was Bernie's main aim; any interpretation of her findings might come only later.

If relationships are considered to be the bedrock of ethical care, then Bernie will have to weigh up how she speaks to Hugh and to Mrs Fox. She will be careful not to betray the trust which Mrs Fox has in her doctor's ability, but that does not mean that she has to cover up for Hugh or make excuses for him. She will also be concerned that how she deals with Hugh will be helpful to him and her and not alienate either of them.

In such situations most people have little time to consider what their actions should be, and what they do and say is therefore guided by deep values which may never have been challenged before. Psychology often makes the distinction between a person's actions, and personal being. In other words, one can criticise a person's actions, but that does not mean that the whole person is under attack or even condemned. If this is someone's deep belief, then it may be easier to deal with a situation which may involve criticism or even disciplinary action.

> *In workshops and discussions I often point this out, and it is surpris-*
> *ing how 'strange' this often appears. People can more easily accept*
> *this principle for others, but find it very difficult to accept that when*
> *they are criticised they may not be totally condemned. It may of*
> *course be true that the person who does criticise us does seem to*
> *imply that we are thereby written off and of no use, but if we can*
> *then also accept that we are criticised for our actions only, this gives*
> *a sense of strength because we do have the possibility to change.*

Ethical actions are, however, actions which are guided by conscience, and therefore by the whole person. It is implied that the action and the person go together, and rightly so, but as ethical beings we do not have the right to condemn a person altogether. The principle of the value of life should be the guide here, as indeed also that of justice and equity. If we are concerned that it matters how we relate to one another, then we have to learn also how to foster and maintain relationships between us when things go wrong.

Bernie's *fitting answer* to Hugh may therefore be one based on these principles: she does not condemn him, but cares for him as a colleague, with compassion, competence, confidence, conscience and commitment. This in no way diminishes the weighty matters of resource constraints and who is deserving of care. Indeed, these are thus put into some perspective. She will also have to apply their consequences to Hugh, but with the long-term view that her help now will 'pay off', for herself, the patients and her colleagues.

The pattern of responsibility

When we look at the pattern as a summary of this chapter, we can see that Bernie's actions determine whether or not the outcome is for good in the practice.

The *challenge* in this situation is the discovery that Mrs Fox was not sent a letter to ask her to attend for a flu injection: a simple fact, a surprise, perhaps even a concern that the Royal Mail might once more not have been as efficient as it might be – but had Bernie assumed that this was the case, she might never have discovered the real reason. The real *challenge*, however, presented itself to Bernie when she discovered what Hugh had done. It was his action which started a whole sequence of events.

The *response* for Bernie can be imagined: she was probably so taken aback by Hugh's avowal that he had eliminated certain patients from the mail shot that her mouth fell open, and she might have stared at Hugh with wide opened eyes and was unable to move. These would have been the physical responses and reactions to her surprise and upset at his treatment of her and of this particular patient.

Bernie might never have been treated in this way before, and her response would therefore have been a completely new and unknown one – that of shock that this could even happen. But, more likely, her reactions would have been informed by past memories of being taken advantage of, being used and abused, and treated as a means rather than an end. If this was the case, her response might also have been guided by the outcome of past situations of a similar kind: if they had had good outcomes or difficult or bad ones. She might have become angry if she had experienced pain in the past without any good outcomes. She might be more aware of the pain than of the anger, and she might remember the people who had caused this pain and this might colour how she will have responded now.

All this will have taken place in the space of a few heartbeats, but she will have been very much aware of this, without perhaps being able to name it all. Her *interpretation* of these past events will convey itself to Hugh and how he interprets what he hears and sees. What is said between the two of them is therefore heavily laden with feelings which may not always be logical or clear, but which are certainly very present and because of that have to be taken seriously.

It is out of this interpretation of the past that the *accountability* comes which will decide what may be the next move. Bernie may actually jump at Hugh and give him a piece of her mind, if she has learned that anger is her best way of dealing with such situations. But she may also be so taken aback that she is speechless. She may perhaps decide simply to say 'thank you' now and look for an opportunity to talk with him later. Or she may be so 'grounded' in herself as a person that she can talk with him in a way which resolves the problem there and then. Her sense of accountability does mean that in whichever way she decides to do it, she must talk with Hugh to clear up what has happened. She herself is implicated in the situation, and her practice has suffered; she cannot just overlook the incident. At this stage she must ask herself what is her *fitting answer* – that is, what is she going to say to Hugh, and how.

The *social solidarity* created will depend on the way in which such a discussion is conducted. If Bernie does manage to talk with Hugh in such a way that she condemns his action but not his person, then she will indeed have acted ethically. Whatever theories or principles act as starting points, the outcome will be a better working relationship between Hugh and

Bernie; a lesson learned for Hugh (and also for Bernie); and no more patients discriminated against.

All this is hard work and particularly demanding for Bernie. If she is able to have support for this, so much the better. If nothing else, it will at least have helped her to see one side of her work in a clearer perspective. But the important point is also that ethical awareness was raised by this incident, which might not have happened had not a mistake been made.

Chapter 8
The principle of
truth telling or honesty (1)

Story

Nora had been a nurse specialist for a long time. She was excellent
at her job and seemed to be able to communicate well with
everyone – doctors, patients and colleagues. She was the specialist
in a unit where patients were diagnosed and prepared for heart,
lung, or heart-and-lung transplants. Nora spent much time with
the patients explaining to them what this would mean and
encouraging them in the often long months of waiting while their
conditions inevitably deteriorated.

The hospital had a policy of not carrying out transplants on
patients who were over 60 years of age. This had led to difficulties
before, but it now presented Nora with her worst problem.

Gloria was just two months short of her sixtieth birthday. Her
health had gradually deteriorated in the last few years. She was of
Nigerian origin and was the beloved matriarch of a big, extended
family. Her GP had originally sent her to Nora's hospital for tests.
Gloria had kept in touch with him, and the GP had mentioned a
possible heart transplant to her. She was delighted at the prospect
and gladly underwent all the tests. She did not know much about
this kind of surgery and appeared to trust the doctors and nurses
implicitly.

Her tests revealed to the surgeons that she might be a good
candidate for a heart transplant, and her enthusiasm and apparent
lack of worry were ideal from the emotional angle. Her large

family and many friends would ensure good care and support after the operation.

However, her age was against her. It was most unlikely that a heart would become available shortly, and the cut-off date was 60. The surgeon felt that he must abide by the policy. If he didn't, he might as well not have such a policy. Everyone concerned knew that if anyone could tell Gloria that she would not be put on the waiting list for a transplant, it would be Nora.

Nora often talked with a colleague about her work and situation. The two supported each other in many ways. Nora was particularly concerned to talk about her feelings. She felt inadequate and very lonely in this particular task. She also felt very close to Gloria because of the way in which everybody was treated as a friend by Gloria. Nora had worked many years in the Third World and she was very acutely aware in herself of a sense of injustice at turning down a black person for a transplant.

Nora felt that it would be best for Gloria to know outright that she would not be having a transplant, rather than letting her go on believing that she was on the waiting list. But the way in which this was done was crucial.

The setting

What is truth? said jesting Pilate; and would not stay for an answer.

(Francis Bacon, 1625)

It is not just Pilate who did not wait for an answer. It sometimes feels as if this principle is necessary simply because, as people, we are usually too much in a hurry to stop and wait for the other person to answer – and for us therefore to hear the truth.

The story of Nora points in particular to the two issues of organ donation and informed consent, both of them closely linked with truth telling. The fact that it was Nora who had to tell Gloria of the decision not to put her on the transplant list is perhaps rather unusual, but specialist nurses often take on tasks which may be seen as overlapping with those of doctors. In a well-functioning team however, it is clearly the person best suited to the task who should be chosen and willing to undertake it.

Perhaps truth telling or honesty is the most delicate of the principles of ethics. When a patient says, 'Tell me the truth,' we do not know how much of the truth he or she knows already or wants to know or is able to cope with.

MacIntyre (1985: 192) makes an interesting point:

> Lutheran pietists brought up their children to believe that one ought to tell the truth to everybody at all times, whatever the circumstances or consequences, and Kant was one of their children. Traditional Bantu parents brought up their children not to tell the truth to unknown strangers, since they believed that this could render the family vulnerable to witchcraft. In our culture many of us have been brought up not to tell the truth to elderly great-aunts who invite us to admire their new hats. But each of these codes embodies an acknowledgement of the virtue of truthfulness.

A debate about truth will always have to include aspects of absolutism versus relativism. There are certain absolutes which we know and which we can verify, such as that Tower Bridge spans the River Thames in London. But there are also absolute moral truths, such as the distinction between truth and falsehood. Relativism, on the contrary holds that everything, including morality, is relative to specific cultures, groups and individuals (Thiroux, 1980: 88). The above quotation is an example of this.

But truth is intrinsic to any moral system: we have to believe what others tell us; how else could we function as a society? In turn, we have to tell the truth.

> *As I am writing, there is a debate going on nationally, sparked by a government minister who maintains that in certain circumstances it is right to withhold the truth and even to lie to Parliament. He quoted a former prime minister as an example, but he in turn accuses the minister of false accusations.*

Since this is a practical rather than a philosophical text, it is not possible to pursue the arguments of absolutism and relativism in any depth. As with all matters concerning ethics and morality, there is always more that can be and needs to be understood on any subject. Our limitations are, however, also our challenges.

It is therefore not only a question of what the truth consists of, but also of how we perceive it. The patient who asks to be told the truth asks this from a background of his or her life, family, circumstances, understanding of health and function and many other known and unknown criteria and values which may have been voiced or not. The nurse responds to this question out of his or her own life experiences, circumstances and standing as a professional. The nurse has, in addition, a tradition and ethos of health and illness to defend, which maintains a formidable value system that may be very alien to that of the patient.

One aspect of 'truth' centres around the giving or withholding of 'bad' news, and to a nurse this may mean mostly the diagnosis and prognosis of a disease or illness. To a patient this may mean very little, but the 'truth' to him or her may be a livelihood shattered, a hidden guilt uncovered, a shame unmasked or status lost. Most of all, it may be that it is a dream or a hope shattered. The truth may also be, as in the case of Pam (see Chapter 6), a sudden realisation that someone is not the person she had always thought she was. 'Bad' news may be 'bad' for nurses and doctors, but it may not always be so for patients. Many patients have said that having cancer diagnosed was the best thing that ever happened in their lives.

Truth underlies any relationship. All our interactions are based on truthfulness. This may be as basic as buying a bag of sugar and knowing that what is in the bag is sugar and not something else. If truth makes sense in commerce, then how much more does it make sense in personal relationships? Yet our relationships are fragile, and in our dealings with others we constantly weigh up what we or the other person can tolerate. Each interaction is interpreted and responded to from that interpretation. Niebuhr (1963) has recognised this as part of the pattern of responsibility. As response and responsibility go hand in hand in relationships, truth and honesty are intrinsic to the pattern. With relationships being ever-changing, the responses we make are governed by a myriad of reasons, most of which have to do with preserving or defending who or what we are. Truth – or falsehood – are rarely the straightforward matters that most of us either wish or imagine.

In English we have very few words for 'truth' but many ways of describing 'untruth' – the 'little white lie' perhaps being the most genteel of these expressions. A politician has been 'economical with the truth', and since economy is one of those values which govern all our lives now, being economical with the truth sounds like a good thing – at least, a clever thing. When we consider how many things in public life are daily covered up and made to appear right, it is surprising that so much truth still does exist and that people still want to be honest.

Thiroux (1980: 135) believes that this 'principle may be the most difficult of all the principles to live with' because of the fragility of human relationships, but that, nevertheless, 'a strong *attempt* must be made to be truthful and honest'. It is this 'attempt' which characterises most of what can be said about this principle.

There can be few nurses who will not early in their career have met a conflict between caring and truth telling. 'Don't tell him' is serious enough from the point of view of maintaining good working relationships; it becomes a good deal worse when it also has wider implications, such as when a patient who is HIV positive is refusing to tell his or her partner. The nurse cannot invoke any rights or duties (this is different from other communicable diseases) to force a patient into a situation for which he or she is not ready. Any consent obtained with partial understanding or under duress is not genuine consent. Where there is no honesty there is also no autonomy for the patient (Jones, 1989).

Any untruth has consequences which may be potentially serious:

- An Asian woman patient in Accident and Emergency has requested to be treated by a female doctor but is told that none is available. A nurse who knows that this is not true but rather an excuse, knows also that the woman may go home rather than be treated.

- An Italian woman, aged 61, requested artificial insemination to have a baby. She admitted that 'she had told "a few lies" in order to make her dream come true. She said she had given her age "ten years less than I was" ' (*Daily Telegraph*, 1992a). This has consequences not only for her obstetrician but also for her baby: does the baby have a mother or a grandmother?

- A surgeon sterilising multiparous women 'as part of the section' when carrying out a Caesarean section, could be in jeopardy of ruining his career as well as the future of the patient.

- 'A 52-year-old lady awaiting a "small operation for the removal of a piece of intestine" ... was listed for major surgery on her bowel following a diagnosis of carcinoma ... became puzzled as to why she had not begun to feel better, but was delighted she did not have "a bag" as she had first been told she might' (Joy, 1990). Should this woman be deprived of the possibility to decide how she would like to live the rest of her life?

The results of any of these lies, white lies and untruths in terms of physical and emotional effects can be devastating. Any nurses caring for such people have a problem with both personal and professional integrity. The responses they make depend on how they understand this principle of truth telling or honesty.

But telling 'the truth, the whole truth and nothing but the truth' is not always the whole answer either, at least not in health care. When truth is a matter of analysis and speculation, as in diagnosis and prognosis, it can never be grasped in the same way as the report of a blood test. Nevertheless, the principle of truth telling or honesty stands as a principle – that is, as something fundamental against which we test ourselves and our actions and words.

Informed consent

According to Duncan *et al.* (1981: 114), 'other human beings are the only mammals for which a licence to experiment is not required in this country'.

Informed consent has long been established as good medical practice. The Patient's Charter (Department of Health, 1991) lists as an 'existing right' 'to be given a clear explanation of any treatment proposed, including any risks and any alternatives, before you decide whether you will agree to the treatment'.

This is clearly more easily said than done.

> Doctors are renowned for their inability to communicate with their patients/
> clients. Most of us must have had the experience of a doctor unable to explain
> in lay terms (a) what is wrong with us and (b) what it entails. If they have
> difficulty when it is merely a matter of telling people what is going on, how
> do they manage when it is imperative that the patient understands what is
> said in order to be able to make a choice? (de Vahl Davis, 1992)

The twin aspects of informed consent which emerge are, therefore, (1) that information has to be given and (2) that it has to be understood.

What information has to be given? The Department of Health, in its *Guide to Consent for Examination or Treatment* (HC(90)22: 2), says that 'Patients are entitled to receive sufficient information in a way that they can understand about the proposed treatment, the possible alternatives and any substantial risks, so that they can make a balanced judgement.' This is a more cautious text than the Patient's Charter (Department of Health, 1991), which gives a patient or client the right to know about *any* risks and *any* alternatives.

de Vahl Davis (1992) quotes the case of a woman 'who had an operation on her spinal column to relieve a persistent pain in her neck. The surgeon did not tell her that there was about a 1 percent risk that her spinal cord would be damaged and she could become paraplegic. This is what did happen to her.' The woman argued that she should have been told, and took her case as far as the House of Lords, where it was finally rejected.

de Vahl Davis points out that such cases are always argued from the point of view of the patient's best interest: 'that is, it would be harmful rather than beneficial to a patient to be told all the risks. Perhaps so, but should a doctor be permitted to decide? The medical profession would call such concern for the patient beneficence: [the patient] might be inclined to call it paternalism.'

While there are experts and lay people, there will always be differences between them. The experts have only acquired their expertise during years of study and experimenting, and it is therefore quite unreasonable to expect lay people to understand the same amount, or even be told about a disease or a treatment in the time available. But May (1975) argues that as doctors are in fact dependent on their patients for their expertise, they are also indebted to patients, and this is expressed in their relationship with patients which should be marked by 'exchange, agreement and reciprocity'. This is not a paternalistic 'doctor knows best', with the patient doing all the agreeing, but it means one person sharing with another person and even asking *what is happening*? by both parties. May makes the further point that this kind of relating (which he calls 'covenant ethics') has truth telling as a basis: 'the moral question for the doctor is not simply a question of telling truths, but of being true to his promises . . . . The total situation for the patient includes not only the disease he's got, but also whether others ditch him or stand by him in his extremity . . . . What the doctor has to offer his patient is not simply proficiency but fidelity.'

Rowson (1993: 39), like May, a philosopher, bases his argument for informed consent on autonomy: when one accepts the importance of patient autonomy, one sees the professional–patient relationship as one in which both participants have an active part to play. The starting point for these two authors is different, but their conclusion is much the same. However, this does also point to the equal importance of all the five principles mentioned here.

The next aspect of informed consent to consider is that the information given has to be understood. Carpenter and Langsner (1975) say that consent should be more than a legalistic process, yet that too often there is 'inadequate informing and inadequate consenting'. What information a patient is given regarding any investigation or treatment does depend on the circumstances. Some innovative ways have been devised to increase the patient's knowledge and understanding of the information given, such as following any spoken instructions with printed notes or leaflets, with patients specifically given time to read and re-read the notes, and perhaps friends and relatives being encouraged to read and discuss with the patient what is involved before any appointments are made or signatures required. Some clinics and surgeries also tape conversations between doctors and patients or clients when specific or difficult issues are to be discussed and the patients are then given the tape to listen to again in the privacy of their home, when again families and friends can discuss and question what was talked about. This takes the pressure off patients who may be nervous, uneasy in clinics, perplexed about medical terms, or too embarrassed to ask simple questions for fear of being thought 'stupid'.

Just as important as the information given freely to patients is the information which is not given. This is clear from the case quoted above, where it was implied that if the patient had asked what the risks were of the operation on her spine, she would have been told; but she did not ask and was therefore not told.

It is not enough that patients are given only information which is positive, encouraging and pushing them in the direction of taking the same view as the doctor. Truth telling involves the truth told and the truth not told. For consent to be true, information has to be given voluntarily. Because patients would not know what else they might ask for, they cannot judge if all the information has been given. Only when all the necessary information has been given can we really say that a patient can give informed consent.

Giving information about proposed treatments is generally the doctor's duty, but it is increasingly also the nurses' duty – as the story of Nora shows. Wells wrote in 1986 that many nurses view informed consent to be entirely within the medical domain, 'yet at the same time talk to one another about their concerns that their patients are not informed'. To counteract this, Carpenter and Langsner (1975) suggest that nurses 'must be better informed about the rationale for, risks of, and alternatives to, medical recommendations'. They also point out that nurses can use their professional relationships with patients to explore the ideas regarding medical procedures because their involvement in informed consent takes place over time rather than in a single discussion; and that nurses should develop their role expectations where their competence, expertise and leadership are utilised rather than inhibited. They talk of a 'collaborative' relationship with the medical team; this is indeed what is happening in the story of Nora.

Health-care professionals are also increasingly aware that their own care and treatments, too, require consent by patients. The more the patient's rights – value of life and freedom – are respected, the more can care be said to be ethical.

Sadly, some nurses feel that the boot is now on the other foot and that some patients are taking advantage of their rights and are harassing nurses. These nurses feel that their 'scope for withdrawing care from people who act unreasonably' (Nursing Times, 1993b) is reduced since the introduction of the Patient's Charter. Not only is one person's right another person's responsibility, but rights are not licences to do as one pleases. The idea of truth telling or honesty is perhaps never so clearly demonstrated as in this example.

Organ donation

Much has been said and written about organ transplantation. It is not the fact that it happens which is in dispute, but how the organs are retrieved and the criteria for receiving transplants which cause problems. These are problems of resource allocation, questions of the mitigating of fatal diseases and the prolongation of life and the avoidance of death (Iliffe and Swan, 1993: 55).

Transplantation is widely accepted as the best option for end-stage disease for which there is no other effective treatment. But it is expensive and labour-intensive. There are also far fewer donors available than the numbers of patients who could benefit from a transplant.

Organs are given free, but the cost to the donor is usually his or her life. The case in 1989 of trafficking in human kidneys obtained from living donors led to the establishment of the Human Organ Transplants Act 1989 which 'prohibits the procurement of kidneys from any living donors unrelated to the intended recipient' (Evans, 1993). Anyone wanting to use kidneys from living donors who are unrelated to the intended recipient must refer to the Unrelated Live Transplants Regulatory Authority (ULTRA), a body set up under the 1989 Act.

The organ donor card scheme in this country is by no means adequate to supply the need. Carrying a card is not an automatic permission to use organs, and in every case where a possible donor is identified, the next of kin or relatives must be asked if they agree. Other schemes for retrieving organs are the *required request*, which 'would require doctors or nurses to ask relatives of all possible donors whether they agree to organ donation'; and the *opting out* possibility, which means that 'unless they have specifically stated to the contrary, or their families object, deceased people may automatically become multi-organ donors' (Iliffe and Swan, 1993: 58).

With so few organs available for transplantation, if they are going to live or die must truly seem like a gamble to the patients. The criteria for selection of patients for transplants vary from centre to centre, but age and clinical fitness are always at the top of the list. Young patients have a better recovery rate and may therefore be chosen in preference to older people. Poor motivation, failure to comply with earlier treatment, as well as psychiatric or emotional instability tend to be contra-indications for transplantation.

For a treatment which is so costly in terms of labour, lifelong medication and technology, issues discussed in Chapters 6 and 7 (resource constraints and QALYs) are also applicable. Subtle and less subtle personal and societal criteria come into play. Doctors and nurses have inevitably to make decisions which may be wrongly interpreted by patients, relatives, friends and society in general. The pressures on doctors 'not to waste money' may be enormous, and refusing treatment to a patient who is a heavy smoker may seem perfectly reasonable as his or her chances for a successful transplant may be drastically reduced from the medical point of view. But the general public may see this simply as discrimination. The notion of informed consent therefore starts rather a long way back, with informing the general public about medical treatments, and perhaps also encouraging public debates about the moral issues of costly treatments versus scarce resources.

The area which nurses often mention as the most difficult to cope with is in the intensive care unit when a patient has been declared brain dead and is being prepared for organ retrieval. Although there are usually no more than a few hours in which the patient is kept ventilated for organ retrieval, caring for these patients often poses a severe emotional problem for nurses. 'Knowing he was declared dead, but having to act as if he were not, made those the most difficult hours I have ever worked' (Sandroff, 1980). Satterthwaite (1990) mentions that the nurses' role at that moment is to provide support for both the patient and the family, and the Royal College of Nursing (1991), in an 'Issues in Nursing and Health' statement says that 'it is essential that appropriate support is available to nursing staff'.

Coupe (1990) describes the policies adopted by the Royal Devon and Exeter Hospitals (known as the 'Exeter Protocol') to ventilate patients electively purely to allow organ donation to take place.

The more questionable use of fetal brain-cell transplants for patients with Parkinson's disease should at least be mentioned. Easton and Lamb (1991) say that 'research on fetal tissue transplantation is still highly experimental, problems with retrieval persist and implantation of tissue into recipient brains is one of the most invasive methods of therapy ever applied'. The Royal College of Nursing has produced some cards in its

'Issues in Nursing and Health' series, and card No 7 is entitled 'Fetal Cell Transplantation, Guidance for Nurses' (1991) and contains some useful advice on this topic.

A related topic is gene transplant or therapy, but as this has far more wide-reaching consequences in that implanted genes will be passed on to future generations, it can only be mentioned here rather than discussed.

Both these last types of transplants are open to commercial exploitation, and their ethical problems lie squarely there as well as in their actual medical use. Nurses may have only limited dealings with these technological rather than medical advances, but their contribution to the debate is vital. Nurses work at the sharp end of resources, and how these are spent will occupy all our minds more and more.

What is happening?

The discussion about informed consent and organ donation needs now to be applied to the story of Nora. *What is happening* to Gloria, Nora and the team treating Gloria?

It is fair to assume that Gloria had never thought of transplants as anything that might happen to her. She had been getting more ill and weaker over the years, but with treatment had managed to live a reasonably active life though slowly getting worse. She might simply have accepted that as part of getting older. Her GP might have mentioned a heart transplant as one way out of a situation which would otherwise leave him with the sense of failure. Seeing any patient deteriorate despite every effort is incredibly difficult for doctors, who are conditioned to save life. Organ transplants of many kinds have therefore often come to their rescue as well as their patients.

Iliffe and Swan (1993) make several cautionary points:

- Patients are sometimes inappropriately assessed for transplant as a way of keeping hope alive and denying mortality. This may arise from the value system held by medical and nursing staff rather than from asking the patient what her or his thinking is on this topic.
- Patients should be allowed to refuse assessment for transplant without feeling that their future care is thereby implicated.
- Patients and health carers must maintain a positive and constructive attitude towards transplant surgery, but must at the same time discuss the risks of organ rejection and death, as well as the possibility that an

organ may not become available and the patient may die. It is emotionally draining to keep two opposite realities alive.

- Patients may feel that they have to be 'good' to be 'worthy' of a transplant by going along with the opinions and decisions of their caring team. They may become unusually dependent on those who care for them and invest them with unrealistic powers. Nurses must be aware of this and encourage patients to be autonomous.

- Perhaps more than other transplants, hearts have an emotional aspect to them which may only come to light after surgery. Iliffe and Swan (1993: 51) describe 'the husband of a successfully transplanted patient [who] felt unable to send his wife a Valentine card with a heart, because his wife no longer had the heart he had married'.

Gloria is here described as one of those 'good' patients who accepts what is told her and goes along with it, perhaps without too much questioning. But when she had been getting worse for years and was then told that she might have a heart transplant, this must have turned her world upside down. The emotional and psychological impact of this cannot be overlooked. But did she really want a transplant? Could she weigh up what might be involved?

Some of the considerations for successful transplants, such as life-style and physical and psychological support after the operation, were clearly present for Gloria. Her large family in particular meant that she would have very good care after a successful transplant. If the family went along with her decision, she would also have good support through the waiting period. But these are the professionals' criteria; much more important, surely, are her own criteria, values, thoughts, feelings, needs and wants.

What is happening? is surely the most important question here, and to ask this of Gloria is imperative. This is where the more long-term and in-depth relationship between nurses and patients can be most helpful. The more intimate contact does not only reveal the persons to each other, but a closer understanding of each other's way of being and acting also emerges. What may therefore appear as eagerness at first may later be seen as compliance. Informed consent here may also be a rather flexible term: the patient will need to give consent to investigations and treatments, but as each new phase of investigations is reached and new facts come to light, adjustments have to be made which each time require new consenting. It is again the nursing staff who may be ideally placed to discuss these issues with the patient as they arise.

Should Gloria be told of the policy not to transplant patients over 60 years of age? If she is simply told of this policy she is not in a position to give informed consent to stop further investigations. She would have nothing more to do than comply because there is no further choice. The fact that she is now in the hospital and booked for investigations means that she already has a choice, and this must be respected.

Gloria may also have talked with other patients who are either awaiting surgery or who have already had it. This will have given her perhaps more insights into what such a procedure might involve and therefore helped her to shape her views.

What is happening to Gloria's family? What do they think, feel, need or want? To the health professionals it may be obvious that they would like their beloved Gloria to be with them for a while longer and that therefore they would want her to have the transplant. They may also think that it is Gloria's right to have a transplant and therefore push her to insist on it. Although she is a matriarch, she may be much influenced by the views of some key members of her large family and feel that she must obey them. Only in this way might she be able to keep her position as matriarch.

What is happening to Nora? When she took on the post of nurse specialist she knew that this would often involve her in difficult situations. She was also aware of her ability to communicate well with people, and she had wanted to use this in a more direct way. She had now been in her job a number of years, and in that time she had gained much experience and become increasingly empathic with her patients and clients. She had also been able to demonstrate to her medical colleagues that informed consent was as much her domain as it was theirs, and she was seen very much as part of the caring team.

Nora must therefore have been involved with Gloria and the team right from the beginning. She will have been present at discussions about Gloria's case and will have been aware of her medical history and of the situation as it presented itself now – in other words, that Gloria would be a good candidate for a transplant, but that her age was against her.

As before when considering *what is happening* to the main actor in these stories, the imagination helps: Nora's own heart may have been sinking as she realised that Gloria was just a few weeks short of the cut-off point of 60. From working with her medical colleagues she will have realised that the surgeon will insist that policies are adhered to, and she will quickly have realised also that she will be the one to tell Gloria that she is not, after all, able to have a transplant.

Nora will probably have had to tell something similar to other patients before, probably those in the waiting period, when their condition had begun to deteriorate and no heart had become available. This would be different from telling it outright even before the start.

Even though a person is skilled, this does not take away the anxiety of actually saying what has to be said. The actual fact – no transplant – is so tied up with other facts that it may even be difficult to remember them all. If Nora remembers that she also has ethical duties and that these are based on five principles, she will probably have covered most of these other facts.

The principle of the value of life is involved here in that Nora needs to respect Gloria for the person she is. The decision has been made that this life cannot be saved with these means, but this does not mean that Gloria's life is morally worth less than that of other people who are younger. She will be cared for as much as she needs and will not be abandoned.

The principle of goodness or rightness demands of Nora that she act in her most professional way and see it as her duty that this is right by the patient, by her profession and by society. It also means therefore that the outcome of this interaction should be good; not necessarily that the patient is compliant, but that the patient is not left unduly distressed or harmed.

The principle of justice or fairness is perhaps the most difficult to defend here. Whichever way one sees this problem, it seems that one has to explain it. Yet without policies, health care would be in chaos. Policies are based on solid facts and are not made arbitrarily. It is simply that, when applied to a particular situation and a particular patient, they appear arbitrary – and perhaps rightly so.

Response ethics asks for the *fitting answer* in each situation, not for the correct or politically correct answer. It starts with the idea of 'co-humanity' rather than with a theory which has to be adhered to or a principle which has to be upheld. If the principle of justice or fairness is rigidly applied here, and Gloria's case is seen in the light of 'economy, efficiency, effectiveness', and the calculations of QALYs are taken into consideration, then we have to say that the surgeon is right to keep to the policy of the hospital.

It is only when we consider the next principle, truth telling or honesty, that we can make sense of justice in this case. Nora had decided that she would need to tell Gloria outright that she would not be having a transplant. Nora had to tell Gloria exactly why: hospital *policy* was not to transplant patients over 60. Only if Gloria knew this, rather than simply saying that it was her age which was against her, could Nora justify the decision. Gloria may be able to accept this, and therefore consent to palliative care rather than technological care. She may then also see that justice in health care is a very hard principle to keep because it has now become an issue of politics rather than morality.

The principle of individual freedom is also compromised here: Gloria is not given a choice of whether she wants to have a transplant or not. Nora may feel that this is perhaps the hardest of all the points as far as she is concerned. Informed consent rests on the principle of autonomy or freedom.

Nora may make the most of her long-term relationship with Gloria to discuss the whole issue with her. Nora's 'truth' is that Gloria is not to have a transplant, but Gloria's 'truth' may be some other aspect; for example, what the family feels rather than what she herself feels. Although Nora had decided that she would need to tell Gloria the medical fact, this does not have to be presented in one discussion of a few minutes.

Given this, it may be possible that Gloria actually decides that she doesn't want to have a transplant. This would be a more informed consenting to the given fact, but it is important that this is not seen as coercion. Nora's relationship with Gloria and the empathy which she particularly shares with her may be 'used' here, but used in the sense that both of them feel that they gain.

What is happening? must also be asked of the medical team. It is they who have drawn up the policy of not transplanting patients over 60. Although Nora is chosen to tell Gloria of their decision, it is a group decision and therefore also a group responsibility. Nora is not simply doing their 'dirty work' for them; she is, after all, part of the team, and will therefore also have taken part in forming the policy and in the decision not to transplant. If Nora had objected to the policy or the decision, it would have been her duty as a professional – and as a specialist in her field – to object.

A team or committee may take a collective decision, but it is usually only one person who can carry it out. In the interests of all concerned, it should be the best-suited person who is chosen to implement the decision – and the rest of the team should support that member in her or his task.

Support is mentioned again and again for people (and nurses in particular) who work in the field of organ transplantation. This must not just be lip-service support, but real and tangible support by people who will again and again ask those involved *What is happening* to you? How are you coping? Can I help you? In what way?

What is the meaning of it?

This is another story of an ethical decision which did not need much deliberation to come to a *fitting answer*: Nora knew that she had to tell Gloria of the decision and she knew that she had to give her the bare facts. Because she knew that this would be difficult for her, one can only speculate that she had some misgivings or that in the process she might have come to some insights which might challenge her values.

Response ethics, with its two questions *What is happening?* and *What is the fitting answer?*, starts and ends with people – persons – rather than principles. It does not disregard any principles but puts people and their communities before any principles. This makes it more flexible as a model for decision making. Hanford (1993) pointed out that 'principlism' has become the dominant model, 'i.e. the practice of using principles to replace moral theory, rules and ideals in dealing with moral problems arising in clinical practice'. She finishes her article by asking for a rethinking and restructuring of ethics teaching, curricula and the relationship between students and teachers 'to create a learning environment that promotes and enhances caring rather than socializing new generations into professional arrogance'.

The *meaning* for Nora in this story may well be to discover anew what she means by caring, by professionalism and by informed consent.

What is the fitting answer?

This story highlights a dilemma in which there is no real *fitting answer* for any of the people concerned. The fact of the policy effectively removes the need for decisions.

Policies have to exist for there to be any distributive justice, as otherwise health care would be in chaos. But it is always hard when this affects a particular person. One can only repeat here that the fact that we have technologies of all kinds does not mean that we have to use them. But who decides to use them, or not, now becomes the moral question. If we take the notion of informed consent to the limit, then surely it should always be the patient who decides.

But is this always realistic?

The pattern of responsibility

It is particularly in this story of Nora that we see a pattern of responsibility: Nora, who took on a responsibility on behalf of her colleagues; but also, that responsibility is not something which is lessened by having policies.

The *challenge* in this story is the decision not to transplant Gloria because she is just below the age limit for such surgery. Younger people · have a much better chance of survival and good quality of life after transplant surgery than older people. Sixty is a reasonable age, and is widely acknowledged as the upper limit for successful organ transplant surgery. This is a medical criterion which has been accepted by health economics, and the two factors together have helped to shape a policy.

The *response* for Nora to the decision that she should be the one to tell Gloria that she would not be considered for transplant was to feel inadequate and lonely. Nora was there when it was decided that she should be the person to talk with Gloria: she could have refused. Like all the others present, Nora knew that she would probably do it best – she was not pushed into doing something which she disapproved of. Nora had long experience – she could not plead that she was inadequate. But yet she felt that this time it was worse than ever before.

Nora may have felt a deep resistance inside her as she realised that this woman who had such a big 'heart' in every way was now not to be given the chance to have a longer life. Gloria's generosity was infectious, and Nora herself had been touched by her friendliness. She was also reasonably well enough to enjoy the life she had. All this must have contributed to the feeling of not really wanting to tell Gloria that she would not be given the chance to continue living in this way. Nora's own sense of justice was also attacked as she realised that here was a black woman who would not be transplanted. Being black and a woman was quite difficult enough without the sense of also being discriminated against. Nora might have felt this less strongly had she not perhaps experienced the reverse of this: being white in a black country. Her response was therefore one of having identified with this patient and now having to 'let her down' – or so it might feel to Nora.

These feelings can be described as irrational and not really based on any facts. Feelings tend to be irrational, but they are there, and that is what matters. They cannot be discounted; they can only be looked at: *what is happening?*

But Nora might also have felt a sense of just recognition and importance. Of all the people in the team she was the only one who could handle such a delicate situation, and they all knew it. Real teamwork is very demanding but also very rewarding because the gifts of each are recognised and used.

The *interpretation* which Nora makes of her response is vital. Her feelings can help her to relate more personally to Gloria. She can understand what Gloria might be feeling and going through, and how she now interprets this can be used to help Gloria in her understanding of what is going on. The insights which this understanding of herself and of Gloria brings will shape how she decides, not only now but also in the future.

Past experience will have taught Nora a great deal about how to talk with patients. If she feels inadequate now it may be that she had a similar situation once before, and it might have been difficult then, or Nora might not have handled it well. The memory can be a strong wrecker of normally simple tasks. Nora's self-awareness will help her to recognise this, and she is well advised to take advantage of her friend's support and help to notice any blind spots and also to build on her strengths.

If Nora is able to take a step sideways, so to speak, and stay with her hesitations and inadequacies, she may also realise that her role might not have been the most courageous. She might have challenged the decision not to transplant Gloria. She might have asked her colleagues if policies have always to be adhered to, to the letter. Why did the surgeon feel so strongly that he would lose face if he did not adhere to this policy? Could Nora have been more of a patient advocate?

These thoughts may go through her mind and form the *accountability* which the pattern describes. This part asks, more or less, what would happen if . . .? In order to give a *fitting answer*, both the past and the future have to be taken into account. There are usually several possibilities which could be chosen. If there is only one answer there will not have been any choice.

The story of Nora shows that there was really no choice in the matter of the transplant because the policy had already been decided; and there was no real choice for Nora except to accept that she was the one to tell Gloria of the decision.

When a *fitting answer* has been given, then a *social solidarity* will also have been created which all recognise. In this story one can only hope that Gloria's response to the decision not to transplant will lead to a *social solidarity*. This would mean that Gloria herself decides not to have a transplant. She is given an ultimatum but she still has to accept it for herself. If she is able to do this, then her family is probably in a better position to do the same. The way in which Nora helps her will be crucial.

There is a very thin line here for Nora between giving Gloria the choice to decide for herself that she does not need or want a transplant and persuading her that she does not need or want it. If Nora is able to use her professional expertise and is given enough support by her colleagues, then a *social solidarity* may indeed have been reached where people are helped and have grown through an experience and have gained from it.

Perhaps Nora might have to ask herself some hard questions about patient advocacy, about truth telling and about informed consent, and consider her role in the light of these. Then there may be even better and more *social solidarity* in future situations where she is involved.

Chapter 9
The principle of
truth telling or honesty (2)

Story

Harry was a senior nurse manager in a large provincial hospital. He
and his family had moved there nearly two years earlier after a time
of stress in his earlier post. He enjoyed his present work and felt
that his life had a new sense of purpose.

Despite his enthusiasm, he began to experience strange feelings
in his hands and feet, and once or twice dropped a pile of papers
for no apparent reason. One evening at home he dropped his
dinner plate in the kitchen. His wife joked that he had forgotten
that he was not on holiday in Greece any longer. Harry brushed it
aside too, but was silently beginning to be very worried.

His symptoms continued and he went to see his GP. After six
months the symptoms got steadily worse, and Harry and the GP
agreed that they should be investigated. Appointments were made
for Harry to go to a neurosurgical unit in his district for tests after
earlier investigations failed to find any organic cause.

While he was in the hospital, Harry called his primary nurse,
Darryl, and told him that he wanted to discuss something with
him. Harry told Darryl that about two years earlier he had had a
test for HIV and was positive, but had not had any symptoms. He
wondered if there might be a connection.

Darryl realised that Harry's condition was almost certainly
related to HIV and that this might be the missing piece of
information. He told Harry that the rest of the team should know
this so that treatment and appropriate care could be started.

Harry said that this was just what was worrying him: that this information would become public and that his position in the hospital would be jeopardised.

Darryl and Harry talked for a long time, because Harry was not easily convinced by assurances that the information would not spread. Darryl pointed out that he was cared for by a team and that they must therefore share information. Harry would not let Darryl go before he had given his word that no relatives or 'friends' would be told of this information.

Harry felt relief, guilt and remorse. During the difficult time before leaving his previous job, he had had a short but intense affair with someone he had met at a conference. He should have known better than take risks with unprotected sex. It was this which gave him most concern.

Ironically, he had himself been responsible for drawing up guidelines for staff in his district who were HIV positive. He had worked hard so that staff should not have to declare their HIV status automatically. In one way he was lucky in so far as he was not directly in contact with patients; in another way it was all the harder for him as he was married.

Darryl passed the information to the team, and there was surprise that nobody had considered that this might be the reason for Harry's condition. No information was leaked, but Harry had the difficult job of explaining to his wife what was the matter with him.

The setting

Informed consent and confidentiality have always been issues in medicine, but it is fair to say that the advent of HIV and AIDS have brought them into the limelight and made people – in particular, health professionals – aware that they had been abusing or disregarding them quite flagrantly.

The most often-quoted American authors on medical ethics, Beauchamp and Childress (1983), and Gillon (1993) in a huge British work on health-care ethics, mention four principles which apply: respect for autonomy, beneficence, non-maleficence and justice. The principle of truth telling or honesty is not included in their list, neither is it in any medical or nursing codes. It is clearly impossible to say, even generally, 'Thou shalt tell the truth', but it is worth considering whether the absence of truth from medical and nursing codes and the writings of influential people has not contributed to some of the legacies in health care with which we now struggle. If truth had been given as much attention as justice in health care, we might have had different problems today, although they would not be more difficult.

The nurse–patient relationship is something which is often discussed, and from various points of view. The medical establishment has often regarded this relationship with suspicion because it is more intimate and perhaps more personal than the doctor–patient relationship, and therefore also more is exchanged between nurses and patients than between doctors and patients. On the other hand, nurses have very easily abdicated their responsibilities for informing patients, and have given this task to doctors, who may be less skilled in communication. Their rather 'cooler' relationship with patients has meant that they could give facts more easily without 'getting involved'. But both this story and that of Pam (see Chapter 6) show that patients have chosen nurses to talk with. The trust placed in that relationship must stem from some instinct which makes nurses ideal recipients of confidences.

Through this close contact with patients, nurses have a different and a complementary knowledge of people, illness and morality from that of other health-care workers – in particular, doctors. This knowledge needs to be shared with those other health-care workers so that it is indeed *health care* which is given.

But it is this sharing of this truth which has often been difficult; doctors may have belittled it, but nurses have withheld it. This may have put nurses in the 'handmaid' position because doctors judged that their truth was not worth listening to; and nurses may have kept themselves as 'handmaids' because they did not share their views and insights out of fear of being misunderstood. By not sharing, but keeping their views and insights to themselves, they did not help their doctor colleagues in their work.

In seeking to be more human ourselves and treating fellow human beings more humanely, we are fostering that co-humanity which Niebuhr advocates. Thiroux (1980: 136) writes:

> since all human relationships are based on verbal and nonverbal communication and since – to my way of thinking – morality is the most important of all human relationships, it is absolutely necessary that truth telling and honesty be considered fundamental and basic to any theory or system of morality.

How much 'truth' we can bring into the nurse–doctor relationship is therefore perhaps the most pressing issue nowadays since it is clear that the nurse–patient relationship is well established. How much we share with others our own 'truth' – that is, the perspectives and insights we have of particular situations and people – depends on our openness and willingness to be vulnerable. Sharing enhances the climate of caring. Fear tries to dominate it and therefore also destroys it. The more we listen, the more we hear truly, rather than making assumptions and thereby missing the point.

Truth can only stand as a principle when all the other principles are also adhered to. The principle of the value of life would ring very hollow if we could not rely on truthfulness that people would respect this principle and keep it. Goodness or rightness, which is concerned with acting ethically in the most fundamental way, needs truth as a guide, otherwise duty is arbitrary and goals become dispensable. Justice or fairness as a principle has always had truth as a companion. Humanity has seen justice as a goal, but this can only be reached if and when those responsible are trusted to keep their promises. Individual freedom is only 'individual' when all people are concerned that freedom exists. When we cannot trust people we cannot believe them and truth is compromised. When there is a breakdown of trust, there is disorder and disharmony. When trust is restored, then truth is also restored.

Truth is not *the* truth, but something fragile which happens between people. In order to find truth and recognise it we must listen to one another. Many of our values are not freely chosen, as we believe they are, but have been specifically taught by such methods as moralising and modelling (Uustal, 1980). Always having an opinion is perhaps one of these values, and in applying it we find that we make assumptions and show prejudice. This devalues the other person's truth about himself or herself.

Prejudice

When AIDS first came on the scene, prejudice was almost universal. The people who had the disease were prejudged, condemned and written off as having brought the disease upon themselves and having only themselves to blame. This attitude was given a jolt when suddenly some patients with haemophilia developed AIDS, as they could not have brought the disease upon themselves. 'Prejudice consists of judging – people, things, or situations – on the basis of preconceived stereotypes or generalizations. A prejudice may be either positive or negative' (Briant, 1976).

It is possible that Harry's reputation as a manager and a person is so favourable that nobody will believe him when he tells them that he has AIDS. But it is much more likely that when he tells them they will think, say and indicate, 'Fancy that; the bastard; I never trusted him anyway'; etc. etc.

Discrimination is a very useful tool when choosing friends, candidates for jobs or showing good taste. When discrimination is based on people's race, creed, colour, sex, age, sexual orientation, ability or looks, then it becomes problematic. Some very common labels given to patients by nurses are 'demanding', 'lazy', 'dirty', 'scroungers'. Any of this may be said about a patient at the end of a long shift by a nurse who may be very tired – for whatever reason – and may not have been meant in a derogatory way. But it is picked up and the label sticks. Once a person is labelled it is almost impossible to get away from it. But the person himself or herself cannot relate to the label because he or she does not know what it is.

> *During a workshop on communication I once took part in a game where every person was given a paper hat with words on it like 'boss', 'willing helper', 'busy-body' and so on. One hat simply had a question mark on it. We could see one another's hats but did not know what was on our own. We were then asked to address the others as the person they were on the label. This was shortly before Christmas and the conversation was about organising a party. It became obvious that very quickly each person took on the 'label' and began to act and speak in the manner addressed. We all agreed that this was one of the most difficult exercises any of us had ever done because we were forced into a role we did not know or want.*

One of the main attitudes required of counsellors is to be non-judgemental. If we judge, we cannot really hear what the other person is saying because we hear everything said through this screen of judgement and prejudice. We therefore never hear the real or true person and we never hear the truth of that person. We must judge and make judgements, but not before we have really heard what the other has to say. It is too easy to judge the situation from *our* point of view rather than let the other person tell us what matters.

Prejudice says more about ourselves than the other person. The prejudice which was so common at first towards people with AIDS was due to our own and society's fears of people who are different from us and who act differently from us. What we don't know we often quickly condemn because it is easier than to listen to a story. As we get more acquainted with AIDS we are less fearful, but in the meantime many people with AIDS have suffered a great deal.

There seems to be a deep need in society to blame: people, things, events, politicians, leaders, the weather – anything and everything gets blamed. When we find it difficult to hear the truth of our own inadequacies and limits we begin to blame. We live in a time of incredible change and we would prefer stability; therefore we blame the change. To listen to one another takes time, and we don't have the time; we blame people for taking too much of our time. We have technology, but it cannot cure our illnesses; we blame the machines. We blame, and thereby increase our prejudices towards anything and anybody because to hear the truth of all these things and people is costly. If we are to act and think ethically, then any labelling and discriminating is wrong because it diminishes the other person as well as ourselves.

'The truth shall make ye free, but first it shall make ye miserable,' says a proverb. Perhaps sometimes we need to be made miserable by the truth because in that way can we understand that 'honesty is the best policy'.

Confidentiality

The International Council of Nurses (ICN, 1973) *Code for Nurses* states that 'The nurse holds in confidence personal information and uses judgement in sharing this information'. The UKCC (1992) *Code of Professional Conduct* states that

> As a registered nurse, midwife or health visitor, you are personally accountable for your practice and, in the exercise of your professional accountability, must: . . . protect all confidential information concerning patients and clients obtained in the course of professional practice and make disclosures only with consent, where required by the order of a court or where you can justify disclosure in the wider public interest. (Clause 10)

The UKCC Code is here, as in other matters, more prescriptive than the International Code. This can be interpreted to be helpful, but equally, it may be considered as not trusting the individual nurse's judgement.

Johnstone (1989: 194) argues that confidentiality can only ever be a prima facie principle, not a moral one, because confidentiality can never be absolute. When stronger moral considerations are present, confidentiality may be overridden. But confidentiality should always be upheld unless harm would occur to innocent others. This is clearly demonstrated by Kitchiner and Toman (1994), who write of their position as forensic psychiatric nurses. As nurses they are bound by the UKCC *Code of Professional Conduct* (1992). But their patients are also people with criminal records, and when one of them absconds, they have to inform the police, who will need to know every medical detail of the person concerned. This often brings them into conflict over this principle of confidentiality.

The UKCC document *Confidentiality* (1987) lists a number of situations in which nurses were seriously concerned about whether or not they should keep some information confidential, or if they were under an obligation to keep or break confidentiality. One of those situations is of a nurse in a psychiatric day hospital who found a patient who had large quantities of controlled drugs on him which the nurse considered to be stolen goods. The case was reported in 1992 (*Daily Telegraph*, 1992b) of a man who admitted himself to North Staffordshire Royal Infirmary in Stoke-on-Trent where he vomited thirty-one rubber packets of pure heroin.

> The hospital management alerted police to the man's presence in hospital when it handed over the drugs to detectives .... But doctors refused to identify the man to the police on the grounds that to do so would breach their code of ethics .... The hospital later identified the courier to police after being threatened with a court order.

Patients have the right to have certain information about themselves kept secret, but this right is forfeited when it impinges on the moral interests of innocent others (Johnstone, 1989: 196). But when are 'the moral interests' of the many more important the moral rights of the one? That decision will always be one which is made in particular situations and particular cases.

People who are HIV positive or who have AIDS do not pose a danger to any other people once very simple precautions are taken which should be routine anyway. It is therefore completely unnecessary to make their HIV status known to anybody.

In 1992 and 1993 a number of nurses and doctors in Britain were identified in the media as suffering from AIDS. Each time this happened, telephone helplines were set up so that the people who had been treated by the individuals concerned could call and be reassured. At the same time, people not affected pleaded that health-care workers should be compulsorily tested for HIV. One can only guess what consequences this might have.

Everyone has secrets, and these need to be respected. Secrets are power, and this is why people are afraid of them. We learn this very early on as children, when secret languages, places and people keep children to themselves and keep adults away. And nothing holds so much fascination as spy stories and thrillers of people intent on getting to the secret which holds the clue to something vitally important.

Confidentiality, say Brown *et al.* (1992: 102), is important because any information is 'property'. This property has to be guarded, and therefore confidentiality is 'a matter of decency, a matter of privacy and a matter of respecting persons'.

These points – decency, privacy and respect – might be said to belong to the principle of the value of life. They are fundamentally concerned with respect for another person's life, way of living, being and behaving. However, confidentiality here is discussed within the principle of truth telling or honesty, as it is clear that all these points apply particularly within this setting. Truth matters, because everyone has a circle of people around them who know the person simply because they interact closely with them. Truth being most vulnerable, it is also most respected. Depending on the way in which we live, our families know most or least about us. In very close-knit societies there can be few secrets about other members of the society, but few are also needed because everybody has much more of a place and function than in more loose-knit societies.

Confidentiality also comes within the framework of the principle of individual freedom. We can only express our personalities when freedom is present, and this needs to be respected and fostered. Confidentiality is vitally important in order that we may grow as persons and remain human.

The principle of justice or fairness is also invoked when considering confidentiality. This is a universal principle, applying to all people. It cannot, for instance, apply to all people except those who are HIV positive. Sooner or later we would find all sorts of categories of people who should also be exempted.

Brown *et al.* (1992: 103) mention discretion as one of the 'virtues' by which a person who upholds the principle of confidentiality, should be guided. They see discretion as a habit of communicating well. Such a person will not take advantage of others' weakness, will not misuse listening skills, will care about people, their privacy and decency, and in general will have developed a sensitivity to confidential information. This person could be said to be 'good' and act 'rightly', and thus the principle of goodness or rightness is also invoked. The point is made by the authors that such a person can also enjoy harmless gossip, is not incurious and will also acknowledge that in certain situations confidentiality has to be broken. But they paint a picture of such a person which comes remarkably close to that of Rogers (1975), who described empathy not as a skill but as 'a way of being'.

What is happening?

The story of Harry is unusual in that it shows how the two main players in this scenario both have to make ethical decisions. Both are within the area of confidentiality, but that is where the similarity ends.

Harry was particularly concerned that his job and the people around him at work were not jeopardised. But his more delicate problem was probably going to be how to tell his family what was happening – or what had happened.

Harry was beginning to show signs of AIDS, and that meant that he was probably not going to get better. People do not normally mind telling others what they suffer from because it helps with sympathy. When the disease is not something 'socially acceptable' this is different. Our society often seems to apply very crude double standards: people in public life need to be seen to be keeping to very strict moral rules whereas the same does not apply to 'ordinary' people. Scapegoating and labelling is very easily done, but the reasons why it is done are much less frequently questioned. Harry, in a high-profile job in a hospital, therefore has every reason to be fearful of what might happen to him and his family when the scandalmongers get going.

It is easy to imagine all the things with which Harry might be labelled: as an adulterer, an egoist, a weakling and worse. Women at his office might feel uneasy working with him. The GP and the hospital doctors might label him evasive and afraid of the truth as he didn't tell them from the beginning that he was HIV positive but let them carry on with investigations. Those who shout about people who have brought diseases and illnesses on themselves by dangerous and immoral living and therefore do not deserve free health care might also put in their twopennyworth of opinion.

But what of Harry the man, the patient – *what is happening* to him? Is it possible to see Harry and not an image of him, or his label? Harry might have been genuinely worried about his symptoms without making any connection with his HIV status. He might not have been so well-read about HIV that he realised that this was what was happening to him. He had drawn up the guidelines for staff on HIV, but that still did not make him an expert.

Perhaps just as likely, Harry was beginning to be aware of what was in fact going on and that he was mentally denying it. The guilt which he had begun to feel might have been so strong that he would have given anything for the awful thing not to be true. He might simply have wished that any and every investigation would vindicate him.

Men are often described as unfeeling, or rather, not being in touch with their feelings as much as women. This may be partly true, but just as likely is the fact that men have exactly the same feelings as women but do not acknowledge them or cannot deal with them. Their only way of dealing with them is by denying them. Harry had no one with whom he could have shared any feelings. Even if his relationship with his wife was good, he might still have wanted to spare her the awful reality. He would have been worried, but until he had any proof or reason to be worried there was nothing he could do about his worries except live with them or brush them aside.

When he finally summoned up enough courage to talk with someone about his situation, he chose Darryl, the primary nurse. He will probably have chosen Darryl for several reasons: he was a man like him, perhaps about the same age, also a manager of a kind – all of which might have given him the sense that he identified with Darryl at some level. Perhaps he felt most of all that Darryl was not going to judge him but help him, and perhaps explain to him what was happening and make sense of his thoughts and feelings. But before that could happen, he needed to be sure that his confidentiality was kept. He had enough of a problem; he didn't need to have it added to by 'helpful' people.

Darryl had quite a job in getting Harry to accept that the caring team should know about his HIV status. Harry needed practically cast-iron proof that his confidentiality was assured. This was difficult for Darryl to give, but as much as was in his power, he certainly did give it. Once Harry was over this hurdle, the real problem was only just beginning.

What is happening, then, is that Harry seems to have layers of problems and one layer can be tackled only after the one before has been eliminated. The ethical problem for Harry was not so much that confidentiality existed and needed to be applied to him, but that he could claim confidentiality in order to deal with the fundamental problem of having been unfaithful and needing the space and help to come to terms with his action.

What is happening to Darryl? As Harry's primary nurse he is particularly concerned about Harry's welfare. Like his medical colleagues, he may have been baffled about the cause of Harry's symptoms and wondered if there might be a clue anywhere which might point in a direction which might help. When, therefore, Harry mentioned his HIV status, he knew that that was probably the clue. Darryl's knowledge of the syndrome was vitally important in the further management of Harry's problems.

It is at this stage that we see how important Darryl's ethical handling of the situation is. Because he was competent, confident and committed (Roach, 1987), he was also guided by his conscience and thus made a compassionate response (see Chapter 6). He was using his discretion to guide him in the matters of confidentiality, secrecy and privacy. He discussed with Harry the need to inform the caring team about the fact that he was HIV positive. It is not so much the fact of this status as its consequences, in terms of medical information and treatment, which counts here.

Had Darryl not asked for Harry's permission and simply informed the team, Harry might have had good reason not only to be angry but also to look for redress. The information might not have leaked outside the caring team, but if Harry had had to make a complaint, then his confidentiality might certainly have been threatened even more.

If Harry had not given Darryl permission to inform the team about his HIV status, then Darryl would have had to respect this. Darryl might have talked with a colleague who was not from his ward or unit and without identifying the patient by name. He might have talked with a supervisor to clarify his position. If he failed to get either realistic help or help which he felt able to accept, then he might also have contacted the UKCC. 'The UKCC's Professional Advisers are experienced in dealing with a wide range of questions', but this 'can only be advisory rather than instructive' (Morris and Knape, 1993). Nevertheless, it is a useful last resort.

One of the points stressed again and again in this book is that patients and clients need to be listened to and heard. It was only by listening to Harry that Darryl could have decided that the information he was given was vital and needed to be shared with the rest of the team. If Darryl had told Harry that he should talk with his doctor, then Darryl would not have made most use of his position as a primary nurse. He would have listened to Harry, but only up to a point. Telling patients to discuss their problems with other people is not taking one's professional role seriously, and it is also showing fear rather than commitment. When we come to difficult places in conversations with patients, it is then that we have to listen hardest. *What is happening?* What is the patient saying? What am I hearing? If we only hear our own fear of being stuck or unable to handle something, then perhaps we need to hear that even more at this particular moment and not be afraid that we haven't got an answer, or know what we should say. *If in doubt, ask the patient.* The patient has asked us in the first instance, and the patient has a reason for doing this; perhaps we need to ask the patient what that reason is. In other words, we need to hear what the patient is saying and also what is only implied.

We are not told if Darryl always dealt so easily with questions of confidentiality. The chances are that in most instances he does and is thus so competent that he does not think about it much. But there are situations even for the most experienced person when questions arise about whether or not they have acted rightly. When we act responsibly, then we can defend our actions even if they are not the best. Responsibility here means being aware of *what is happening* to all the people involved.

Harry's family also need to be considered under the question of *what is happening?* At the time of the incident in the story, they are not aware of any wrongdoing on the part of Harry, but they will at least be worried. Their effect on Harry will influence his thinking and acting. Anyone who will be helping Harry with his physical and emotional care will have to care as much for them as for Harry, though in a different way. Since Darryl helped Harry to see that the purpose of his disclosure is that his total care can be better managed, he might suggest to Harry that help for the family needs also to be considered. They, too, need to learn how to 'handle' confidentiality if they are not to have more problems than they already have.

What is the meaning of it?

This question needs also to be asked of both Harry and Darryl, but no doubt for Harry it will have very different consequences. Once Harry had become aware of the link between HIV and his present symptoms, many things will have fallen into place. Harry would not have had an HIV test if he had not had reason to suspect that it might be positive.

When Harry was assured that confidentiality would be kept about his HIV status, this gave him at least a firm basis from which to think and plan. It gave him a space in which to be himself. When Brown *et al.* (1992) talk of confidentiality being 'a matter of privacy and a matter of respecting persons', it can be seen that this is what it feels like here.

Harry had probably asked himself a thousand times already *What is happening?* and what has happened? Now that he can link his HIV status and his present symptoms he can at least give rather more concrete answers to these questions. Undoubtedly, this will lead him to ask further, *What is the meaning* of it all? Why did the affair happen? Does he deserve to be HIV positive? Is it a punishment?

When considering this story as it is told here, it is very easy to see cause and effect and say, 'Yes, it is a punishment for an indiscretion or a wrong'. But that is how an outsider sees it. To the person concerned it may look very different. And what matters is how it looks to the person concerned.

If we want to help anyone with this question, then it is not a matter of being able to walk in that person's shoes, as the saying goes. It is a matter of understanding how that person feels in his or her shoes, and walking alongside the person. That, indeed, is the heart of ethics. That is social solidarity.

Darryl will also be asking *What is the meaning of it?* both for himself and for Harry. As he will have been there when Harry needed him, he will be anxious to help Harry in whatever way he can, with empathy and care. But he will also ask himself, at least in passing, why Harry chose him. What is it about him that made him the recipient of this information? As he asks himself this, he will understand himself a little more, know himself a little better and have grown in his humanity.

What is the meaning for Harry's family of all this? That may yet be the biggest question of all, and the one they will have to work out gradually if they are given the space, the respect and the privacy to do it in their own time.

What is the fitting answer?

From the point of view of acting ethically, the fitting answer in this scenario is Darryl's stance with Harry, in that he told him that the information he had just given him was vital and that he would therefore need to pass it on to his colleagues in the caring team. Darryl was clear about that. He told Harry that the team should know. In this way he did not say, 'I must tell the team of this' or 'You must give me permission to tell the team', but he simply said that the team should know. This gave Harry the space to voice his further doubts about Darryl's confidentiality.

Confidentiality is indeed about discretion, as Brown *et al.* (1992) say, and as such discretion is about communication. Discretion is perhaps not the easiest of terms to use. Discrimination was used above with regard to prejudice, and judgement, too, is sometimes used, both of them in the positive sense. 'Discernment' is another term used in the helping professions. Whichever word is used, it points to the fact that we need to be aware of *what is happening* at the moment of interaction and use our powers for communication in the best way possible.

The *fitting answer* is not simply the best one from the point of view of communication, but the one which expresses best what is most appropriate for all the people concerned. In this situation, Darryl had to consider Harry, the team, Harry's family and indeed himself as a fellow human being, with Harry committed to him at this point because of his professional choice to care. May (1975) made the point that professional relationships are about 'exchange, agreement and reciprocity', and this has certainly been demonstrated in this instance.

The pattern of responsibility

The *challenge* in this story was that Harry called Darryl to discuss with him the fact that he was HIV positive. Had this not been the missing piece of information in the search for a diagnosis, it might simply have remained a piece of information which nobody need have been concerned about. It was not the sensational aspect of HIV which mattered here, but the fact that it was information which helped the understanding of the wider health picture.

The *response* which Darryl may have experienced on being told this news might perhaps have been excitement. He realised that this was some vital piece of information, and he might have been proud to be the person to receive it and make the link. It is not every day that nurses are in this position.

When considering the response to the challenge, Niebuhr (1963) says that this is first of all a physical response, and that it is often experienced as a change in the heart rate, or a dry mouth, or a feeling of weakness. In this instance, the response which Darryl may have experienced might have been the heart actually missing a beat, as if in acknowledgement that something exciting was happening.

The response stems from the initial feeling experienced, and if this was excitement at being the person to make a discovery or use one's knowledge in a positive way, then this gives a boost to one's feelings of self-worth. This is necessary in any professional's life in order for him or her to continue functioning.

The *interpretation* of these initial feelings is usually based on past experience of such feelings. It is likely that Darryl will not have been in a situation like this before, but he will have heard of others who have, or he will have had smaller successes. Since these are good feelings he will remember them well, and they will have helped him to feel more in control and more assured that he is acting in the right way.

The *accountability* – the response he will eventually make – will be shaped by the interpretation made so far. Darryl will have realised that he is in a very important position and that what he says to Harry will determine Harry's future. It is important that Harry gives him permission to pass on the information. How he asks for this is therefore crucial.

Darryl made his request well, and Harry was satisfied that his confidentiality would be respected. Thus there was going to be *social solidarity* – that is, a good outcome for all concerned. The outcome might have been social disintegration if Harry had not agreed that the information should be passed to the team, or if Darryl had not asked for permission but told the team anyway, or if confidentiality could not be assured, or if the information had been leaked to people who had no good reason to know it.

The *challenge* for Harry was the need to talk with someone and to clear his mind of a worry which could not be contained any more.

His *response* might have been relief at having confirmed what he had feared for a long time. His response might not have been very strong because all these thoughts had been going round in his head for a while and he had weighed them up again and again. His response might therefore have been slowly growing over the two years and might not be particularly acute now.

On the other hand, Harry's *interpretation* of his challenge and response might now begin. Together with his *accountability*, the interpretation may become like a game of chess: 'If I make this move, the other – any of the people involved in Harry's life – will make that move'. 'If I say this, they will respond in that way.' Interpretation and accountability are now a process of weighing up the possibilities and the impossibilities. Given the fact that Harry has confidentiality, he can do this, and make his present situation one of *social solidarity* rather than of division and more problems. But this is not achieved overnight, and a great deal of further help and support is needed for all concerned if this is to happen. It may not be accomplished completely, but at every turn it is possible to ask afresh *What is happening?* and *What is the fitting answer?*

Chapter 10
The principle of
individual freedom (1)

Story

Ed and Laura were two Enrolled Nurses (Mental Handicap) on the
staff in a house where ten people with fairly severe learning
difficulties lived. They had been with this group of people as their
carers for a while now. They lived with the group during the day
and one of the staff always slept on the premises. Despite the fact
that the staff were not there all the time, together they had become
integrated as a group and were very close.

Ed and Laura took parties of five people on various trips and
outings. On one of these outings the following incident took place.

The party were on their way to one of the London museums.
They were going to have lunch first in a pub and then go on to see
a particular exhibition. They had to go rather a long way on the
Underground, and the train they were on was very crowded. Peter,
one of the residents, stood slightly apart from the rest of the group.
He was a gregarious character and liked by all because he always
made them laugh. In the train he was standing beside a young
woman who was carrying a large bag of shopping. From the bag
stuck out the end of a baguette. Peter, aware of his hunger, thought
that he could smell the delicious French bread, baked not very long
before. When he thought that nobody was looking, he broke off a
piece of the bread. The party had to get out at the next stop, and
Ed had signalled to Peter to this effect. Peter understood the signal
and moved towards the door.

As the train stopped the whole party got out, Peter at one door and the others at another. Peter was a few steps ahead towards the exit and was tucking into the bread with great gusto. Ed, surprised to see Peter eating, asked him where he got this bread from. Peter laughed heartily and said that it was just there. Where? Ed realised that Peter had been up to his pranks. A little huddle formed around Peter and another passenger then joined the group, saying that he had seen Peter break off the bread. By this time the train was well on its way out of the station. Ed said that he could do nothing about it, but the other passenger was not so sure. He said that he was going to speak to the station manager. It may not have been money, but another passenger had been robbed and he had seen the thief. Ed, if he was in charge of this group of people, would be responsible – and with this he ran up the stairs, making sure that he got to the ticket barrier before Peter, Ed and the rest.

The setting

The idea of personal liberty, says Baird (1993), is firmly linked with the market economies of the West. In more traditional societies it is not the individual who counts so much as the society, and each person's role and status in it. 'Liberty – like money – grows in the hands of the powerful and shrinks in those of the disempowered' (Baird, 1993). This is perhaps why Marx had much to say about the human condition, as people were only at liberty when freed from the bonds of the bourgeoisie. But were people under the Marxist regimes free? Perhaps each generation needs to free itself from its own shackles.

The ethical principles described by Beauchamp and Childress (1983) and Gillon (1986, 1993) comprise autonomy, beneficence, non-maleficence and justice – in that order. To this Noddings (1984: 6) says:

> An important difference between an ethic of caring and other ethics that give subjectivity its proper place is its foundation in relation. The philosopher who begins with a supremely free consciousness – an aloneness and emptiness at the heart of existence – identifies *anguish* as the basic human affect. But our view, rooted as it is in relation, identifies *joy* as a basic human affect.

Noddings writes from a feminist perspective, not in order to 'divide men and women into opposing camps' but rather to 'enter a dialogue of genuine dialectical nature [to] achieve an ultimate transcendence of the masculine and feminine in moral matters'. This shows clearly that there are different ways of approaching the idea of autonomy or freedom. It is therefore interesting that Thiroux (1980) places his principle of individual freedom at the end of his list rather than at the beginning. Niebuhr (1963) seeks 'social solidarity' in his response ethics, which equates more with the ideas of the 'traditional societies'. Noddings (1984) sees 'receptivity, relatedness and responsiveness' (p. 2) to be the basis of an ethic of caring, and these three authors have therefore a good deal in common.

Thiroux (1980: 128) says that he presents the principle of individual freedom last 'so that it is understood that individual moral freedom is limited by the other four principles'. Only when the necessity of each of these principles is understood and upheld – the need to respect and protect human life; the need to do good and prevent harm; the need to treat people justly and the need to speak the truth and be honest – can each of them function. Perhaps Hartley Coleridge (1796–1849) summed this up well when he said, 'But what is Freedom? Rightly understood, A universal licence to be good.'

We do indeed need freedom in order to express ourselves as human beings. But this can never be understood as absolute freedom. In daily life we are bounded on every side by laws and regulations which 'restrict' our freedom; the compulsory wearing of seat belts in cars is only one example in which the infringement of personal liberty was debated at length. We do not have the freedom to drive at any speed on any roads; we do not have the freedom to help ourselves to a loaf of bread sticking out of a bag; we do not have the freedom to burn any fuel we like. At every turn a person's individual freedom is subject to the freedom of the common good.

Autonomy or freedom in health care is important because it leaves the patient or client in charge of his or her own life. The paternalism so beloved of old and now so decried certainly restricted a person's choice. But more than that, it controlled that person's life according to its own values. It could hardly be said to have respected the patient's life; it was a beneficence which was very differently understood from what it is today – 'sparing' the patient any decisions and thus keeping him or her in a subordinate position; it was the justice of 'all people being equal but some people being more equal than others'. And truth did not come into it because that was the province of the doctors.

A person's autonomy depends on the ethical stance of others. We cannot be free ourselves unless others respect us and our lives, treat us in a good and just way and are honest with us. Jones (1989; see Chapter 8) says that 'where there is no honesty there is no autonomy for the patient'. We can say this of every principle in relation to autonomy (and also of every principle in relation to every other). But it is particularly in relation to autonomy that communication in health care has changed drastically. Truth is no longer the province only of the carers. But how much truth is needed to enable a patient to make a free and fair choice?

The proliferation of Local Research Ethics Committees (LRECs) must be a good thing, preventing patients from being used or given inadequate information. The practice of all these ideals is, however, far more difficult than the theory. We have a huge legacy of culture and tradition to contend with which militates against many of these principles. It is only gradually that we see more and more what needs to be changed if health care is truly to be 'care' and patients and clients are truly to be autonomous. If we take this seriously, then we will always have to contend with 'economy, efficiency and effectiveness', because personal freedom cannot simply be measured in terms of mathematics. Perhaps one of the challenges of an ethic of caring and an ethic of nursing is to affirm the supremacy of the *caring* relationship over the standpoint where everything is seen as 'value for money'. Giving patients their choice means giving them time and listening to them and their needs and wants, and time is more and more a precious commodity.

Empowerment

Empowerment has become the buzz word of the alternative and complementary health care scene. By being more open and honest with patients and clients, it is believed by carers in that field that this gives the power back to its clients. This is surely so most of the time, but it must not be forgotten that as soon as a new theory or treatment appears, it is quickly surrounded by a science and a language of its own which excludes the lay person. It is not easy to pursue 'receptivity, relatedness and responsiveness' (Noddings, 1984: 2) all the way.

Empowerment, according to the *Chambers' Dictionary* (1993), is 'the giving to individuals of power to take decisions in matters relating to themselves, especially in an organisation, in relation to self-development'. It is often seen that empowerment is necessary to redress the excesses of paternalism. Charters and bills of rights seek to give people – patients and clients – something which belongs to them by right. Coleman (1993) is somewhat cynical when he says that 'claiming to act in the public interest, ... institutions devise codes of etiquette that are more about defending territory and position than respecting patients' wishes for autonomy'. It is not only personal relationships which are often difficult to maintain; official and professional relationships are just as delicate and have to be handled with care. Therefore they are carefully defined in charters and codes.

It is reasonable to ask why powers were taken away from patients in the first instance, so that they now have to be given back. When we start from the standpoint of moral equality, then there is nothing to hide and nothing to lose.

⅄ When professionals set themselves up as experts, then they create an atmosphere of dependence, and this has been the case, particularly in medicine, for a very long time. Patients have become used to being dependent and in this way they have lost the power to decide and choose. Autonomy, as described above, has led to that essential aloneness and anguish which needs to be respected but cannot get close because it has to defend its territory. The autonomy which is rooted in relation brings a sharing and therefore a joy (Noddings, 1984).

Sherwin (1992: 28) describes medicine as being characterised by 'crisis management'; that is what it is good at. But the '*institution* [emphasis added] of medicine should be transformed from one of crisis management to one of health empowerment. Perhaps the nurse–patient model is worth examining in this context, for, ideally, nurses define their role as one of informing and empowering patients, rather than controlling them'. We see, therefore, yet again, the two different approaches to patient care: that of medicine and of nursing, or perhaps also of a masculine and feminine approach. They are necessarily different, and perhaps they need to be, but they also need to be available on an equal basis, as equal partners. In order to achieve that equality, nurses need to be clear that their approach is just as important as the medical approach, and their different relationship with patients is the one which empowers and sees empowerment as the 'natural' way.

The story at the start of this chapter shows an attempt at empowerment which was not very successful as far as Peter was concerned. Empowerment of patients does not mean an abdication of responsibilities on the part of the nurse, and Ed, too, had to look at his position. This will be discussed below, after a brief examination of professionalism.

Professionalism

Professionalism and power are often subtly, or not so subtly, linked. A profession characterises itself by teaching its own members and by having a code which applies to all qualified members. Those who have received that teaching then have a knowledge which is associated with privilege, and this gives power. But 'simply because one person has power it does not follow that another individual is powerless' (Chadwick and Tadd, 1992: 51).

There has been much debate about whether nursing is a profession or not; what is clear, though, is that nurses behave in a professional way. If medicine as a profession has power, it does not necessarily follow that nursing, not being a profession in the same way, has to be powerless. Medicine may have power in matters of medicine, but doctors are not therefore also experts in ethics. When issues of an ethical nature arise, it does not mean that they exercise any particular power; nor are nurses powerless.

Quinn and Smith (1987: 9) make the point that nursing has traditionally been associated with affective care and emotive devotion to patients, and Benjamin and Curtis (1986: 89) say similarly that 'hands and feet' rather than 'brains' have been seen to be the hallmark of nursing. Both sets of authors dispute this view vigorously in the light of what they see nursing to be today. Nurses diagnose and treat, make judgements, engage in research – all of which requires knowledge ('brains') as well as good-will and affection. The divisions and stereotypes which have so long kept health care locked into a system of power are not applicable any longer. Holism is more than just an idea; it is something which has to be accepted as the only way towards health in the widest sense, and therefore each part of the health system and its professions has to work together. This is not only the best for patients but also for the professionals, who can only be and become more human when there is acknowledgement that they too need to give and receive in a holistic way.

Professionalism is not only about what a group of people are but also what they want to be. Nursing therefore has to ask itself what it wants to be and stand for. This has led to the debate about the 'extended' or 'expanded' role of nurses. In *The Scope of Professional Practice* (1992), a companion to the *Code of Professional Conduct* (1992), the UKCC has given the thumbs down to extension of practice as limiting the parameters of practice and concentrating on activities and detracting 'from the importance of holistic care' (Paragraph 13). The *Scope of Professional Practice* does not elaborate on expansion as such, but points towards 'principles for practice'. This gives nursing practically a free hand to develop in any way it desires, which exemplifies the principle of individual freedom. As freedom is bounded by all the other principles, so this freedom given to nursing is bounded by the areas covered by the other principles: nursing has to respect the value of life of its clients, concentrate on what is 'good' and 'right', what promotes justice and equity and what is honest.

Professionalism has to concern itself with the profession as a whole while not overlooking the individual members of it. It is always the individual who makes an impact in one area first, and this may or may not then be taken on by the profession. It is an individual who first blows the whistle and then others can follow; who questions the practice of electro-convulsive therapy before others are also able to follow their conscience and question it; who exposes repressive practices in children's homes; who sees the need for better care of dying patients and a whole movement in the same direction follows; who is convinced that nursing practice can be different, thus starting a shift in attitudes towards nursing diagnosis and care which cannot be reversed. This 'bottom-up' approach needs to be fostered because it is the 'powerless' who are at work here. Empowerment is not just something for patients but does need to be seen as part of what nursing as a whole is about.

The 'top-down' approach, from the profession's governing bodies, is much easier because it has the power of officialdom behind it. The balance between individual (personal) action and professional need is addressed in the UKCC *Code of Professional Conduct* (1992) but as the Code is not a legal document, the interpretation of the Code is each nurse's own duty and responsibility.

What is happening?

The story of the stolen bread is both funny and pathetic, simple and very profound in its implications. Every one of the players involved tells a story of their own.

The main character is Peter, a young man with learning difficulties. It is possible that some years ago he had spent his days in a large institution, and because of government legislation he and the other people moved together into the house they now occupy. This will have been a difficult, but also an exciting move to make. The outings were not just for pleasure but also for helping the residents to be, and be seen to be, part of the wider community.

It seems that Peter always had a good appetite and was therefore always happy to be given a little extra food. This may have been his motivation on the underground train. But it seems that playing a trick was just as much a part. He was standing slightly apart from the group and so he was just a little more independent. It is fair to assume that this was Peter's own choice, asserting his independence when he could. It was not so much the bread itself which tempted Peter, as the smell which he imagined went with it. The smell of freshly baked bread is enticing for most people, giving them a sense of comfort and satisfaction. Presumably the bread in the bag was actually cold and could therefore not have had much of a smell about it. But when one is always hungry one can also smell bread even when it is not there.

Peter was presumably also well enough aware of the boundaries of property. In the house, he will not have been able to take what belonged to someone else and he will have known the difference between personal and common property and that to take from someone else without permission was not right. It is in this sense that Ed, Laura and the other staff will have educated the residents and gradually have empowered them to play their part in society. *What happened* to Peter then? In a moment of opportunity – or temptation – he forgot his personal code of behaviour and let himself be guided by his instinct, hunger or showmanship.

The saying that we can resist everything except temptation is not only apt but mostly true. Most of the time we have no difficulty in deciding rightly and correctly, but then something presents itself and we act contrary to better judgement.

> *Perhaps I am more aware of these possibilities because I am writing this book. . . but recently I have found myself in any number of situations in shops, where I could have helped myself to goods without being noticed, could have slipped through turnstiles without paying, was given things which were intended for other people, and so on. Reflecting on this I wondered in particular how this principle of individual freedom affects other people. Thiroux (1980) says that the principle of truth telling or honesty is the most difficult one to keep, but I wonder if these days freedom might not be just as difficult?*

What is happening to Peter, then, as he breaks off the piece of bread? Why had he not learned his lesson? Had Ed and Laura and the other staff not taught him well enough? Had he been doing similar things at home and got away with it? Did the staff not notice or not want to notice? It may be that he showed off and everybody thought that it was funny. It may indeed have been funny, but did Peter then know the difference between what is funny and what is wrong? When we ask *What is happening?* we need to consider many of these aspects – and perhaps many more which might only emerge once we ask this question in reality.

What is happening to Ed and to Laura? When Ed realised that something was wrong, he questioned Peter but guessed quickly enough what had taken place. When the other passenger joined the group, Ed said that he could do nothing about it.

Ed said nothing and did nothing. In this way he indicated that Peter was responsible for his action and that he, Ed, was not going to take over.

What is happening, then, is something like this:

- Ed implies that Peter, being a responsible member of society, is responsible for this act – he should speak for himself;
- Ed assumes that since he and the staff have empowered their clients, they are now not going to take that power back;
- Peter may be baffled, because when he played pranks before, everybody thought it was funny, and now they suddenly don't and Peter is at a loss what to say;
- Laura hides behind Ed and takes no part at all, thus denying any responsibility;
- the other passenger clearly thinks that Ed is 'in charge' and therefore he is responsible – Peter may have done something wrong, but being handicapped, is not in control of his behaviour;
- everyone is shifting responsibility on to someone else, therefore. There is a vacuum and a third party – the station manager – has to come in and sort it out with the law rather than in a spirit of 'receptivity, relatedness and responsiveness' (Noddings, 1984: 2).

All this happens in a matter of a few seconds. It is also based on a whole set of assumptions. When this is the case, there is blame first of all and then accusation. It then takes a great deal of tact and good communication to get it straight, because by that time everything has become distorted.

One could look at this scenario from the standpoint of every one of the principles discussed because, as already mentioned, when one of the principles falls, they all fall like dominoes. When we look at it from the point of view of individual freedom we need to see that

- Peter was not free to take the bread;
- Ed had a professional responsibility towards Peter and the rest of the group – he was not free to abdicate this even though Peter had been taught what was right and wrong;

- Laura was free not to say or do anything, but this freedom did not remove her duty of care when with clients;
- as adults we cannot be responsible *for* one another – that would be reducing the others' freedom – but we are responsible *to* one another. In the area of mental handicap and people with learning difficulties it may often be very unclear where one rather than the other applies. Staff working in these fields must therefore be even more aware of this point and be prepared to question deeply *what is happening* in order to be effective with their clients and their own professional practice.

What is happening with and to the other members of the group? They do not have the problem of being responsible *for* one another, but should be aware that they are responsible *to* one another in a unique way. If they are not, then their living together would be very difficult. They may not fully comprehend the finer details of this idea, but the way in which they interact and support one another will show how they understand this responsibility. How they now treat one another, and in particular Peter, will be crucial for him and for their future together.

Finally, *what is happening* to the passenger who saw the incident? He makes himself the spokesperson of the injured party. This happened perhaps only because he saw that Ed was not doing or saying anything which he would have thought appropriate. If Ed had acted differently, he might not have stormed off and caused an incident which would have had to be reported.

Even if we assume that he was well disposed towards people with learning difficulties and had not thought that they should not travel on public transport, this incident will have tarnished his image of their nurses, carers or even social workers.

It is hardly possible to separate the personal from the professional image. Ed, who might have thought of himself not so much as a 'nurse in charge' but as one human being caring for another human being, is nevertheless not free to do as he pleases because he is responsible *for* Peter and the group *vis-à-vis* the public.

What is the meaning of it?

Ethical situations like the one described in this story of Peter, Ed and the rest of the group, are not the kind which make it into the textbooks of philosophers. It is not enough of a dilemma of life and death. But it is one of those stories which make up our lives and by which our values are shaped just as drastically as when there has to be agonising over a decision. Indeed, it may be said that this 'bread-and-butter' story is even more powerful because it is the sort of story with which we might be faced every day, whereas the other kind usually only happens once in a lifetime. To look at this story, then, from the point of view of the meaning is essential in raising the self-awareness out of which any understanding and possible change can come.

It is clear that at the time of the incident only *What is happening?* might be asked as a question; asking for the *meaning* then would have been out of place. But later, when everybody will have had to reflect on what had happened, there might emerge a sense of new understanding which will then come only because there will have been some new *meaning* in it all.

Depending on Peter's level of awareness, he will have understood the meaning of property from a new angle. He will have realised that he cannot simply help himself to anything tempting. He might have done it in the past and it might have been seen as a joke within the circle of the people of the house, but when it concerns people who are strangers, he is not free to do as he pleases. The notion of 'citizen' may have to be taught him in a new and perhaps better way. How this is done may indeed be enlightening for the persons concerned as it may throw new light also on their understanding of freedom and how to teach it.

People with learning difficulties or who are physically challenged have occasionally used the term 'body fascism' to describe the attitudes of society towards individuals and groups who do not fit the social norms. Peter might have become acutely aware at that moment that he was not like other people and that this might have been a strong reason why the passenger marked him as a thief rather than walking on and saying and doing nothing. Would the passenger have acted in the same way if the roles had been reversed and Peter, visibly handicapped, had been carrying the bread and a pretty young woman had taken his bread?

Once we begin to look into *what is happening,* we are often able to see also into the *meaning* of unexpected areas of life which then shape future thinking and behaviour.

What is the meaning of it for Ed and for Laura? It may be that Ed was jolted by the incident. He may have had to re-evaluate his ideas of personal and professional responsibility. He may have had to think carefully for the first time in his life what 'everyday ethics' is about; how he behaves ethically with his staff and with the people he cares for. He may have to consider again what is *meant* by empowerment of people who have no power, and autonomy for those who do not know how to use it. He may indeed want to ask himself why he works with the underprivileged and powerless – what this means in his life and with regard to his own power and freedom.

Clearly, not every daily incident can be used to reconsider one's values in depth, but then again it is so often a small and even insignificant event which makes us face some issue in a new way. When that happens we need to take the incident seriously. It presented itself for a reason: we must try to understand the reason.

What is the meaning of this for the passenger? Some of the possible aspects have already been outlined. What is certain is that he will not forget this incident and he may even dine out on it a few times. In the process the story will get embroidered. The chances are that his anger at Ed, the nurse in charge of the group, will not diminish. Ed said nothing to Peter and seemed to wash his hands of the whole affair.

This man may build an image of nurses in general from this, not just of nurses caring for handicapped people. Unconsciously, he may tarnish every nurse with the same brush, and if and when he has to go to hospital or be cared for by a nurse he may be frightened or feel that he cannot trust any nurse. This may be quite painful and lead to misunderstandings and problems. It may also just possibly be that someone will point out to him that he could have been discriminating against a person or group of persons and that this might have set him thinking about personhood, power and ethics.

Inevitably, this scenario is speculation, and nothing so drastic may happen at all. It simply shows yet again the kind of consequences our ethical or unethical actions have.

What is the fitting answer?

This question applies most of all to Ed. What would have been his fitting answer? Should Ed have said something to Peter, and what?

According to *The Scope of Professional Practice* (UKCC, 1992, Clause 21):

> the Council requires that registered nurses employed in [the residential care sector] will use their judgement and discretion to identify the nursing needs of residents and others for whom they may have responsibility, and will comply with any requirement of the Council.

Was this a 'nursing need'? Would Peter understand more if Ed said nothing? Should Peter be told off in front of the other residents? These are more issues of pedagogy, and clearly Ed would need to use his 'judgement and discretion' in how to handle the incident.

What is perhaps most obvious from the account is that by saying and doing nothing, Ed seems to have relinquished his professional responsibility. As such, he compromised the principle of individual freedom because he did not have the freedom to do that. He did not have the freedom to shift his responsibility on to Peter, who clearly showed at that moment that he was not capable of taking personal responsibility.

Freedom is only freedom when all people can share it equally. Peter could not, at that moment, handle his personal freedom, and, being in a crowd and on an outing of which Ed was in charge, Ed had to assume the responsibility. Peter misused his freedom, but that did not mean that Ed could also misuse his. Of the two, Ed was more in the wrong because he should have known what he was doing, whereas Peter did not. When Peter showed that he had not been fully empowered, Ed should have empowered himself and acted in some way appropriate to the situation.

What would have been Ed's *fitting answer*? It would probably have been to identify himself as the person in charge to the passenger and to have told him that he, Ed, would deal with the culprit. If the passenger insisted that the station manager be told, then Ed might have said that he would do this. Ed might have told Peter that he had done wrong and asked him if he understood why. He might have asked the whole group of residents, there and then, what they saw the problem to be and perhaps even what they should do with Peter. They might have had a simple procedure or policy at the house for helping one another to understand what they had done wrong and for some kind of 'punishment'. If necessary, they might all have gone to the station manager to say what had taken place. In this way they might all have learned rather than been shouted at and frightened by the passenger. In this way they would have acted ethically towards one another and to the wider public.

What would have been the *fitting answer* for Laura? She was not considered in charge, but she was part of the staff. Seeing that Ed was not taking responsibility, Laura might have said something to Ed to make him see his duty. As a member of staff, she might also have handled the situation herself. The fact that she did and said nothing, either, was not fitting in the circumstances.

Was the passenger right to do what he did? If he acted as an advocate on behalf of the wronged person, then he was probably right; if he picked on

Peter because he could see that he was handicapped, then he was not. The motivation is a strong pull to action. It depends what the motivator is and what drives the motivation.

The pattern of responsibility

The *challenge* in this story is that Ed is confronted with Peter eating a piece of bread. This is compounded a few moments later by the passenger speaking up and then taking an angry course of action. It is this which then presented the real *challenge*.

For Peter, the *challenge* might have been to see the bread and smelling it, thus becoming aware of his hunger. Put like this, it seems all too similar to the story of Adam and Eve, each blaming someone or something more remote. How easy it is to blame an instinct, rather than to accept that a *person* is addressed by a challenge. By blaming an instinct we back out of responsibility at the very first hurdle.

The *response* which Ed demonstrated first of all towards Peter was to see what was happening. It was only when the passenger came that Ed seemed not to know what to do. His *response* then was speechlessness.

The *response*, in the way Niebuhr (1963) describes it, is a physical reaction first of all, but one stemming from emotions which may be quite deeply hidden and not easily accessible at the moment. But they have been triggered by something in the challenge, and they are now evident even if not understood.

The *interpretation*, the next element in this pattern, goes to those feelings and interprets what has come as a challenge in the light of these emotions. What has happened in the past that was similar to what is going on now? What was the outcome then? What happened in the past may be crucially important for the present, because its consequences will colour our future experiences.

We *interpret* what the other person is doing, saying, implying or showing, and our response is an interpreted response to what the other said. That person, in turn, interprets what we say, and so every situation 'grows' as the people respond. The longer Ed refrained from making any move, the more the passenger interpreted this as dereliction of duty or irresponsibility.

The *accountability* – that is, the sense of weighing up the possible ways forward – did not seem to have taken place for Ed. He was stuck in his unresponsiveness, and therefore from his point of view nothing was happening to change the present.

But for the passenger, the *accountability* grew steadily. He may have been in a situation much earlier in life where he had not acted as he later thought he should have done. This might have left him with the need to act now. He might also have been the sort of person who always acts, whatever the incident. Or he might simply have been concerned for the person who lost a piece of bread; he might identify with people who are robbed. Whatever his *interpretation* of the situation, his *accountability* now meant that he needed to act. If Ed did not act, *he* would – something had to be done. The longer Ed refrained from acting, the more he acted. He saw perhaps only one way forward, and that was justice: an injustice had been done and it needed to be rectified, and by him. He could not let such an incident go by.

The outcome of any situation which presents a challenge should ideally be *social solidarity*; that is, something which benefits the whole community of people involved. In this case, the outcome could not be called 'solidarity' and was rather 'unsocial' into the bargain: an irate passenger, a speechless Ed, presumably a helpless Peter and a baffled group of fellow-residents, and in the end a station manager who would probably have much preferred to do something else than sort out other people's problems.

Social solidarity is possible even in the most difficult situations. But it does demand that all concerned do act in the most ethical way possible. This is normally the way which regards the common good as well as the personal good, values all life and respects individuals and their ways of life, seeks justice and is concerned for equity and speaks and acts truthfully. These are the basic facts; at each turn it is necessary to interpret anew *what is happening* and to give the *fitting answer* in the light of the principles outlined.

Chapter 11
The principle of individual freedom (2)

Story

Ellen was 23 when she first went to work in the community. She had always said that this was what she wanted to do most. Her area covered two residences for elderly people. She was particularly interested in patients with diabetes, and she was deft with her injections.

In one of the residences was Roy, a 58-year-old man who had to retire early because of diabetes and severe complications – in particular, leg ulcers. Ellen had to go to Roy to give him his insulin injections every day and to care for his legs. While she did this she talked with Roy, who told her often of his son, Mike, who had a good position and visited him regularly, though he could only ever come at night because he was so busy.

Roy always had the insulin ready but could not draw up the injections because of his deteriorating eyesight. Ellen told Roy that the insulin should be injected straight from the fridge, and that she could very easily go there and take it out when she came. Roy agreed to this, but every day the insulin was there again on the table when Ellen came. She tried to tell him several times more not to take the insulin out of the fridge, but Roy simply seemed to ignore her.

One day Roy was not well at all when Ellen called. She feared that he had had a stroke just before she had arrived. She called the warden and the GP, who said that he would come shortly, but in the meantime Ellen wanted to give him his insulin. The warden arrived quickly and they discussed what might have happened.

Roy became agitated when he realised that Ellen was going to the fridge to get his insulin. Ellen was surprised by this and the warden tried to reassure him. When Ellen opened the fridge she saw several plastic bags full of tablets, unmarked and unlabelled. Now she knew why Roy had never wanted her to go to his fridge before. Ellen imagined that these tablets were either stolen or secretly manufactured and stored with Roy for safety. She quickly made the connection with Roy's son – but all this was guesswork.

She gave Roy his injection and then she and the warden discussed with the GP, who had arrived a few minutes later, what would be the best way of caring for Roy. They talked among themselves but in such a way that Roy could hear everything, and they addressed him even though he was almost unable to answer or take part in the conversation.

Roy was taken to hospital a little later by ambulance. Ellen also left, very concerned what she should do about her discovery.

The setting

Many people would say that there is freedom *from*, and freedom *to*: freedom from violence, injustice, lying, repression and discrimination; and freedom to think, speak, believe and move about unhindered. We need to be free in order to make any choices, and, in particular, if we are to decide ethically, we need to be morally free. The concept of 'the market' so revered in today's world is based on economic freedom, which, however, is not an egalitarian freedom since it presupposes an economic starting base which is certainly not available to everybody.

If one person is to have freedom, then all persons need to be free. If we are to have freedom, then we first need equality at every level of human dealing. Like so much in society, this is more an ideal than reality. But all over the world people fight for these ideals. Most wars have been fought so that people would be free to live in their own country, in secure borders and according to their own beliefs and traditions. Ibsen's famous saying, 'You should never have your best trousers on when you go out to fight for freedom and for truth', must be all too clear to any soldier.

But it is not only on the level of territory that this might apply; maintaining freedom of thought, belief and speech is not easy either. We are quick to condemn anybody who does not hold the same views as ours or maintains some beliefs with which we do not agree. Particularly in health care this can lead to some very unpleasant scenes (as the story of Pam in Chapter 6 shows).

Maintaining individual freedom or autonomy is therefore one of the responsibilities of health professionals. If we say that we maintain the principle of the value of life, then we have also by extension to maintain the principle of individual freedom because we cannot respect life without respecting autonomy. But we need to be on our guard; paternalism may be 'out' officially, but it is still often around in very subtle ways. The use of the word 'we' betrays this attitude quickly: 'we will give you this medication; we should like to try this treatment', and so on. Who is 'we'? And should not the patient have been asked if he or she agrees, rather than be informed that this will happen?

> *A friend who had received wonderful help and support from a GP at a time of a personal crisis was very disturbed when this same GP then said, 'We will try these drops first and we will see what happens'. She was furious that she could be treated so considerately at one level but when it came to actual medical care, this GP was still in the old mode of paternalism.*

While people are capable of holding their own values, it does not follow that they always follow these values. Most people value their health very highly and do much to maintain it. But they also smoke and eat and drink too much, and put their own and other people's lives in danger by driving dangerously or crossing busy roads haphazardly. Health professionals see this in the way in which patients and clients fail to keep to diets despite their declared intentions, or take risks after life-saving operations despite clear instructions and advice. It may then be difficult to respect such people's freedom and value their lives.

A perennial difficulty here is the wish of members of the Jehovah's Witnesses Church not to receive blood transfusions. They will accept any treatments and operations so long as blood is not transfused. Doctors find themselves in the difficult situation of wanting to treat and even save life, but the beliefs of Jehovah's Witnesses in effect prevents doctors from carrying out their duties. Whose life is then valued? Whose freedom is upheld?

It is at this point that the other principles also come into play. The principle of truth telling or honesty is heavily involved here, in that a patient should be thoroughly informed of what is happening, what is possible and what is impossible. The practice of getting a sick Jehovah's Witness into the operating theatre and then giving a blood transfusion without him or her knowing is not acceptable any more. The principle of goodness or rightness comes into this situation because of the injunction to do good or to avoid harm. But then it must be established what is meant here by 'harm'. 'Prevention of harm to others is sometimes considered sufficient reason for limiting a person's autonomy' (Quinn and Smith, 1987: 34). This may apply in the case of children of Jehovah's Witnesses who cannot give consent on their own for any treatments which might include blood transfusions. In this case, a child would probably be made a ward of court, thus limiting the parents' autonomy.

Nurses have understood the concept of patient autonomy almost instinctively. The idea of empowerment is rooted in the 'receptivity, relatedness and responsiveness' (Noddings, 1984: 2) which generally characterises the nurse–patient relationship, and in the sense of equality which this creates. Patient advocacy is therefore also related to this, and so is accountability.

Accountability

According to the *Chambers' Dictionary* (1993), to account means 'to reckon; to judge, value; to recount; to give a reason or explanation; to answer as someone responsible'. Marks-Maran (1993: 123) combines all these elements in her statement that

> an accountable person does not undertake an action merely because someone in authority says to do so. Instead, the accountable person examines a situation, explores the various options available, demonstrates a knowledge-able understanding of the possible consequences of options and makes a decision for action which can be justified from a knowledge base.

In order to practice, professionals have to have a knowledge base, and within their sphere of practice they have to exercise their knowledge responsibly. They also have to be given the freedom to exercise their skills.

The traditional problem in nursing has been that nurses were given a fair amount of freedom and responsibility, but a strict hierarchy prevented accountable practice. There was always someone higher up the ladder who was held accountable. This meant, in effect, that many nurses never learned to think for themselves but 'very quickly learn[ed] the necessity of obedience to those over them, and realise[d] what a difficult and responsible job it is to be a sister or matron (Way, 1971: 17). Although this now reads like a caricature from a different world, the fact that Way's little book was still in print in 1971 indicates that this sort of teaching was still around then, and old habits really do die hard. It is therefore not surprising that the UKCC *Code of Professional Conduct* (1992) has to stress accountability so much.

Marks-Maran (1993) lists four different areas of accountability: legal, managerial, professional and moral. Legal accountability refers to keeping the law. This may not be so difficult when it comes to keeping traffic regulations. It is more difficult when a patient's prescription specifies 20 mg of a given analgesic and the patient is still in severe pain. Is it possible to give another dose after only a short while? This may not pose a great problem when a doctor is quickly available, but is not so easy at 03.00 hours, when the doctor has already been disturbed a few times before.

In the case of Ellen, legal accountability might also be asked of her in respect of her find in the fridge. If these were stolen goods, or indeed illegal drugs, then she could be legally responsible for reporting this find.

Managerial accountability is the kind most advocated by the Code: on the basis of professional knowledge and experience, a nurse weighs up a given situation, makes a decision and acts on it. If and when questioned about it, she or he can give good reasons for acting in that way. Problems often arise when a nurse has taken a decision which a doctor might regard as his or hers alone to make, such as letting a patient die and not calling the emergency team when a patient has a cardiac arrest. If a decision is made in good faith, not simply out of neglect or malice, managerial accountability has taken place.

The UKCC states in its Advisory Document *Exercising Accountability* (1989: 18) that 'Professional accountability must be exercised in such a manner as to ensure that the primacy of the interests of patients or clients is respected and must not be overridden by those of the professions or their practitioners', thus acknowledging that there will often be tensions between the various professional groups. If there is any doubt whose interest is at stake, then the patient's must have priority. But this is very easy to maintain in theory; in practice there is a problem precisely because it is not clear whose interest is questioned. The question *What is happening?* may then help all concerned to see more clearly what is going on simply because this question takes a step sideways and allows other possibilities to enter the discussion.

The discussion in the previous chapter about expansion is also relevant here because professional accountability is about practice and the constant change in practice. Accountability is thus not only an interaction between different professional groups but also between the various disciplines of nursing – in particular, between education and practice.

Exercising Accountability highlights the 'tension between maintenance of standards and the availability or use of resources' (1989: 7). This is perhaps the single most obvious factor to cause stress among all health-care professionals in the present climate of cuts and 'value for money', particularly when one considers 'resources' to be money, people, space, time, goods and services.

> *Many nurses have wished that their attributes of angels and good*
> *fairies would occasionally become reality and that they could*
> *change an awful situation with wishes of peace and goodwill.*

Moral accountability considers the personal values. The stories so far outlined in these chapters all point to situations in which personal values were clarified in the process of searching for the fitting answer to a problem. Values only become important when they are questioned. In difficult situations our 'instinctive' values come to the fore, but then they are also questioned and re-examined and very likely rephrased. The issue of conscience is relevant here, but so is the fact that any professional morality is based on personal morality. What we are in the privacy of our own home we are also in the wide-open spaces of professional practice.

Professional autonomy

Are nurses really free to act upon their own judgement? Should they be able to be free? If they are not free, what would make them free?

Throughout this book it has been shown that nurses have again and again acted upon their own judgement and paid a heavy price for it. This may be in the form of other professionals taking action against the particular nurse, or nurses finding that they cannot square certain practices with their conscience any longer. The stress resulting from such situations becomes too great, and nurses either give up and leave the profession disillusioned or give in and then function like robots rather than human beings.

One of the difficulties is that nurses have two 'masters': they carry out the doctors' orders, but they are legally responsible to the nursing hierarchy. If nurses make a medical mistake it is not the medical profession which disciplines them but the nursing profession. But this is precisely where so many of the issues arise which demand of nurses that they use their own professional judgement. Medications are prescribed in doses which nurses question, investigations are requested which nurses find inappropriate and treatments are ordered with which nurses disagree.

In all these cases nurses have to have an extensive knowledge of medicine to make any judgement. They need to know the normal doses of medications and their effects and side-effects in order to judge if a prescription is questionable. If they question a dose or a treatment, they may be told that they are interfering in something which is none of their business. If they 'do as they are told', they may later – too late – be told that they are 'professionals' and not morons. They are damned if they do and damned if they don't.

Should nurses be free to make their own professional judgements? In several areas of practice nurses are as independent as possible, given other professional restraints. Midwifery practice is clearly an area where a group of professionals is more and more independent. Certain groups of nurses, mainly in community and practice care, are now able to prescribe a number of specified medications. Reid (1993) describes the Tile Hill Health Centre in Coventry, which is 'unique in terms of the extent to which nurses . . . are autonomous and responsible for their own professional practice. Managerial interference is low and edicts from the top are few . . . . The working environment allows nurses to be creative in the way they deliver care and come up with, and see through, their own care initiatives, using the UKCC Code of Conduct as personal guidelines.' In the same category is a 'nurse-led minor injuries unit at St Charles' Hospital in West London – which is an integral part of St Mary's NHS Trust – [and] is a very successful example of how nurses can implement innovative new methods on behalf of clients' (Baker, 1993). Given the climate of the market place, nurses are much freer than ever before to take advantage of the areas where they can indeed be free to use their professional judgement.

But this should not only apply to a few specific situations. All the professions and professional groups are expanding on several fronts, and with this must always go a discussion of the legitimate use of and right to autonomy. Being able to use one's professional judgement in everyday decisions is perhaps even more important for the health of individual nurses and nursing in general than a few models, important though these are in their own right. It is only when professionals are able to use their personal and professional faculties to the full that they will be fulfilled as persons and not be demoralised.

Professional nurses should therefore look for opportunities to use their autonomy to the full. This should surely include any number of imaginative innovations covering all areas of care. One area where nurses could be innovative as well as autonomous and put patient empowerment into practice is in finding ways of identifying patients. Wrist-bands and electronic tagging are not only unsightly and demeaning of the person, they also have an air of possessiveness about them. Anything which 'reduces' patients also 'reduces' nurses; anything which gives patients and clients autonomy also gives nurses autonomy.

The UKCC *Code of Professional Conduct* (1992) states that,

> as a registered nurse, midwife or health visitor, you are personally account-
> able for your practice and, in the exercise of your professional accountability,
> must ... avoid any abuse of your privileged relationship with patients and
> clients and of the privileged access allowed to their person, property,
> residence or workplace. (Clause 9)

This clause is generally interpreted to mean that one should not take advantage of patients however such an opportunity might present itself. It could also mean seeing accountability to patients not only as applying when something has gone wrong, but also as that which unites nurses and patients in the first instance. It is generally understood that nurses are accountable to an employer, society and the profession. When we see that we are in the first instance accountable to the patient, then this changes the emphasis of the nurse–patient relationship. If we therefore ask if nurses should be free to act upon their own judgement, we need to answer that they can only be free in so far as they can and do account for their judgement to the patient.

What, then, would make nurses free to use their judgement? The answer to that question would depend on our understanding of accountability. Accountability is the outcome of responsibility. The type of ethics advocated here is based on responsibility, and accountability is simply the measurable part of responsibility.

Niebuhr (1963: 57) speaks of 'ourselves as responsive beings'; May (1975) says that the professional relationship is marked by 'exchange, agreement and reciprocity'; and Noddings (1984) suggests that a moral attitude which longs for goodness is 'rooted in receptivity, relatedness and responsiveness'. Niebuhr, with his play on the words 'response', 'responsive', 'respons*i*bility' and 'response-*a*bility', perhaps encapsulates the ideas of the other two authors as well, making the word 'responsibility' into a résumé of all the other expressions.

Professional independence can therefore really only be seen in this context of relating to others. Nursing can never be completely autonomous because it is too much dependent on relationships – with patients and clients as well as other professionals.

Just as the principle of individual freedom only makes sense when seen within the confines of the other ethical principles, so autonomy can only be understood within the confines of relationships. Professional independence is, like human independence, much more an *inter*dependence.

What is happening?

How do these deliberations fit into the story of Ellen? When looking at *What is happening?* we see that they all shape the context and all help to answer this question. The question needs to be asked of all the people concerned if we are to understand this story, and others similar to this one, which readers may have experienced.

What is happening to Ellen? Ellen finds herself with a patient who, she realises, has probably had a stroke and therefore needs attention. Being insulin-dependent, he needs his injection, but at this stage probably also a different dosage from the one he has normally, and Ellen is able to adjust the dose at this moment. When Ellen opens the fridge to take the insulin out she notices some bags containing tablets. She realises that these do not belong to Roy, her patient, and that they are probably in the fridge as a hiding place. Ellen has no idea what these tablets are, but she knows that tablets rarely need to be kept in the fridge, and she is therefore suspicious, particularly because of their quantity. Roy had never wanted her to have access to the fridge, and she now realises why. Perhaps she is also beginning to make a connection with Roy's son, who, she was told by Roy, has a business and only ever comes to visit his father in the evening. Is there something shady in this business? If Roy is really storing – or hiding – tablets for his son, then surely there would be a safer place than the fridge where Roy also keeps his insulin? There is something not quite right about this arrangement.

But with the arrival of the warden and the GP, Ellen has to concentrate on Roy and her discovery has to wait. Yet she will have to act fairly quickly, otherwise there might be wide repercussions.

What is happening here? Ellen is suspicious that these tablets are either stolen, counterfeit or indeed dangerous drugs. She believes therefore that they are illegal. If they are illegal drugs, then she believes that she has a duty to notify the police. But if she does this she puts a patient of hers under suspicion and she is bound to keep her patients' and clients' information confidential. She would also put the warden of the residence at risk and, because such places seem to have eyes and ears everywhere, rumours would probably spread like wild-fire and generally make life difficult around the house. It is fair to assume that Ellen was wondering where her primary loyalty lay: towards her patient, now unable to speak and look after himself, or towards the wider public in that illegal actions of any kind should be investigated and those involved prosecuted.

Ellen may have feared that something like this might happen at some stage because, probably, several of her colleagues will have had to deal with situations where they saw and heard things which challenged their practice. Perhaps she only vaguely knew about such incidents because colleagues would not disclose information. Knowing that colleagues might have had such difficulties and not been able to share them might have made Ellen realise what a burden confidentiality can at times be. Now she found herself in the same situation. Who was she going to turn to for help? At this very moment Ellen was alone and perhaps more aware of that aloneness than she cared to admit. She could not even explain to the warden and the GP why Roy appeared to be more agitated than he had been just a few minutes before.

If someone were to ask Ellen at that moment *What is happening?*, she might have answered that she was confused or disturbed, perhaps angry that this had happened to her and perhaps also irritated with herself that she had not been able to understand Roy's behaviour earlier and was now left with this difficult problem. In moments of stress it is very difficult to concentrate because many conflicting messages and demands present themselves. One of the best things which might happen to Ellen is that, as soon as she is free and Roy is on his way to hospital, she could talk with a supervisor or trusted friend in complete confidence, and without disclosing the identity of her client. If this person is then able to ask Ellen *What is happening?*, she might be able to begin to see a picture. She may be aware of her feelings but also aware that they may cloud that picture at this moment. But they are there and they have to be taken seriously, because this is what she is aware of.

She may be aware of professional duties, such as keeping confidentiality; promoting and safeguarding the interests and well-being of her patients and clients; and avoiding any abuse of her privileged relationship with her patients. She may also be aware of her duties as a citizen, and she clearly thinks that she has witnessed something illegal. She has a duty to bring this to light.

Ellen may be more concerned with any outcomes than with duties. She may be concerned that she may just have made a big fuss and that the tablets are completely legal and rightfully in Roy's possession. They may be something totally innocuous, and she should not have meddled in something which did not concern her and she should have trusted Roy. If that were the case, then her relationship with Roy would be destroyed if she acted now without his knowing, as he was in hospital and unable to speak for himself.

She might even consider doing nothing at all and simply 'forgetting' that she saw anything suspicious. After all, nobody would probably be any the wiser. She might argue that Roy might not be able to come back to his flat, and if so, the son would probably have to clear it and that would be the end of that.

She might also argue that in the first instance it would be the warden who would need to see that everything was all right in Roy's flat while he was in hospital, and if she had reason to look in the fridge then it would be the warden's responsibility to do something about the tablets if she thought fit. The warden might not make the connection with the insulin and Ellen having had to give Roy his injection that morning and therefore seeing the tablets.

Ellen might have argued from the two traditional points of view of deontology (duty) or teleology (goals or outcomes) and have had to decide quickly.

But she might also have argued from the point of view of responsibility. In this case, she would first of all consider two human beings responding to each other, each interpreting what the other is saying. In responding to the other there is an exchange, a receiving of the other, a relating to the other, a hearing of what the other is saying. But it is more than the words are expressing: it is trying to understand what the other is about and what his or her life is about in the present context. This would allow her to step sideways for a few moments. Response ethics does not deny duty or considering goals, and it does not refuse quick decisions, but it takes a different starting point. Ellen would start by considering her relationship with Roy and what this meant and how this might lead to a *fitting answer* in her present situation.

Ellen's relationship with Roy is a professional relationship; they have met because of his need and because Ellen can supply some of this need.

Their lives have coincided because of a need: the patient has a need for professional care and the professional has a need to maintain and improve her experience and therefore she needs the patient. The idea of 'exchange' in the professional relationship stems from this need (May, 1975).

As Roy talks to Ellen – little snippets here and there; some important event remembered; what his son does and what he thinks of him; the way he greets Ellen and the way in which he always has the insulin ready – so these elements combine to make up this life story. Ellen, too, tells a story: the fact that she is particularly interested in patients with diabetes; that she is good at giving injections; that she would rather that the insulin be fresh from the fridge; that she realises by the way Roy gets the insulin ready that he anticipates her – all these give a sense of 'receptivity' and relatedness or 'getting involved' which now has a purpose: that of making both persons in the relationship more human.

Once two people have related to each other they cannot 'unrelate'. If the relationship is broken, then something fundamental is broken. This happens constantly in nursing when patients suddenly leave or die, or nurses are moved to other areas or units without being able to say goodbye. This causes anxiety and pain. Menzies (1960) was aware of this in her famous study of the functioning of social systems as a defence against anxiety. It seems that we are learning only very slowly that anxiety is not always such a bad thing and that we grow more by facing anxiety than by avoiding it. Thus Ellen is now faced with anxiety because of her relationship and 'involvement' with Roy. If she takes this relationship seriously, then she will not be left with painful, nagging and unresolved anxiety.

When we get to this stage in the deliberations on *what is happening*, we are reaching the point of asking for the meaning of the relationship. Before doing that it is useful also to look at *what is happening* to the other people in this story.

The GP presumably knows Roy well, but he has nothing obvious to do with Ellen's deliberations. If there needed to be an enquiry, he might be called to give evidence, but this is not a consideration at the moment.

The warden will probably never have had reason to look into Roy's fridge, nor would she in the future, if everything goes straightforwardly. If Ellen decided to take any action, then she would have to tell the warden what she was doing and why, and this might involve the warden. The warden would then, no doubt, also be part of any investigations. At this stage Ellen might want to consider what would be best or least harmful to the warden, but she will see this through the eyes of the relationship with Roy.

What is the meaning of it? _____

When Ellen has looked at the relationship with Roy and seen it as the decisive element in her present situation, then she cannot help but see meaning in everything connected with this relationship.

Clearly, not every ethical decision which has to be taken can go to the length of considering *meaning*, nor does it have to. It is only at moments of 'truth', when something stops us or brings us up short with inadequacy, that we are faced with ourselves and our ways of dealing with a problem. If we then push the problem aside, we simply damage ourselves and probably do not make a good decision.

When Ellen began to think about her relationship with Roy she will have had to look, however briefly and maybe without using specific words, at what it *means* to her to be a nurse, what she understands by the idea of caring, compassion, commitment, professionalism, confidentiality, consent, autonomy, beneficence, justice, truth, value of life – and almost all the topics touched on in this book. In the context of this chapter she may have concentrated on the idea of individual freedom and what this means in relation to responsibility and accountability. What might this *mean* to her?

It is possible that this is the first time that she has been faced with a major professional decision in her life. Perhaps always before there have been other people involved with her; this time she is alone. She may always have found making decisions on her own difficult, and realising this now she may become aware that this particular situation is so difficult because of this background. She would therefore be wise to seek help.

It could be that she had to make some important decision in the past which was not a good decision, and she was left with anxiety and now this presents itself as a memory, obscuring her decision-making capabilities in this instance.

It may be that she likes making decisions on her own and is confident that she will find the *fitting answer*. This too, may come from an experience, but one where she had seen a good outcome. The *social solidarity* which she had experienced earlier may now determine how she *interprets* what had happened then and how she may now see her *accountability* for looking forward.

In this interaction between past, present and future lies the *meaning* of what is happening.

From the story as it has been recounted so far it is possible to deduce that Ellen was in fact anxious because she had to make a decision quickly and on her own. If we assume that, for whatever reason, her *response* to the *challenge* is to be fearful, this may now be seen as the main feature. The situation with Roy and the tablets *means* that she suddenly has to face herself and her fear of being alone in tricky circumstances. She may realise that this time she cannot let anyone else take on the responsibility. As a professional, she has to account for her actions herself. Like a ticket, accountability is not transferable. She may have held to this principle and advocated it throughout her nursing career, but now it becomes reality. When this happens the first time, it is usually traumatic and will be remembered for the rest of one's life. This insight then constitutes the *meaning* of the 'story' for her.

Because Ellen considers responsibility as part of the relationship with Roy, she may be wise to work this out in a relationship. People who are aware of the strength of relationships are more likely to seek help from others than people who are more concerned with autonomy. Ellen may instinctively have turned to someone to help her, and this may have helped her to see the *meaning* of her dilemma. This *meaning*, as she began to understand, was loneliness. Having to facing this loneliness, rather than having simply known it at an intellectual level, now becomes the focal point. Thus the search for *meaning* will have helped her to understand herself. It will also have helped her to understand in a new way the *meaning* of responsibility. She will have understood that one cannot make decisions without affecting other people, and therefore such decisions have to be based on the relationships we have with the people concerned rather than only on memories and issues which come from other situations.

What is the fitting answer?

Having looked deeply at *what is happening* and having seen there a *meaning* not only for this particular situation and relationship, but also for those of the past, Ellen will find it much easier to come to a *fitting answer*. This is not the 'right' answer or the 'best' one, but the one which is most suitable in this situation and given these circumstances. In other situations and circumstances the answer might be different. But this does not point to inconsistency as much as to being deeply rooted in the present and *what is happening* in this present.

When Ellen has looked at all the people and aspects involved and considered also the ethical principles of the value of life, goodness or rightness, justice or fairness, truth telling or honesty and individual freedom, she cannot help coming to a point where a decision has to be made and carried out. Deciding ethically is simply deciding consciously and responsibly.

If Ellen decided to talk her dilemma over with a friend or colleague she would probably have moved to the *fitting answer* during the course of the discussion. Such a discussion may not have needed to be very long. Someone with even a minimum of helping, communication or counselling skills will have been able to ask Ellen *what is happening* and hear what she was saying. This will have helped Ellen to find her own answers.

Given, therefore, what has been described here, Ellen's *fitting answer* in this situation will have taken into account her relationship with Roy. What action should she take in the light of this? It is possible that Roy will regain at least some of his speech, and the tablets will not disappear, and these two things combined will mean that Ellen's choice is to wait. This may have become clear when she had considered her fear of acting alone; waiting may not have appeared to be a choice earlier. Now her relationship with Roy is more important than her fear of loneliness and her earlier fear of having to act quickly and alone. By waiting she is not putting off a decision, but she is in fact facing a very real problem in herself: a compulsion of having to act and a fear of loneliness. As she decides on this as part of her relationship, this is the most *fitting* thing to do here.

In a few days Roy's condition will have stabilised and Ellen will then either be able to talk with him and tell him that she had seen the bags of tablets and had wondered what they were, to which he will probably be able to give a reply which satisfies her. If his reply does not satisfy her, she can tell him, and she can also tell him what she intends to do further about it. Thus she will have acted responsibly and not jeopardised the relationship.

If Roy does not improve enough for her to talk with him, then Ellen will have to face a completely new dilemma: what to do without Roy's consent, because he would then be 'incompetent' in the legal sense. Ellen might consider talking in confidence with the warden about her concerns. She, in turn, may want to approach the son. If she does not get any cooperation from the son, then she might be justified in taking further action.

It is possible to say that this is beneficence: doing good and avoiding harm. But sometimes it is difficult to see where doing good comes from and on what it is based. By having considered the professional relationship as the main element, it is easy to see that doing good is part of that relationship. In this way it is not only the action itself which is good, but the outcome will be a *social solidarity* which is stronger than 'the greatest good for the greatest number'. The people themselves will have gained and grown as individuals rather than simply the greatest number of people having gained.

The pattern of responsibility

The *pattern* has been visible throughout this story, but when the story is summarised in the pattern, some points may be highlighted.

The *challenge* in this story was that Ellen saw some bags of tablets in the fridge of her now incapacitated patient. Roy had always 'guarded' his fridge. This may not have been evident to Ellen until she realised that he was agitated when she had to go to the fridge to take the insulin out for his injection. This made her suspicious that the tablets she saw were there illegally.

Ellen's *response* to this was probably one of inner panic. She might have become white for a few moments and might have had some difficulty in drawing up the insulin. She might not have known quite why she reacted so strongly to the sight of some bags of tablets – she might also have laughed, or not reacted at all – but she was aware that something here had triggered some very strong emotions.

When Ellen had been able to talk about these emotions and reactions, she would have known that she was *interpreting* some event from the past and that this had left her with feelings of anxiety when faced with having to make decisions alone. A fear of being alone when decisions have to be made and a sense of having to decide quickly or else be seen to be unprofessional might all have been reasons for irrational fears. Feelings are always irrational in such situations, but *they are there*, and therefore they matter and have to be taken seriously. When we are able to look at them and *interpret* them, then they also help us to see *what is happening*.

When these elements have been seen and understood, and their *meaning* has been elucidated, then there comes an *accountability* – that is, the need to set all this in context and to act on it. A decision has to be made – even if at times it may be to decide not to act, or as in the case of Ellen, to wait. Waiting is not doing nothing but is in fact a most responsible thing to do, because in waiting we trust the process and we trust the people concerned. Waiting then becomes empowerment.

The outcome then is invariably one of *social solidarity*. This does not mean that 'everything in the garden is rosy'. It might not be so at all. It might have thrown up more problems and more issues to be faced, but this might have been necessary. *Social solidarity* is something which relies on relationships and on responsibility and their continuing importance; and the trust that, because of this process, people will have become more human.

References

Baird, V. (1993) 'Liberty, ideals and low deals', *New Internationalist*, **249**: 4–7.

Baker, B. (1993) 'Model methods', *Nursing Times*, **89** (47): 33–5.

Beauchamp, T.L. and Childress, J.F. (1983) *Principles of Biomedical Ethics*, 2nd edn. New York: Oxford University Press.

Benjamin, M. and Curtis, J. (1986) *Ethics in Nursing*, 2nd edn. New York: Oxford University Press.

Benner, P. (1984) *From Novice to Expert*. Menlo Park: Addison Wesley.

Briant, N.J. (1976) 'Prejudice in nursing', *The Canadian Nurse*, **72** (6): 26–30.

British Association for Counselling (1990) *Code of Ethics and Practice for Counsellors*. Rugby: BAC.

Brown, J.M., Kitson, A.L. and McKnight, T.J. (1992) *Challenges in Caring*. London: Chapman & Hall.

Callahan, D. (1993) 'Pursuing a peaceful death', *Hastings Center Report*, **23** (4): 33–8.

Campbell, A.V. (1984) *Moral Dilemmas in Medicine*. Edinburgh: Churchill Livingstone.

Campbell, A.V. (1987) *A Dictionary of Pastoral Care*. London: SPCK.

Carkhuff, R.R. (1987) *The Art of Helping VI*. Amherst, MA: Human Resource Development Press.

Carpenter, W.T. and Langsner, C.A. (1975) 'The nurse's role in informed consent', *Nursing Times*, **71** (26): 1049–51.

Castledine, G. (1993) 'The Bland Truth: 2', *British Journal of Nursing*, **2** (5): 285.

Chadwick, R. and Tadd, W. (1992) *Ethics and Nursing Practice*. Basingstoke: Macmillan.

Chambers' Dictionary (1993) Edinburgh: Chambers Harrap.

Coleman, R. (1993) 'Patient power', *Nursing Times*, **89** (49): 50.

Coupe, D. (1990) 'Donation dilemmas', *Nursing Times*, **86** (27): 34–6.

Crawshaw, R. (1991) 'Oregon sets priorities in health care', *Bulletin of Medical Ethics*, **69**: 32–5.

Crisp, R. (1991) 'QALYs and the mentally handicapped', *Bulletin of Medical Ethics*, **67**: 13–16.

Curtin, L. (1983) 'The nurse as advocate: a cantankerous critique', *Nurse Management*, **14**: 9–10.

Daily Telegraph (1992a) 'Mother at 61 told lies about her age', 1 August.

Daily Telegraph (1992b) 'Heroin smuggler freed by hospital', 7 July.

Department of Health (1990) *A Guide to Consent for Examination or Treatment*, HC(90)22, London, DoH.

Department of Health (1991) *The Patient's Charter*. London: HMSO.

de Vahl Davis, V. (1992) 'How informed is informed consent?', *Bulletin of Medical Ethics*, **76**: 13–18.

Dickson, A. (1982) *A Woman in Your Own Right*, rev. edn, London: Quartet Books.

Dimond, B. (1993) 'Who deserves care?', *British Journal of Nursing*, **2** (15): 743.

Doyle, C. (1992) 'Dominic and the ethical tightrope', *Daily Telegraph*, 1 Sept.

Duncan, A.S., Dunstan, G.R. and Welbourn, R.B. (eds) (1981) *Dictionary of Medical Ethics*, rev. edn, London: Darton Longman & Todd.

Easton, S. and Lamb, D. (1991) 'Transplanting fetal tissue', *Nursing Times*, **87** (31): 39–40.

Eaton, L. (1993) 'Open to abuse', *Nursing Times*, **89** (44): 16.

Evans, M. (1993) 'Moral costs', *Nursing Times*, **89** (37): 34–5.

Fleet, M. (1992) 'Death case nurse tells of threats and abuse', *Daily Telegraph*, 8 Oct.

Fletcher, J. (1955) *Morals and Medicine*. London: Gollancz.

Frankl, V. (1962) *Man's Search for Meaning*, London: Hodder & Stoughton.

Fromer, M. 'Ethical issues in nursing care', in J. Tingle, (1990) 'Accountability and the law: how it affects the nurse', *Senior Nurse*, **10** (2): 8–9.

Fox, J., Scaman, H. and Wilmot, S. (1993) 'Caring: a new framework for analysis', *British Journal of Nursing*, **2** (20): 1008–11.

Fuchs, V.R. (1983) *Who Shall Live?*, New York: Basic Books Inc.

Gillon, R. (1986) *Philosophical Medical Ethics*, Chichester: Wiley.

Gillon, R. (ed.) (1993) *Principles of Health Care Ethics*, Chichester: Wiley.

Hanford, L. (1993) 'Ethics and disability', *British Journal of Nursing*, **2** (19): 979–82.

Harris, J. (1987) 'QALYfying the value of life', *Journal of Medical Ethics*, **13** (3): 117–23.

HM Government (1992) *The Citizen's Charter: First Report*, Cm2102.

House of Lords (1993) Airedale NHS Trust (Respondents) *v* Bland (Acting by His Guardian *ad litem*) (Appellant), London: House of Lords.

Hubert, J. (1993) 'Speaking up', *Nursing Times*, **89** (44): 59–61.

Hunt, G. (1991) 'Professional accountability', *Nursing Standard*, **6** (4): 49–50.

Hunt, G. (1994) Personal communication.

Husted, G.L. and Husted, J.H. (1991) *Ethical Decision Making in Nursing*, St Louis: Mosby-Year Book Inc.

Iliffe, J. and Swan, P. 'Heart and heart–lung transplantation', in V. Tschudin, (ed.) (1993) *Ethics: Aspects of Nursing Care*, London: Scutari Press.

Independent (1993) Editorial, 24 May.

International Council of Nurses (1973) *Code for Nurses*, Geneva: ICN.

Johnstone, M-J. (1989) *Bioethics – a Nursing Perspective*, Marrickville, NSW: W.B. Saunders.

Jones, C. (1989) 'Little white lies', *Nursing Times*, 85 (44): 38–9.

Joy, A. (1990) 'White lies and deceit', *Nursing Standard*, 5 (10): 49.

Kitchiner, N.J. and Toman, M. 'Care of people in controlled environments', in V. Tschudin, (ed.) (1994) *Ethics: Nursing People With Special Needs (I)*, London: Scutari Press.

Kuhse, H. and Singer, P. (1985) 'Handicapped babies: a right to life?', *Nursing Mirror*, 160 (8): 17–20.

MacIntyre, A. (1985) *After Virtue* (2nd edn), London: Duckworth.

McTaggart, L. (1993) *The 'What doctors don't tell you' Guide to Women's Screening Tests*, London: The Wallace Press.

Marks-Maran, D. 'Accountability', in V. Tschudin (ed.) (1993) *Ethics: Nurses and Patients*, London: Scutari Press.

May, W.F. (1975) 'Code, covenant, contract or philanthropy', *Hasting Center Report*, 5: 29–38.

Meilaender, G. (1993) 'Terra es Animata – On Having A Life', *Hastings Center Report*, 23 (4): 25–32.

Menzies, I. (1960) 'A case-study in the functioning of social systems as a defence against anxiety', *Human Relations*, 13 (2): 93–121.

Morris, S.E. and Knape, J. (1993) 'When and how to seek professional advice from the UKCC', *British Journal of Nursing*, 2 (21): 1084–5.

Morrison, A. (1991) 'The nurse's role in relation to advocacy', *Nursing Standard*, 5 (41): 37–40.

NHS Management Executive (1993) *Guidance for Staff on Relations with the Public and the Media*, London: DoH.

Niebuhr, H.R. (1963) *The Responsible Self*, New York: Harper & Row.

Noddings, N. (1984) *Caring, a Feminine Approach to Ethics and Moral Education*, Berkeley, CA: University of California Press.

Norberg, A., Hirschfeld, M., Davidson, B. *et al.* (1994) 'Ethical reasoning concerning the feeding of severely demented patients: an international perspective', *Nursing Ethics*, 1 (1): 3–13.

Nouwen, H.J.M., McNeill, D.P. and Morrison, D.A. (1982) *Compassion*, London: Darton Longman & Todd.

Nursing Standard (1993) 'News: "special empathy" can help smokers quit', 8 (9): 16.

Nursing Times (1993a) 89 (45) (extracts).

Nursing Times (1993b) News item, **89** (51): 8.

Pence, G.E. (1983) 'Can compassion be taught?', *Journal of Medical Ethics*, **9** (4): 189–91.

Pettifer, B. (1987) 'Person', in A. Campbell (ed.) (1987) *A Dictionary of Pastoral Care*, London: SPCK.

Pyne, R. (1987) 'A professional duty to shout', *Nursing Times*, **83** (42): 30–31.

Quinn, C.A. and Smith, M.D. (1987) *The Professional Commitment: Issues and Ethics in Nursing*, Philadelphia, PA: W.B. Saunders.

Rachels, J. (1986) *The End of Life*, Oxford: Oxford University Press.

Reid, T. (1993) 'Joint input', *Nursing Times*, **89** (47): 30–32.

Roach, M.S. (1987) *The Human Act of Caring*, Ottawa: Canadian Hospital Association.

Rogers, C.R. (1975) 'Empathic: an unappreciated way of being', *Counselling Psychologist*, **21**: 95–103.

Rowson, R. 'Informed consent', in V. Tschudin (ed.) (1993) *Ethics: Nurses and Patients*, London: Scutari Press.

Royal College of Nursing (1991) 'Issues in nursing and health', card No. 7: *Fetal Cell Transplantation; Guidance for Nurses*. London: RCN.

Royal College of Nursing (1993) 'Harvesting of organs: the nursing issues', *Nursing Standard*, **7** (40): 25–6.

Sandroff, R. (1980) 'Is it right?', in H. Satterthwaite (1990) 'When right and wrong are a matter of opinion', *Professional Nurse*, **5** (8): 434–8.

Sawyer, J. (1988) 'On behalf of the patient', *Nursing Times*, **84** (41): 28–31.

Sherwin, S. (1992) 'Feminist and medical ethics: two different approaches to contextual ethics', in H. Bequaert Holmes and L.M. Purdy (eds) (1992) *Feminist Perspectives in Medical Ethics*, Bloomington: Indiana University Press.

The World's Religions (1982) A Lion Handbook, Tring, Herts: Lion Publishing plc.

Thiroux, J. (1980) *Ethics, Theory and Practice*, Encino, CA: Glencoe Publishing Co.

United Kingdom Central Council (1983) *Code of Professional Conduct*, 1st edn, London: UKCC.

United Kingdom Central Council (1984) *Code of Professional Conduct*, 2nd edn, London: UKCC.

United Kingdom Central Council (1987) *Confidentiality*, London: UKCC.

United Kingdom Central Council (1989) *Exercising Accountability*. London: UKCC.

United Kingdom Central Council (1992) *Code of Professional Conduct*, 3rd edn, London: UKCC.

United Kingdom Central Council (1992) *The Scope of Professional Practice*, London: UKCC.

United Nations (1948) *Universal Declaration of Human Rights*, New York: UN.

Uustal, D. (1980) 'Exploring values in nursing', *AORN*, **31** (2): 183–7.
Voluntary Euthanasia Society (1989) *The Last Right*, London: VES.
Warren, M.A. (1973) 'On the moral and legal status of abortion', in M-J. Johnstone (1989) *Bioethics – a Nursing Perspective*, Marrickville, NSW: W.B. Saunders.
Watson, D. (1993) 'Can memory survive the storm?', *New Internationalist*, **247**: 14–16.
Way, H. (1971) *Ethics For Nurses*, London: Macmillan.
Wells, R. (1986) 'The great conspiracy', *Nursing Times*, **82** (21): 22–5.
Williams, A. (1985) 'The value of QALYs', *Health and Social Service Journal*, 18 July.
Wright, S. (1993) 'What makes a person?', *Nursing Times*, **89** (21): 42–5.

Index

Note: The principles of response ethics are illustrated in each chapter by a case history, and the format is the same in each. The components of response ethics (e.g. pattern of responsibility) are indexed once only.

THE CAMBRIDGE CURRY CLUB

Saumya Balsari

KT-163-796

BLACKAMBER BOOKS

Published by BlackAmber Books Limited
3 Queen Square
London WC1N 3AU
http://www.blackamber.com

1 3 5 7 9 10 8 6 4 2

A full CIP record for this book is available from the British Library

ISBN 1–901969–28–2

Typeset in 12.5/13.5 pt Garamond Three
by RefineCatch Limited, Bungay Suffolk
Produced by Bookchase (UK) Ltd
Printed in the EU
Printed in Spain
L.D.: SE-3713-2004 in Spain

For Sudhanshu,
Sárica Robynn and Sanna Linnéa

Prologue

THE SLY OCTOBER wind tore through Cambridge, boldly lifting the prim skirt of the Junior Bursar as her court shoes, indignant at a male colleague's promotion, clicked briskly through a college archway to meet the waiting porters and bedmakers. It scattered the papers of the student vaulting fluidly over the rhododendron bush near the Buttery, and waltzed through the hoary trees of the College Backs, rocking *Venezia*, a derelict punt on the river. It tousled the hair of the Japanese tourist posing in front of the Victorian pillar box and the lamp-post outside King's College. A few yards away on King's Parade, a passerby lingered inexplicably in front of a Bible in the display windows of the Cambridge University Press, and the bells of Great St Mary's chimed grandly as a bird wheeled through St Edward's Passage, past *G. David, Booksellers since 1896* and over the Fen farmers unloading produce at Market Square.

The wind paused to reflect on its own past glory; in its time it had circled the Roman settlement at Castle Hill and rattled the round-headed Saxon windows of St Bene't's Church. At Christ's College, it had swept the

1

conversations of Charles Darwin and John Milton, two centuries apart; at Corpus Christi it had been Christopher Marlowe's whirling Muse. The wind also shook the trees in the orchard of Isaac Newton's family home in Lincolnshire. An apple fell.

The wind had been the harbinger of revolt urging the students fleeing the Oxford riots in 1209 towards Cambridge; it had hastened their staggering steps to the medieval brothels in the area surrounding Magdalene College. It knew where Oliver Cromwell's head was secretly buried in the chapel of Sidney Sussex College. Centuries later, it still whispers envy to townspeople pausing to watch new graduates in gowns and hoods file through the streets towards the Senate House.

The bird perched on the segment of missing stone ball on the parapet of Clare Bridge until the wind whipped its wings, whirling it into the autumn sky. Together, bird and wind sailed jauntily through the Gate of Humility in the Master's Garden at Gonville and Caius College, departing humbly through the Gate of Honour and soaring high over Parker's Piece and Fenner's Ground to seek the homely pleasures of Mill Road.

Colourful Mill Road bore no resemblance to the shops of elegant Magdalene Bridge, nor, for that matter, did Covent Garden, a side lane of Mill Road, recall its London namesake. No riverside café served steaming latte and mozzarella panini here, no leafy towpath walked the sluggish dog or mind; instead, a daily brigade of bargain-hunters sniffed their spoils, their hard noses pressed against the display windows of the charity shops. With its rows of small houses, ethnic food stores, hair salons, curry houses, Internet cafés, bookmaker, health shop and dry cleaners, Mill Road was the city's pumping heart.

Spotting a homeless drunk lying outside the book-makers, the wind swooped, tossing the shivering man into dreams of Salvation soup and death. Next, it flirted with a large Asian woman bent over a black bin bag on the pavement outside the charity shop called IndiaNeed. Lasciviously lifting her blue silk sari, it revealed sensible men's socks above sensible women's sandals. The large woman's neck showed traces of talc. A white van halted at the traffic lights opposite the shop. *Wish my wife was as dirty as this van* was scrawled on its dusty side. The driver leaned out of his window and whistled at the bending woman. She straightened hastily, feigning indignation, but a smile hovered over her lips at the moment that the bird circled above. Plop, plop, plop. Everything auspicious was always in threes; it must have been an Indian bird in a previous life. The green-white slime slithered down a rolling mountain of flesh, splaying rivulets over the plains of her unsuspecting back.

The bird hopped away, and the triumphant wind scampered back over Silver Street and across the Bridge of Sighs to slip into the waiting willows nearby.

CHAPTER ONE

Many hands make light work

SWARNAKUMARI WAS BENT, innocent and ungainly, over a black bag lying on the pavement outside the charity shop IndiaNeed, her posterior turned heaven-ward like an overturned duck scrabbling in the shallow brook that runs along the Botanic Garden overlooking Trumpington Road.

She hauled the bag from underneath the vandalised sign that read *Do   lean bicycles against the windows please* and dragged it into the shop. Watching her from the windows of Flamenco, the salon opposite, the hair-dresser James alias Juan slipped warm Mediterranean vowels into his Glaswegian accent and waited near the Rexine customer chairs. Once inside, Swarnakumari bent over the displays in the shop window. Three amused women watched from the till as she carefully placed a pink china plate depicting a grinning bulldog next to a framed Jubilee photograph of the Queen.

Heera leaned with both elbows over the counter. 'Just look at Swarna, how that woman bends . . . she can bend for England! You know, Durga, my grand-father used to go to the village temple and feed the cow there every day. He was such a naughty man! One day he pretended to be blind and he patted a fat bending woman as if he was stroking a cow, and then he pulled her long plait just like a cow's tail. She thought he was blind, so she didn't get upset, but when she bent again to remove her slippers, what d'you think happened? He did it again!'

Heera dug an ebullient elbow into Durga, chuckling into the folds of her chin; her body shook under the shapeless black sweater and elasticated trousers she wore, and her short hair bobbed in mirth. Swarnakumari straightened, patted the flower in her neat bun and retrieved her handbag, calling over her shoulder as she headed for the Staff Area behind the green floral curtain, 'Window display is done now. Just going to wash my hands, *hanh*.'

Hunched over the till, Durga twirled a strand of shiny shoulder-length hair. She was slim in jeans and a cream turtleneck. Sudden laughter had creased the solemn lines of her face, skimming lips ashamed of their fullness. She observed, 'Every time she touches anything in here, Lady Macbeth washes her hands over and over with her Sainsbury's soap dispenser, but the damned charity shop spot remains like a turmeric blob on a white English hob, staining her Brahmin sensibilities.'

Eileen muttered, 'Sixteen times. Swarna washed her hands sixteen times last Thursday.' Eileen had been a gifted mathematics teacher; she knew her numbers. Born in Armagh, Northern Ireland, she was tall and wiry with wispy grey hair, and was dressed in a long black skirt and matching knit cardigan accompanied by a silver cross around her neck and silver bracelets on her wrist. Her mother had been a hungry seamstress

6

raising a family of six children; the exhausted father ran away and jumped aboard a ship called *Providence* bound for New York. Young Danny Watts of Cambridge met the twenty-year-old Eileen on a camping holiday in Cork and was entranced by her dark eyes and hair, creamy neck and ready laugh. The smile had faded first; her black hair followed twenty years later.

Swarnakumari's handbag contained the soap dispenser, a tiny towel, a prayer book, a tortoiseshell comb and the distinctive red Shantiniketan hand-crafted leather money purse. The colour of the folded towel was different every week.

On Thursday nights Swarnakumari lay in bed, eyes turned upward and away from her sleeping husband, Shyamal Chatterjee. On her bedside table stood a tube of Neutrogena cream; an application after dinner ensured that her fingers had shed the chalky film covering shop rejects and other rejections unnamed. Once the ceiling above her bed no longer reflected the passing lights of street cars and desire, unguent calm had been restored.

Swarnakumari was a charitable woman, and her thoughts, like her puja table for the gods, faced eastward. She had initially read fiction every Wednesday to Jean Ward, a blind woman in a Cambridge nursing home, but her strongly accented English proved too much for her elderly listener, who promptly fell asleep each time. Swarnakumari had enthusiastically recited an entire novel, unaware that her listener had not progressed beyond the first page. Jean Ward passed away peacefully in the Prologue of the second novel.

The charity's name, IndiaNeed, led Swarnakumari to volunteer in a shop whose proceeds benefited deserving villagers in a desert region of Rajasthan in Western India. The director on the Board of the charity, Diana Wellington-Smythe, was mockingly nicknamed 'Lady Di' by her staff. Her hyphenated surname had found immediate approval with Swarnakumari's husband Mr Chatterjee. A link with a village project in West Bengal would have been ideal, but a Cambridge charity shop had its limitations, as did Mr Chatterjee, thought Swarnakumari.

Heera played idly with a basket of small leather purses. She wondered why Swarnakumari had volunteered at IndiaNeed; she had the look of a pukka Bengali madam in a paisley silk sari presiding over a sitar soirée, and on the first day of the shop orientation meeting with Lady Di and the volunteers two months ago in that very spot, she had known Swarnakumari would be a strange one – she simply didn't belong. Those silly Korean student volunteers didn't belong either, and were there to practise their English one afternoon in the week, but in the end they jabbered away together in their own language, and if a customer approached, they pulled out a superfast translator to slowly make a sentence and a sale.

Heera sighed and rearranged the brooches on the jewellery shelf. What could be cured in life was little, whereas what had to be endured was a coiled snake around the neck, her Aunty Buddi Mai used to say. Durga with her clever remarks was another strange one, thought Heera, and Eileen was even stranger. Those two were both so secretive about their lives that getting any masala – any juicy bits – out of them, was like trying to make a stubborn camel move. And why did those two *eediots* Bitter Butter Betty and Quite

Contrary Mary volunteer four days a week if they were going to complain all the time?

Swarnakumari returned, deposited her handbag on the table and held out a small plastic Tesco box sporting a humous label. Inside was a powdery concoction of sugar, ghee and roasted flour.

'My hands are washed now. Today is Her Holiness, my Guru Ma's birthday. I am also fasting today. *Cholo cholo*, come, come, hold out your hands and take *proshad*. Take more, Eileen,' she urged.

Heera, Durga and Eileen dutifully held out their palms and licked off the crumbs as she continued, '*Bhalo*. Good. We are all blessed now, and today will be a good day, so now we shall start sorting the bags that came this morning.'

They approached the long wooden sorting table directly behind the curtain that concealed the Staff Area. Above it was an oversized notice: *Sort out any bags stored under the table. Put all rejects into bags and onto skip outside. Do NOT take home, or throw away in bin. Remember to check the pockets of all clothing and contents of all purses, wallets and handbags. Do NOT take away contents, especially money or jewellery.*

Two entwined hearts and the words *Pamela and John forever* had been anonymously etched into the table's far right corner; eternity was evidently to be seen in a grain of wood.

The area under the large table was the depot for the black bags arriving from the pavement outside. The bags were wrung tight with yellow string, startled plump chickens strangled at the neck by their donors. After dark, the wind rummaged the other bags left in an alleyway outside the shop, and the crumpled plastic morphed into flapping ghouls of the night. Black bags and charity shops were an inseparable pairing, like 'chicken' and 'egg', 'honour' and 'killing'. Like Pamela and John, forever.

Swarnakumari opened the first bag with suppressed excitement, gingerly retrieving lingerie and men's tweed trousers. She dropped the trousers in horror. '*Chee, chee*, I am not going to check another man's trousers; that too, the backside pocket. So dirty, *na?*' *Na* in Swarnakumari's speech was a statement of finality rather than a search for validation.

Holding the offending trousers by their waistband, Heera twirled them slightly. 'Yeah, they are quite manky. By the way, girls, did you know one in four Englishmen never washes his favourite underwear?'

Swarnakumari emitted an exaggerated wail on cue. 'You are always teasing me. You know I do not like touching unwashed clothes of others. What would my people in Kolkata think of me? Oh, look at this swimsuit, so transparent – you can see everything!'

'If you hate all this touch touch, then why so much rush rush to open the new bags? *Arre*, I know all your tricks. If there's something new or nice to buy, you'll say you saw it first.'

As the shop's manager, Heera could have vetted the goods first, but an Indian deference to age had prevailed. Swarnakumari was fifty-seven; Heera was forty-seven. Eileen was three years older than Swarnakumari, but showed little interest in the bags, only in the arrangement or disposal of their contents. The previous week Swarnakumari had profited from the delivery of a manufacturer's bag containing new sweatshirts in S, M and L sizes. After pricing them herself, Swarnakumari purchased six for her favoured Kolkata nieces. Durga intervened; black sweatshirts would not find favour in India. Swarnakumari had hesitated, but in the end, the words *Cambridge University* emblazoned in red had settled the matter favourably.

'And by the way, this isn't a swimsuit, it's a teddy,' explained Heera.

'Teddy?'

Heera continued, 'Yes, teddy. Listen to this, Swarna. On Ritu's anniversary, Raj went home with one yellow and eleven red roses and two plane tickets; he made her pack her bags in one hour. First he gave her a flower, then he gave her one hour.'

'That's flower power,' interjected Durga.

'She told me they went to the Moulin Rouge. So romantic, can you imagine? He bought her a teddy in Paris,' Heera gushed.

Swarnakumari was perplexed. 'Why buy all the way from Paris? Ritu comes to the shop so often, and she could have bought the teddy bear cheap from here, *na.*'

'Not teddy bear, *teddy.* You really don't know what a teddy is, do you? *Arre*, can't you see it's so transparent, how can it be a swimsuit? It's lingerie. Underwear. Honestly, Swarna, sometimes you're worse than those Korean volunteers.'

'These young English girls are wearing anything nowadays, how was I to know? Shameless girls. Their clothes for wearing outside look like underwear, so *baba*, I am confused, *hanh.*' Swarnakumari fussed, 'Are these garments washed? Heera, I am asking you the same thing again and again – remind Mrs Wellington-Smythe, we must have gloves when we are doing the

11

sorting.' She retrieved further items in haste and distaste. 'And what is this, now?'

'A blond wig and a whip,' said Eileen flatly.

'And such tiny white knickers! They've got *Punish Me* embroidered in black. Let's write a note for Lady Di: *Awaiting instructions*. Then just watch the fun, because the knickers will disappear, poof, into the air. Like the inflatable doll that came in two weeks ago,' laughed Heera.

The inflatable doll had not mysteriously disappeared; it had been sold by the Korean volunteers to a dejected young man swathed in a black scarf. He carried it home for target practice and shot several toy arrows of rejected love into its plastic heart. As the doll collapsed, the air oozing out of its red duck lips, the student had opened a celebratory bottle of beer and slashed his wrists on its broken glass.

'What doll? I never saw it. You should at least have shown it to me. I love dolls; I used to buy so many. Heera, such good things have started disappearing from the shop: new video recorder, antique brooch, necklace, watches, camera. And tell me, what is the thief going to do with my reading glasses from Vision Express? Why did he steal them? Can it be he has the same prescription?' demanded Swarnakumari.

'One can only speculate, Swarna. Why don't you arrange the teddy, the blond wig, whip and knickers in the window? We could pull in a few more customers that way. And where's that magazine we got the other day, Heera? It could go into the display, too,' suggested Durga. 'It had a double-spread of a punk hunk who was once a monk.'

'I threw it out,' said Heera curtly.

12

'Fascinating, isn't it? The monk became a gay hunk. Maybe the pay was better,' continued Durga.

Swarnakumari was curious. 'What private talk is going on?'

'It's about a gay magazine. And don't pretend you don't know what that is,' teased Durga.

'Of course I know about these things. So unnatural, but anyway, thank God this problem is not there in good Indian families.' A practised angler, Swarnakumari fished in the black bag. 'Look, a fur coat. Fur. Can it be real?'

Eileen gave the coat a brief examination. 'Fake.'

Swarnakumari continued as she found a hanger for the coat, 'So many people have so many problems in this world; look at these poor villagers in Rajasthan for whom we are raising money. They have no running water, no electricity. Guru Ma says we must always remember there are many more who have much less.'

Durga mused, 'My former supervisor here in Cambridge was gay, and he had more than most. Termtime tutorial visits were only between one and three in the afternoons. Whenever I left at three, I saw a Lebanese student bounding up the stairs for "happy hour". And I could tell you a story or two about the Formal Hall dinners. Some female students at the tables wore more or less nothing under their gowns. You might say those who had less had much more.'

Swarnakumari looked shocked as Heera asked, 'Really? I always wondered what went on behind those college gatehouses. What's a Formal Hall dinner?'

'College dinner in an echoing hall a few times during term. Stern portraits on the walls. Sherry in the Fellows' Drawing Room. Grace in Latin followed by

13

dinner of warmed tart of broccoli and red onion topped with Emmental and watercress, escalopes of beef, dauphinois potatoes, apple and cinnamon flan with vanilla ice cream, finishing with coffee and Cambridge mints. Everyone waits until High Table departs, and then the fun begins.'

There was the sound of a drill. Heavy boots crossed the floor overhead.

'There he goes again,' cried Heera in irritation. 'Vroom vroom. One of these days, I am going to ask that man what he is doing in the room upstairs.'

'Perhaps he could use the blond wig and whip?' suggested Durga.

'Who?' asked Swarnakumari.

'The man upstairs, who else could we mean?' replied Heera.

'What do you want to do with these crutches?' demanded Eileen. 'They were lying next to the same bag.'

'Crutches and whip from the same donor? Which of the two gets a person walking faster?' wondered Durga.

'Heera, why should we keep these crutches in the shop? Can we not offer them to Ritu's mother-in-law? You told me she has recently broken her leg, *na*,' proposed Swarnakumari kindly.

'Has she really broken her leg, or has her son broken her heart by marrying Ritu?' Durga was intrigued. 'Anyway, who is this ever-ready to beddy, teddy-wearing Ritu?'

'She lives on Fendon Road. Her husband Raj always looks deep into her eyes. He squeezes her waist like a lemon all the time,' sighed Heera wistfully.

'Juicy stuff,' was Durga's comment.

14

'How is it that they can always be so romantic, even after so many years? It must be all those dates they ate when they were living in Dubai,' concluded Heera spitefully.

'Fake,' repeated Eileen before disappearing to replace a roll in the till machine.

Raj was inseparable from Ritu's waist at parties, and as soon as the women disappeared into the kitchen and the men held their whisky glasses aloft in the living room, he challenged other husbands into true confessions. When was the last time they had sent flowers or chocolates to their wives? He, on the other hand, knew the gift for Ritu's every mood. Her favourite bouquet consisted of eleven red roses and a single yellow stem. Wispy teddies were her undoing, he admitted with a wink. Mohan Karnani bent forward in bluff incomprehension. What were 'teddies'? Raj roared, patting Mohan's shoulder affectionately as he described the garment. It was short and didn't stay on long, he said, with another wink, as the other men shuffled with guilty feet.

'If only Raj would escort his mother to the Moulin Rouge instead, voilà, she would ditch the crutches and kick the stick habit,' said Durga.

'So what do you want to do with the crutches?' asked Eileen doggedly, as she reappeared clutching a book on mountaineering in the Balkans.

Every object handled by Eileen had its place, a number, a weight, a size, a shape and a space at IndiaNeed – and in her ordered universe. Chaos belonged to scientific theory, not in a charity shop.

'How many are there?' inquired Swarnakumari.

'It's a "Buy one, get one free" deal,' teased Durga.

'Two. Do you think we all need crutches, metaphorically, that is, to get through life?' She gazed at the passersby bent against the curling wind. 'Perhaps crutches can never be given up or away. They are the desire and the dream that keep us breathing. And from walking. Away, that is.'

Durga was accustomed to the silence that invariably followed her observations. Eileen hovered until Heera spat impatiently, '*Arre*, just put them anywhere.'

'And what is this, now?' demanded Swarnakumari, retrieving a large box. 'Oh, it says on the cover that it is a machine for checking blood pressure.' She forced open the lid.

'It's a toy gun,' said Eileen with her usual grim composure as Swarnakumari recoiled at the contents. 'What do you want to do with it?'

'Scare the Korean girls? Price it and put it in the window?' mocked Durga.

The shop bell tinkled, and Heera emerged from behind the curtain as a young woman entered.

'Oh, hello, where are the children's bicycles?' asked the eager customer. 'I'm looking for one for my little girl, a pink Barbie one.'

'I'm sorry, but we don't have any.'

'You did have one. I saw it outside your shop last week,' insisted the woman.

'Yes, but we sold it, madam. You can see for yourself, there are no more bicycles here.'

Heera returned to the Staff Area as the customer departed. 'If we get one bloody bicycle in six months, does this mean we've become Halfords?'

'We could rename the shop Wellington's Wheels and Deals, or Smythe's Bikes for Tikes,' quipped Durga.

16

As she returned to the table, Heera continued, 'Girls, today's black bags are very strange. First manky trousers, then blond wig, knickers and teddy, then whip, crutches and blood-pressure kit with a toy gun inside.'

'Send the whole lot to Rupert darling,' Durga drawled.

'It is rude to talk about the husband of Mrs Wellington-Smythe like that,' admonished Swarnakumari.

'D'you know, the Heart to Heart shop got a 1917 diary the other day?' revealed Heera. 'A woman had sent love letters to her soldier fiancé, and she kept writing to him even after she knew he was dead. It was in the papers, didn't you read about it? And look at us – when we got a decent oil-painting two weeks ago, those stupid Korean girls sold it while it was waiting to be valued.'

'You mean the portrait of the dimpled heavenly cherub? Its hands were a bit fluttery. I'd get rid of it in any language,' Durga ventured.

Swarnakumari was defensive. 'We do get good things in this shop. Otherwise I would not be working here, *na*.'

The shop items passing through Swarnakumari's keen hands underwent a primary test of usefulness to the Chatterjee family, other volunteers at the shop and selected members of the Cambridge Indian community, after which time-consuming procedure she reluctantly considered the items for window display. A consignment of red and black porcelain mugs with *Mad Cow Mother-in-Law Disease* inscribed above the face of a scowling woman left Swarnakumari unmoved despite the magic words *Made in England* on the underside.

Durga used one for coffee breaks at the shop, but the rest lay neglected on a shelf until purchased by a taciturn Bulgarian language student who was brilliant at mathematics but struggled with his English. Eileen had silently pointed to the words *Mad Cow Mother-in-Law Disease*, and he had merely nodded. The meeting of minds over mathematics never took place. It was one of those encounters bursting at the bud, like the thousands in the lifetime of an individual, that, but for chance or fate, lead nowhere.

Heera moved forward to answer the insistent telephone. 'IndiaNeed . . . Yes, Mrs Wellington-Smythe, it is Heera here . . . No, I'm sorry, I was a little late today because I wasn't feeling . . . It was only ten minutes after ten . . . Yes, the shop should be opened on time, I am very sorry. Next time I'll . . . Yes, it is important for the customers . . . Yes, they come first . . . No, we haven't heard anything new about the missing items . . . Yes, of course I shall let you know . . . You've found a new volunteer to join us? That's very good . . . Yes, goodbye.'

She stormed back to the sorting table. 'How many times does Lady Di need to ask me about those missing items? *Arre*, once they're gone, they're gone. Is the thief going to come back and say, "Here, you can have them back, I'm having a bad hair day, now please arrest me?" And making such a big fuss over my coming late this morning! I wasn't feeling well, and I almost didn't come at all. Everyone has his or her problems, right? And every time I answer the telephone, why does she ask me who's speaking? Shouldn't she recognise my voice by now?'

A female pensioner entered as Eileen continued to

count the pieces in the cutlery boxes. Despite her record as an inspiring mathematics teacher, Eileen had been dismissed by the Village College where she was Head of the Department, as soon as she crossed her sixtieth birthday in June. A number had been the final betrayal. Her husband, a plumber, had recently discovered his body's tendency to spring leaks of its own, and so the pipes were no longer calling 'Danny Boy' as he retired, driving Eileen out of their home in secret desperation.

There had been a child once; an engaging curly-haired boy of six, struck down by a speeding van outside the school gates as Eileen watched. For days she stayed in his room, rocking back and forth on his bed, hugging his clothes close to her chest. Mathematics and the Catholic Church had provided succour, and she had plunged gratefully into the worlds of numbers and rosary beads.

Eileen had been the shop's first volunteer. Every Thursday, she bustled quietly, her bright eyes inquiring of the objects she constantly rearranged whether life was an endless equation. The shop items became mathematical digits to contemplate in endless combinations: she placed a bunch of yellow recycled pencils at five pence each along with elephant key chains and beaded pens and colourful Rajasthani cloth puppets and McDonald's Happy Meal toys in a wicker tray near the till, returning almost immediately to remove the pens and look anew at the configuration.

Heera continued to fold the clothing in silence. She had been appointed the manager of IndiaNeed ten days after her seventeenth wedding anniversary, and sought solace in work with fierce dedication, a quality Diana

Wellington-Smythe astutely exploited. It was on their anniversary that Heera's husband Bob had told her of his terrible secret, unwittingly timing it to the day when she began her first course of hormone replacement therapy.

CHAPTER TWO

A trouble shared is a trouble halved

It was 15 August, the anniversary of India's Independence and of their marriage. Heera Malkani Moore still celebrated the first of the two with pride. She looked at her husband, Bob; he was sprawled across the bed, his mouth slightly open in sleep. How thin his lips were, she thought, a gingery grey for a sunny day.

'Adam!' he had called out gruffly, and she awoke instantly. Who was Adam? she wondered.

Heera's transparent, bubbly exterior concealed an edgy sexuality; she was a forgotten kettle boiling over. Only once had she known real passion, at eighteen, with lithe Javed in his tight blue Terylene trousers. He had exuded an animal vigour, demonstrating clever stealth in their assignations. Heera cherished a velvet memory; they had watched the teen romance *Bobby* in the back row at the local cinema in Hyderabad, and Javed's fingers had splayed interrogatively across her breasts while he popped peanuts into his mouth with his other hand. He had retained a last peanut for the moment when the lights came on, despatching it with studied nonchalance as other couples leaped to their feet to shuffle demurely out of the hall.

Bob's contribution to the anniversary was a generous Marks & Spencer gift voucher. On the advice of his aunt he had presented Heera with English cookery books to mark the first, and Heera had dutifully noted the recipes for Yorkshire pudding and mince pies. On the second anniversary he took her to a caravan site in Cornwall. Heera now used the vouchers to buy white six-pack tummy control undergarments.

On every anniversary and several times through the year, Heera entertained the local Asian community as well as Bob's friends and colleagues in their spacious semi-detached house on Tenison Road. The front door was decorated with an Indian floral garland from which a green chili and lemon were suspended. The men huddled over the whisky and the women flocked to the large floral Chesterfield and overflowed onto the red Persian carpet. The guests departed at midnight with a lover's lingering touch of Indian spice in their hair, coats and eyes. 'I should call this house "Heera Hotel", complained Heera. 'I get absolutely knackered with all these people coming and not going.' It never occurred to her that she had a choice.

Once inside the door, her overnight guests succumbed to the languorous air, moving from one calorie-laden meal to the next in a stupor, too soporific to consider the red Cambridge sightseeing bus that departed hourly from the station. Bob frequently returned to slipper-shod strangers wandering with easy familiarity in his home. Standing on his doorstep one evening a few years ago, he was welcomed by a large woman in a shimmering red salwar kameez. She giggled

22

coyly. Several perspiring strangers were executing various dance poses on his carpet, a large woman whacked a *dholak* with podgy fingers and her listless companion sang tunelessly to the strains of a wheezing harmonium.

Another woman and her bowed daughter were straining over the guests' outstretched palms, squeezing intricate mehndi patterns with weary flourish through tiny cones.

'*Arre jaan*, where did you come from?' cried Heera, aghast. 'You had said you were coming home late. We are having a mehndi party. No men allowed.'

The large woman gushed, 'Poor man, let him be. He can be the gora Krishna, our white Krishna among the gopis. Come, come, *chalo* Bob, you must also dance!' She dragged him into the circle of giggling women. A shrill Bollywood tune sprang to life on his stereo system operated by a hard-faced stranger with a diamond stud in her nose, and the large woman shook her hips suggestively, hiding her face behind her shiny dupatta. The women tittered as Bob ducked like a diver in a scuba suit wandering into a May Ball by accident.

'Come, Heera, I will read your hand before you have your mehndi put,' offered a large woman in a purple sari, who fanned herself vigorously. Bob watched as Heera was led to a couch.

'Heera, you give only happiness wherever you go. It is in your bhagya, in your destiny,' declared the woman. 'Your husband is a very lucky man.'

Heera smiled.

'But what is this?' queried the woman in deliberate tones. '*Hai*, what is this? You are blessed by the Goddess Lakshmi herself, but you were not meant to have any children?' Deliberately ascending an octave, she repeated, 'There is no line at all in your palm. How can that be?'

Heera glanced at Bob in the silence. She had looked stricken, he thought later, as he stood in front of the mirror, removing his tie. Unfathomably stricken, for he recalled his question to her in Hyderabad: could she contemplate a life with him and without children? She had appeared not to hesitate in accepting his proposal.

Their announcement to Heera's flabbergasted family led to the appointment of a lynx-eyed chaperone waiting for gora Bob to make an unlicensed move. Cinema visits were conducted without peanuts and in the company of curious relatives eager to behold Heera's white fiancé in the dark.

Tonight, on the evening of his seventeenth anniversary party, Bob felt constricted by the tight collar of the white sherwani he wore, although a frail little man in a black sherwani holding a whisky glass appeared to suffer no such discomfort.

'Brahma-ji, you are such an expert in English Literature, and we haven't heard your recitations for a long time. Why don't you give us all a demonstration?' prompted Heera gaily.

'Su-er,' assented the little man in a pronounced Sindhi accent. He handed his whisky glass to Heera and moved to the centre of the room to sit cross-legged on the carpet. There was a hush as, arm raised to render a qawali, he announced, 'Hamlet'. It sounded like 'omelette'. His voice boomed:

To beeeee (he paused overlong, looking meaningfully around the gathering)

24

Orrrr (long pause)
Not to beeeeee (he shook his grey locks), *that is the*
qu-ushtion:
Whether 'tish nobler in the
Mind to suffer
The s-lings and arrows of outrageous fartune,
Orrrr (meaningful look) *to take up arams against*
A sea of troubles,
And by opposing end them?

There was a thin ripple of applause. Brahma Mansukhani was a retired doctor from Bradford, who had once
been travelling in a minicab that was blocked by a red
Ford Fiesta. Three young men wearing balaclavas
sprang from the darkness, brandishing knives at the
driver, wrenched the car door open, punched his face,
took his money and vanished. They failed to notice the
tiny terrified doctor slumped low, cowering in the back.
The next day his son, a locum at a pharmacy, appeared
before the Royal Pharmaceutical Society, charged with
the unlawful sale of prescription painkillers. The combined shock could have rollercoasted the little doctor to
drink, but he had turned to the Bard instead.

His mentor's birthday on 23 April filled him with a
religious fervour of such potency that he undertook an
annual pilgrimage to Stratford-upon-Avon. Then he
read of the controversy over the Bard's precise date of
birth in April. A cautious man, he now celebrated at
home for an entire month.

The chance discovery of an anagram website that had
rearranged the letters 'William Shakespeare's birthday'
into 'April's skies: we may hail the Bard' filled his days
with activity as he created his own anagrams from

25

various Shakespearean plays to post on the Internet. His attempt to rearrange his own name 'Brahma Mansukhani' concluded abruptly after the emergence of the embarrassing configuration 'Bra Man Khan'.

While 'Shakespeare' trilled in the centre of the living room, Bob stood on the patio, a large, bluff man like a farmer without his wellingtons. He thought again of Heera's wounded glance. Charlie (Chandru) and Barry (Bhagat) called out goodnaturedly for whisky refills as they admired his artificial Japanese garden. A few minutes earlier, Bob had slipped upstairs, crossed over to the window and looked out onto the street, deliberating before he dialled. 'Adam Russell,' answered a man's voice. Bob replaced the receiver without speaking. His palms were sweaty as he descended the stairs to serve apple juice to the owner of a London frozen food company who urged his sympathetic listeners, 'We need more burial sites in this country, and we must have burial within twenty-four hours.'

'Have I ever introduced you to Lord Bijlani?' asked Heera, linking her arm in Bob's, guiding his reluctant feet across the room.

'A peer?'

'*Arre* no, *jaan*, his first name is "Lord". What clever parents – why didn't they call him "Lakhu"? This way, everyone thinks he's an MP sitting in the House of Lords. Anyway, he's in the manufacturing business, he makes leather seats for luxury cars. He was also in some insurance scam. His bossy mother lives with him and everyone knows she sits on his head, so he can't find a wife,' whispered Heera in a tumble of words.

Lord Bijlani wore a black leather jacket and tight leather jeans; his fitted shirt was unbuttoned to display

26

a gold chain. He squealed and kissed Heera soundly and roundly on both cheeks. Was the leather of his jacket the same as the fabric of his car seats? wondered Bob, as he offered him a drink, aching to hear the cool voice at the other end of the telephone. On his way upstairs, he was stopped by a man with greasy hair and piercing eyes. 'I am Dr Sridhar T. I cure incurable illnesses,' he announced, thrusting a visiting card into Bob's hands. He moved away, but returned an instant later. 'Slight spelling mistake in card. Printing was done in India, but do read.'

Bob read obediently: *People loose valuable things in life. Without Health life is nothing. Patient cured includes many Business magnets, many M.PS, M.L.A's. Successful treatments by Dr. Sridhar T for Intestine disc's, gynaecological disc's, sexual disc's, baby of choice.*

Dr Sridhar was a 'world-renowned miracle doctor' visiting England. His previous surgery had been conducted three evenings a week at a school hall in his Indian hometown. A new patient entering the hall was presented with a token and seated among a few hundred people in perpetual motion. The newcomer was then sent to men and women in white coats in a tiny room, and Dr Sridhar stepped forward. As the patient opened his mouth for a mandatory inspection, several heads peered in as one, notes were taken, glances exchanged and little white pills prescribed by Dr Sridhar, to be taken twice a day after meals. Despite the fact that only the tongue was on display, the patient came away feeling undressed.

Dr Sridhar's wife, Manjula, was a tall woman with a face the shape of the full moon. Placid and calm, she bore her sister-in-law's harassment with equanimity.

27

Radiant in her third month of pregnancy, she initially dismissed a mound of curly human hair, red chillies and a doll stuffed with pins on her pillow as a childish prank. When she gave birth to a deformed child, Manjula shrieked it was the hand of voodoo, but remained unsupported in her conviction. The baby died within days, and a year later Manjula became the wild-eyed mother of a healthy boy, but still slipped into postnatal depression, a condition that remained undetected by her husband. She attempted suicide, mistakenly swallowing the pills he prescribed to his patients instead of the sleeping pills purchased for the overdose, but survived, recovering the calm of thin ice. Manjula was living testimony to both the failure and success of her husband's little white pills.

Bob slipped away from the doctor, excitement driving him upstairs.

'I know it's you, Bob,' accused the voice.

Bob stared silently out of the window, telephone in hand.

'We can't go on like this. You know that. Tell her. Tell her now.'

O Romeeeo, O Romeeeo, wherephore art thou Romeeeo, wailed the cross-legged 'Shakespeare' as Bob wandered in a daze into the hallway and into his study. Eight children were on the carpet watching a Bollywood film in a room overflowing with laundry baskets, books and a computer on a tiny table. A photograph of Heera in a bridal sari stared back at his shuttered eyes as a plate of tikkis and chutney hovered over his shoulder. 'There you are, *jaan*,' chided Heera. 'Why are you here? There are so many people you must meet – how can you neglect your guests? Come outside, come look after them.'

A voice yelled, 'Heera, forget your *bak bak*. Talk later, go to the kitchen, your kebabs are going to burn.'

Heera peered into the oven and retrieved a steaming tray of kebabs. 'This is Sam. She works at Smith's. You know, the curtain shop on Burleigh Street. She's the one with the tattoo on her thingy,' said Heera on her way out to serve the kebabs.

'Shall I show you my tattoo?' challenged the girl called Sam.

'That's entirely your decision,' replied Bob.

Sam swiftly unbuttoned her blouse for an instant to reveal a black rose tattoo nestling between her Wonderbra-enhanced breasts, before turning to the aloo tikkis in the microwave. 'I used to work in a salon on Green Street. I do hair, nails, mehndi, threading and facial. I used to do full body wax also,' she continued archly. 'You know – *full*. Where does she keep her pickles?'

The young woman hunted in a cupboard. She walked closer to Bob, scrutinising his face. 'You need to look after yourself. If you don't, who will? Anyway, I'm saving up for a boob job now.'

Bob felt no obligation to respond.

'What's that about boobs? Take some of mine, they're too big.' Heera turned to Bob, who was perched on a kitchen stool. '*Jaan*, again hiding? Sam, what magic are you working on my husband? Leave him alone. Come, *jaan*, look who's here – it's Manoj Daryanani!' she announced flirtatiously.

Manoj Daryanani was a tall, slim man with an unlined face. Dressed in a spotless white kurta pyjama, he greeted people from afar with folded hands, backing away as if from contamination.

'*Jaan*, look after Manoj, give him some pakoras,' advised Heera.

'No fried things! He has a problem, you know, with his digestion,' warned Manoj's wife, a silent fellow sufferer.

Charlie and Barry waved their whisky in wobbly unison. 'And do you remember what Karnani said at the end of the shareholders' meeting?' asked Charlie. 'That he must thank people "on the backside".' The two men roared at an old joke, the ice in their glasses rocking in merriment. Another voice roared from the carpet, reaching a crescendo:

> *The evil that men do lives afater them;*
> *The good is oft interred with their bones*

An elderly Englishman declared as he waved a kebab in his listener's face, 'I do agree, without Asian medical personnel, the NHS would collapse.'

> *When shalla we three meet again*
> *In thunder, lightning,*
> *Orrrr in rain?*
> *When the hurrrlyburrrly's done,*
> *When the battle's losht and won.*

Heera hurried over to 'Shakespeare'. 'Brahma-ji, you must be so tired, dinner is served on the table.'

'Su-er.'

Bob turned to leave the room. 'Where are you off to, Bob? Aren't you going to cut the cake?' cried his sister Sarah.

'You're a lucky man, Bob,' observed his cousin Jonathan.

30

'Heera's a lucky woman to be married to my brother,' contradicted Sarah. 'Let's raise a toast to the happy couple.'

'Speech, speech!' clapped a woman with flaming henna-dyed hair and blue clanging bangles on her wrist.

Bob put his arm around Heera and addressed a speck on the floor. 'She's everything to me.'

A murmur went round the room. 'Ah, bless.' Heera sniffed, before twisting herself out of his embrace to cry, 'Who wants tiramisu, who wants apple crumble, who wants ice cream and who wants rosogulla?'

'Mustn't be naughty!' vowed Sarah, a hand fluttering over her abdomen, as she greedily surveyed the desserts. 'Ooh, shall I give in this once?'

'Wouldn't you rather have the cake and eat it, too?' asked her husband Brian sourly.

Sarah always surrendered to her sweet tooth, but rarely to her husband. She had persuaded him to exchange their house in Royston for a dilapidated farmhouse outside a Tuscan village, hoping to convert the barn and stables into luxury tourist apartments. The legalities of the transfer of property deeds were as much a nightmare for Brian as working the ancient water pump and cleaning out the well. He harvested the grapes and olives and struggled to find a match for broken kitchen tiles. She never wanted sex, only olives by the truckload to sell in the local market. He was ready to return to England, but Sarah refused. He wished he could write an autobiography with the title *My Grapes of Wrath*.

'Anyone for coffee?' Heera approached Manoj

31

Daryanani, who asked for a glass of hot water. His wife explained, 'For his voice.'

'Why, what's wrong with it?' queried Heera.

'He sings.'

'*Wah ji*, you are a gayak, you are a singer, and you did not even tell us! That means you must perform for us right now. Yes, yes, I'm not taking a "No" from you. It's my anniversary, you have to please me. Come on, *ji*,' cried Heera persuasively.

Manoj Daryanani, who needed a straight-backed chair, now occupied the carpet so recently vacated by 'Shakespeare'. Heera carried out a harmonium and a pair of tabla, but he looked disdainfully at the instruments and waved them away as he cleared his throat. '*Hari, meri itni suno*,' he intoned. It was the first line of a devotional song.

'Why don't you sing a film song instead? How about "Yeh Shaam Mastani"?' suggested Barry, now on his third Scotch and viewing the world through heavy-lidded eyes. Barry was recovering from a disagreement earlier that day with his teenage son. The drink would dull the pangs of parenting.

He ached to leave it all and return to India. Perhaps he was not too old; he might still find a job in an Indian company. Life wouldn't be the same, of course, none of the luxuries they took for granted in England, but at least he would never again feel the fear, the black pounding of his heart as he discovered the cannabis hidden behind his son's physics textbook. It was still not too late to take his son back to India. Ari was a good boy in bad company, but what would Shanti say? It would kill her, the way she pampered that boy, as if he were a prince from Patiala. It was all her fault, spoiling him, letting him think he could do whatever he wanted, money from his mother any time, so what if Dad didn't give it to him, the manipulative little bugger went to Mummy. 'Come to Mummy, son, Mummy understands her *beta*.'

He had told Ari from the very beginning, 'Yes, it is hard to live in this British society. You can't be mediocre if you want to be accepted here, you have to show you are the best at something – swimming, maths, science, computers, something at least – then they will admire you. But instead you have become a zero, a nothing, a charsi, a drug addict, and what do you think, just because you can fool your mother, you can do the same with me? You will know what your father is made of if you ever touch that stuff again.'

'Yes, why don't you sing "Yeh Shaam Mastani",' repeated Barry jovially, as he hitched his trouser waistband.

Manoj Daryanani frowned at Barry's levity. Thirty minutes later, during his rendition of 'Raag Bageshree', the bolder members of the audience had already escaped via the conservatory door. Those who remained trapped leaped with unapologetic haste after the last prolonged note and scattered, beads of a strung note onto the carpet.

The guests disbanded at the moment that the Trinity College clock struck midnight over Great Court. Heera surveyed the empty living room with satisfaction. She had already guessed Sarla's gift by its contours; always the same Indian wrapping paper bought in bulk and the same box of chocolates without an expiry date or manufacturer's label from a shop in Wembley. Sarah and Brian's gift was olive marinade.

Bob was lying on their bed, staring at the ceiling. What was it that ridiculous little man 'Shakespeare' had recited about a tide in the affairs of men taken at the flood, and was this such a time, to submit, release the torment and anguish within and allow it to take its course, let it take him to good fortune or to defeat? Or would he regret it forever afterwards, and would the shame be a torment far greater? Would he be forever damned, or should he plunge, surrender?

> *This above all: to thine own self be true,*
> *And it must follow, as the night the day,*
> *Thou canst not then be false to any man.*

The crumbling sensation in his throat all evening turned to fuzzy warmth as he remembered. The meeting had been in a small conference room. As the executives streamed in, Bob's secretary hurriedly handed him a copy of the Finance Director's memo before the heavy oak door closed. Bob nodded to his colleagues, his eyes roaming the room, a swelling bubble of excitement as he recognised the dark, bent head of a man reading by the window. The man turned and looked at Bob, eyes a cool smoky grey that clashed and tumbled into his own, and Bob turned from the flint of the other man's gaze to take a seat at the table. As the diminutive Finance Director talked, a powdery thirst invaded Bob's throat, and he reached for a jug of water, staring involuntarily at the golden hair on the wrist of the man beside him. The lights dimmed as they looked at the first chart in the PowerPoint presentation on the wall at the far end of the room.

Bob felt tingling heat on his thigh as the brushing

movement of a hand left its searing imprint. He continued to stare at the wall. As Adam teased Bob's ankle with his own, Bob grappled this new, daring reality while tortured angels tumbled and frolicked in a forbidden fountain, resisting banishment. At the end of the meeting, he hurried towards the door. A cool voice behind him asked if he would like to stop by at the pub. Without meeting Adam's eyes, Bob mumbled that he had to get home. 'Another time, then,' Adam had said smoothly, turning away. 'No, wait!' flung Bob. It was a strangled, torn sound.

As Heera entered the bedroom, she knew something was wrong, something far worse than unwrapping stale chocolates from Sarla for the third consecutive year. She had found Bob pacing the room, a half-empty whisky glass in his hand. He never drank upstairs, and usually shared a pot of Chinese green tea with her before retiring. He told her he had something important to say, but that it could wait until she was ready, and she had looked at him, wordlessly taking her perspiration-stained pink nightgown and matching robe from the room, returning drawn and anxious a few minutes later.

Afterwards, she had asked Bob in the dim bedroom light why he had chosen their anniversary to tell her. All he could say, standing ridiculous and pale in his faded blue striped pyjamas, was that big occasions made his decisions seem smaller. He had finally found the handle to the door of his closet, and he was coming out. He could no longer conceal, only reveal; he would not hide, he would announce with pride – he was a bisexual.

Then Bob crumpled at the hurt she would feel, the

disgust and repulsion, her accusations of trickery and fraud. He had never meant to deceive or dissemble, he beseeched, he was fragile and frail.

If he was frail, so was she, Heera thought fiercely. It wasn't only her depleted hormones that needed replacement; she needed implants of reassurance. He had never really been by her side, she decided; she had been living with a phantom, hollow, filled with straw, lit and brought to life by another. What had he expected her to say? she thought dully, head exploding, as she lay awake in the dark. What did he think she would do with his revelation? And it had to be a coincidence, one of those amazing ironies of life, that her cousin had told her of Javed's divorce and of his forthcoming visit to England.

Bob had a dream that night; he was a boy in his father's cottage near the moors, running home through the heath to his mother, who was wearing a blue and white floral dress. She scooped him into her arms for a warm embrace, and he hugged Adam back. Heera responded sleepily. As suddenly, his arms fell away from her, and he turned on his side again, heart thumping in the darkness, afraid that she might be awake.

It was Adam who banished Eve from the Garden of Eden.

CHAPTER THREE

The customer is always right

THE WIND PROWLED for new victims as cyclists wobbled, their nostrils filled with the sniff of fresh bread snaking out from the bakery on Mill Road. The smoke from its blackened chimney was whirled away over the grey rooftops, and three doors down from IndiaNeed the handpainted sign *Wright and Sons, Bookbinders since 1930* flapped noisily above the entrance to the shop. A young man in a black leather jacket and merino russet scarf announced his arrival; inside, an elderly man shuffled towards him in the dim light, weaving through stacks and piles of theses, glue, buckram, bookbinding tools and overalls. The young man took delivery of a Cambridge thesis bound in black, pressing it proudly to his chest as he left.

The blonde florist arranged the blooms in buckets on the rack outside the Sunflowers Florists shop, waiting for her boyfriend to propose. The wind spotted two Pakistani women walking slowly past the solicitor's firm towards IndiaNeed, and playfully buffeted the elderly lady and her stick into the shop. Abandoning her mother, the younger woman swooped on the soft toys, gathering armfuls of teddy bears that were as suddenly dropped back onto the shelves.

'One ear or two – does it really make a difference? *Arre*, tell the child that they are special designer teddies. Doesn't that expensive Steiff teddy always have a button only in one ear? See, I am giving these to you at a special discounted price. One for a pound,' urged Heera.

The young woman needed little persuasion; the one-eared toys were shiny and new. Shabbier toys were always removed by the volunteers and despatched to the skip, along with the reject clothing that often only missed a button or a thread. A firm regularly collected the contents of the skip and paid the shop fifty pence per bag. Heera's neighbour was an airline manager, who offered to send the reject bags to any charitable institution in India free of charge, but Diana Wellington-Smythe's grey eyes had narrowed at the suggestion; she was convinced the contents would be distributed or even sold among Heera's relatives and friends.

The elderly Pakistani lady examined a furry black monkey lying in a basket next to her chair. Its giant tail had been mistakenly sewn on in front, and she looked at the freak toy in silence. Swarnakumari frowned and whispered, 'This is not good, Durga. What will that lady think of us? I thought we had thrown that dirty thing away. Who put it there again?'

'The Korean girls?' suggested Durga.

'Auntyji, this is not for you,' appeased Heera smoothly, attempting a seamless exchange with a blue Beanie Baby teddy announcing *It's a Boy* across its chest. 'Take this, only two pounds.'

'Who put that blue teddy there again?' asked

Swarnakumari, perturbed. 'I had thrown it into the rejects bag.'

'I did; there was nothing wrong with it. Why did you throw it away?' Eileen was surprised.

Swarnakumari remained silent; some secrets were best kept buried, like the stories the black bags never revealed.

The elderly lady held the monkey firmly in her grasp, waving Heera away with her stick as the daughter spotted the sign *IndiaNeed* and the photograph of the smiling Rajasthani villagers on the wall.

'Does the money you make go to India?' she probed.

'Yes, of course.'

'And only to India?'

'Yes,' repeated Heera, surprised.

The daughter catapulted her protesting mother out of the chair. The monkey tumbled onto the floor, where it lay brazen, its furry tail on display. They left without a purchase.

'We are all the same here, the same brown skin fighting for respect in this society. Why carry on India–Pakistan enmity here? Even the leaders of both countries have started peace talks now, so what's the problem with these two? The daughter was pretty, though. She reminded me of Nafisa,' observed Heera. 'You know, Swarna, Nafisa coolly sent her mother-in-law back to Lahore, and I hear the room has been given to three Japanese students. Of course, it's not far from the Bell Language School, so the room must be in demand. She's making good money, but how do those poor students all fit? I know Japanese girls are tiny, but still, three? By the way, her sister Razia is with Nafisa's neighbour's husband now. He was helping Razia build her extension.' Heera chortled. '*Arre*, if you ask me, he should have looked after his own extension, if you know what I mean. Anyway, long story, some other time.'

Eileen bent to pick up the monkey. 'I'm off to rearrange the soft toys,' she announced, her quick eyes noting their disarray. She placed the monkey on the shelf next to a blue-eyed china doll. The story of *Beauty and the Beast* had always been a favourite with her.

'Girls, why are the English so mad about their teddy bears? Teddy waiting on their beds, telling Teddy their secrets . . . Bob has a teddy called Charlie, you know. Such a shabby teddy! Only one eye. When I first met Bob, I actually offered to sew the other eye on.' Heera chuckled. 'You know how it is in India, those dhobis wash the clothes so carelessly sometimes, the buttons become loose, so my mother had a huge collection of assorted buttons, all colours, all sizes, in a big biscuit tin. I could have found an exact match. But Bob said he preferred Charlie with one eye.' She called out, 'Four out of four Englishmen don't wash their teddies, Swarna!'

Two startled elderly ladies sifted through the pile of net curtains, eavesdropping with bright bird eyes. 'Are you all Alsatian, then?' chirruped one, turning to Swarnakumari. 'I have a lady next door who is Alsatian. She's very nice, very nice, very well-spoken indeed. Lovely dark eyes. Dear, when you're ready, could you measure up this curtain for me?'

Swarnakumari turned to Durga in bewilderment.

'Forget it. Asian or Alsatian, what does it matter? No point trying to explain to these sweet *buddi* biddies,' whispered Heera. 'Half of them can't hear, half can't see, half can't walk, half can't talk.'

'Dogs and Indians once had to use the back door,' mused Durga.

'The Irish too,' added Eileen as she disappeared down an aisle. She was fiercely proud of her heritage. Annoyed by Durga's appropriation of the Diaspora to signify Indian sub-continental migration alone, she usually remained silent. Some things were felt, and not always said.

A middle-aged woman had been standing uncertainly in a corner; she rummaged in her bag and removed a plain gold band and a platinum ring studded with a large ruby. 'There, you can 'ave 'em both and good riddance,' she rasped, flinging them on the counter in front of Heera. 'Me old man's done a runner, gone an' left me, so I took me engagement and wedding rings to the jeweller's down the road.' She jerked her head sideways to indicate the location of a Mill Road shop. 'An' what d'yer know, they're worth no more than five quid after all these years. Five quid, I tell yer!' she repeated, her voice rising. 'I been with 'im all these years, and the bugger couldn't even give me a decent gold ring. So I says I'll take 'em down to the charity shop and get rid of 'em. You can do what yer want with 'em,' she told Heera. 'Don't never want ter see 'em no more.'

Heera handed the rings silently to Eileen, who placed them on a little velvet fold and slid them onto the jewellery shelf below the till counter.

A wedding ring always reminded Durga of Pooja, the popular, leggy prefect at her school in Bombay, now Mumbai. Pooja and Anil had married, won a *Wills Made for Each Other Couple* contest and a new car. A year later, Durga had sat uncomfortably in a living room in a

41

Cuffe Parade apartment overlooking the bay, witness to a marriage rotting twig by twig. Pooja had initially turned a blind eye to Anil's affairs and embarked upon revenge romps of her own. Her husband's Malayali chauffeur with jasmine oil-greased hair was startled, but willing. It was her discovery of the maid's gold earrings tucked under Anil's pillow that impelled a dramatic confrontation between the couple. He must choose, Pooja said imperiously. Anil obeyed with alacrity and stayed with the maid; humiliation sent Pooja out of her marriage and house into obesity. Durga had heard later that a week on a health farm in Bangalore had restored Pooja's holistic balance. Two months later, she wedded the masseur and flashed a new gold ring on her finger; jewellery was both the bane and balm of her marriages.

'They're new, don't you want them?' asked Eileen, handing a pile of net curtains to Swarnakumari.

'I have already got net curtains, *na*. Your Uncle says our house must look English from the outside.'

Swarnakumari never referred to her husband by name, oblivious to the confusion caused by 'Your Uncle' as the substitute. She had initially refused to arrange the display when asked to 'do the window', and announced with a vigorous shake of her head, 'I am not here to clean. Your Uncle would not like me to do that.' Diana Wellington-Smythe had merely arched an eyebrow, enunciating in slow English thereafter to Swarnakumari and the Korean volunteers.

'White wisps of respectability,' commented Durga, examining the net curtains. 'Give the immigrant net curtains and he simply blends, like the tea packet labels that say *Product of more than one country*. But to blend or

42

not to blend into the diasporic cuppa — that is the question.'

Swarnakumari picked at a loose thread on the curtain. 'Durga, my Mallika is not listening to me at all nowadays. See, she is now twenty-two. She has finished at Emmanuel College and she wants to do postgraduate also, but I am thinking if she settles down with a good Bengali boy, she can also continue her studies, but she is not agreeing. Early in the morning she was fighting with me when Your Uncle was not there. Tell me, if your parents find an intelligent boy from a good family for you, you will agree to see him, *na*? At least you will not say "No" straight away?'

'What's this got to do with me?'

'You both are similar — see, you are twenty-nine, your studies are over, now you are doing this research on charity shops for the television, and soon you are going to London for your new job. But you must also think of marriage, or it will be too late. That is what I keep telling Mallika.'

Heera bent to pick up a basket of baby clothes. 'Too late? Too late for what? You know, girls, when I was eighteen I was in love with a boy called Javed. He was our neighbour. He used to write beautiful Urdu love poems. Then my parents found out. Usual Hindu–Muslim problem and both the families immediately stopped it. Javed was sent to Dubai; he owns a big construction company now. Three days before he left, we met for the last time and we went for a walk on the beach. He suggested a camel ride, and we sat on the same camel, but the camel wouldn't move. It just sat there in the sand. People were staring and laughing and suddenly there were many stalls there — peanut-seller, balloon-seller, coconut-waterwala. People even threw peanuts at the camel to make it move. Then the owner told us to get off, and he kicked the camel hard on its bottom.'

Heera paused; no one said anything. She continued, 'We went back home. Javed didn't say a word to me again, and he left for Dubai. For many years, I refused to see any of the boys my parents showed me. After all, if you fall in love, you fall in love, right? The heart remembers its broken song for ever. Then Bob came to Hyderabad. He knew one of my brother's friends, and that's how we met. There was such a big fuss when Bob proposed – you know, how could I like a gora, an Englishman, how could I leave India forever and go to England and all that – but we got married anyway.'

'Your Bob is a good man, just like Your Uncle,' confirmed Swarnakumari.

'Yes,' replied Heera, 'he is a good man, otherwise why would I follow him to this country?'

'Javed was a Muslim, and you a Hindu. *Baba*, it would not have been possible. Love is blind, I know, but I am telling you, such marriages are very difficult,' Swarnakumari said sagely. 'There is too much difference. Too much adjustment for both parties.'

'And your esteemed opinion is based on . . . ?'

Ignoring Durga's sarcasm, Swarnakumari persisted earnestly, 'See, in arranged marriages, quarrels about basic things are not there. Everything is matched. That is why these marriages work, *na*?'

'Work. Marriage is work,' muttered Eileen, who had been listening with interest as she returned with an armful of boy's clothes, looking as if she would hold them forever.

44

'Tell me, Swarna, do you love your husband?' asked Heera moodily.

Swarnakumari was surprised. 'Of course. You always give your love to the man you marry.'

'I didn't mean that. What sort of love is the love for a husband?' said Heera.

'A mistake,' said Durga.

Swarnakumari continued patiently, 'A marriage should also be blessed by the gods, but it is the woman who has to make sure everything is in its proper place. Then only it works. She must accept that there are things she wants but cannot have. The tragedy is our young girls these days don't know themselves what they want. They are confused, and they feel pressure. They are trying to be like these English girls. Parties and clubs, drink, wearing those clothes showing everything, and they want—'

'Wild sex with white blokes,' interrupted Durga.

Swarnakumari was shocked. 'My Mallika needs—'

'Wild sex with black blokes? Oh, of course, sorry, these things don't happen in good Asian families.'

'What dirty talk is this? It does not suit you, Durga. Take my advice, and let your parents help you get married. They can easily find an intelligent boy, good personality, same values, same social background.'

'Leave my parents out of this. And what's with you first-generation Indians, anyway? You came here thirty years ago with a suitcase you never unpacked. It's all about tradition, family, culture, honour, isn't it? Why are you so keen on carrying on tradition? It's as if you're scared – you have to obey, or else. But does tradition exist? Is it real for us to taste, smell, feel and hold?'

A customer approached the till. 'Er, could you . . .'

45

'Anything wrong with what I said? One day when you girls become mothers you will understand your own mothers. Each generation will not listen. It will understand only later. That is the tragedy of life. Tell me, Durga, who are you without your roots, *hanh*? It is because of our roots that we can survive in this society. Why do you want to deny our Indian culture, that's what I don't understand.' Swarnakumari matched Durga's passionate outburst with one of her own.

'Don't you see that you seize upon "Indian culture" out of desperation and fear? Fear of erosion and erasure of identity. Why not welcome the churn of East–West encounters instead, take the plunge into the flow and see what happens? Diaspora isn't only about displacement; it's a progression, a moving to a new location of the liberated self.'

'*Baba*, I do not understand this high talk of yours. What I am saying is there is nothing wrong if parents guide and advise children even when they are older. That's all. Your parents must surely be telling you the same thing.'

'Blankets,' interjected the customer.

Durga cried, 'Leave my parents out of it!'

'My Arthur used to say—' reported the customer unsuccessfully.

'Why, your parents should not worry about you just because you are grown up?' pursued Swarnakumari.

'I said, drop it.'

The customer grew bold. 'Could I just . . .'

'Yes, madam?' inquired Swarnakumari, noticing her for the first time.

'Do you have any electric blankets, dear?'

'No, madam, but do look in that section there. We

46

have some new Edinburgh wool blankets,' replied Swarnakumari as the customer moved away.

She continued, '*Baba*, forget it, why are you getting so upset? You know, so many things have changed for the better from twenty-five years ago. You must have heard how we used to buy baked beans to make an Indian dish, and in those days we could not even get coriander. What could we teach our children about India, living here in Britain? That is why I am thinking there is nothing wrong at all if youngsters like these Bollywood films nowadays.'

'Did you understand anything I said? Oh, and about Bollywood, let me tell you, the only reason you welcome those films is because at last there's something much bigger than a bunch of coriander to reflect your "Indian values". But I think Bollywood has stereotyped us further in this country, shut us all in a cage called "Asian". One size fits all, so my Asian bum doesn't look big in this. Do the J. Kumar grocer and I have anything in common? No, but we're all Asian, so let's party.'

'I don't understand—' Swarnakumari began.

Durga interrrupted sharply, 'At last, Mr and Mrs Jones next door know the real me. I'm Asian, right, so *of course*, all I do is I boogie my belly and bounce my bosom to the bhangra beat. Jerk and jhatka, ooh, that's hot, that's Asian cool! Swarna, the future is so bright it's not orange, but brown.'

'Durga, what are you talking about? Everything is so easy for your generation now. Let me tell you something. Mallika's father and I got married in Kolkata. He left, and I came later to England. In Kolkata my family had five servants – *five*. And first day in England, he gave me an empty milk bottle in my hand and told

47

me, "Roll out chapattis with this!" The kitchen window must be kept shut also. "No Indian cooking smell should go to the neighbour," he warned me. You cannot imagine the shock; it took me such a long time to forget my Kolkata, to like this country, even other Bengalis, the weather, even my own house . . .'

The eavesdropping customer agreed. 'Don't blame you, dear. I still don't like the weather. No good for me bones – got arthritis you see, just like me sister Maud. She's the younger one, holidaying in Spain at the moment she is, but our poor Edith was buried with her pacemaker she was, and ooh, what a problem she used ter have going through metal detectors in airports. She went on a holiday to Rome and those Italians thought she was a terrorist. Bleep, bleep, bleep, the detector went off and poor Edith got such a fright, I can tell yer. My Arthur used to say—'

'How can we help you, madam?' prodded Swarnakumari.

'Er, well, yes, I wanted an electric blanket, you see, but you don't have any, so I thought I'd donate these ten pounds. Mary did say to me ter make sure the money goes ter those wee cats. My Arthur always said—'

'I think you mean the cats' charity next door, madam. It is called Catnap. This is IndiaNeed. Our money goes to poor Indian villagers.' Swarnakumari shook her head vigorously. 'No cats here.' She pointed to the photograph on the wall behind her of the group of smiling Rajasthani villagers. A larger photograph of Diana Wellington-Smythe shaking hands with the Duke of Edinburgh hung adjacent on the wall.

48

'Oh, but we do have one,' contradicted Durga. 'Her name is Mrs Well—'

Swarnakumari frowned.

'Well, dear, I'll be off, then. Goodbye. You too, dear, goodbye,' sang the customer, opening the door. 'My Arthur always used to say . . .' The traffic outside drowned her voice.

Durga wanted to call her back, ask about Arthur. What did he always say? Who was he? Husband, lover or son? He was dead, or perhaps he was alive and now said something different, something he had never said before. And what if everything Arthur had ever said was gone, washed away like the ashes and flowers floating on an Indian river, and one human being had the power to keep his spoken word alive in an echoing universe?

The customer returned, popping her head through the door. She paused, lost in thought. 'There was something I had to remember,' she announced amiably. 'And I've forgotten what it is. Never mind. Goodbye.'

Memory was a capricious tool; it airbrushed the cavities of time. Javed no longer wrote Urdu love poems – he wrote invoices. After a successful career as a builder in Dubai, he had recently purchased a plot of land in Harrow, north-west London, for the development of offices and residential flats. His wife had custody of the children, for whom he felt affection but no pangs of separation. Javed was now a new man, and he intended to behave like one. 'Freedom by fifty' was his new life slogan.

He had never sat on a camel again, although fate had

confidently despatched him to the land of camels. As long as he was within sight of a dromedary, it was clear that his marriage to Shabana would remain doomed. Shabana was a Pathan, fair and loose-limbed, with light grey eyes and silky brown hair; she was also a deeply religious shopaholic. He had indulged her excesses, and even when her two younger sisters and mother joined a household already bursting with servants, his protests remained benevolent and mild. With the sunlight pouring onto his desk one afternoon, he stumbled upon her latest bank statement. Blinded by the intensity of the light, he misread the digits and decided that Shabana had stretched both her credit and credibility too far; he had reached his limit. In a moment of insight, Javed discovered his was a marriage by numbers.

His thoughts turned to Heera pickled in time, and of her soft arms and bubbly optimism. He had heard she had married an Englishman. His lip curled. What did an Englishman know of love, of its obsessive sweep, rain-drenched passion, mystic couplets of yearning divided by immeasurable distance? Of the glance like a sweetly poisoned arrow and the tender curve of lips, of the dusky, honeyed surrender of being and soul, of the tortured wait for an answering echo of devotion? What ardour could an Englishman produce in that miserable weather, when the rain and the cold could only dampen the blood to congeal into colourlessness? He tried to recall the poems he had written to her more than two decades ago, but remembered nothing. He wondered if a fragment was what his life was, she the other; together were they meant to be whole, for what had driven her to an Englishman, revenge or indifference?

She had haunted him. She could not be happy with an elegiac Englishman.

He looked at the slip of paper on which Heera's disapproving cousin had reluctantly written the telephone number and address of the charity shop. He was driven by dread; would she be as he remembered? A man needed a dream, a passion to live and die for, or what was life worth? He had made a mistake once in relinquishing her love. Far worse to yearn and ache, never knowing, than to try to make it happen and fail; far better to reach for the dream than pluck air.

Despite his roguish looks, Javed was in torment as he glanced in the mirror at his dyed black hair, the tiny wobbles of flesh fanning his cheeks and the portly frame. He was forty-nine, and dissipated. The doctor had warned him about his cholesterol. He took three tablets twice a day and had to remember the large white pill was to be taken first, before the smaller two. His lips twisted ruefully. Romance had to be more than a weak-hearted, pill-popping middle-aged man, who couldn't chase a bus any more, asking a lost love if she had ever thought of him again. Then the image of the jeering crowds and the camel arose before him, and he was filled with new resolve. The camel had not moved then, but today he would move mountains with his hope. He would go to Mill Road to see Heera.

The telephone rang. 'Sir Puzzle', who had been standing near the till, jumped like an electrocuted cat. Every Tuesday and Thursday the elderly man wandered into the shop, lifted his cap with gallantry to greet the women and request new jigsaw puzzles. The harder the

51

better, he pleaded with a twinkle in his eye, preferably with a piece missing.

'Good morning, IndiaNeed,' said Heera. 'Heera here . . . *Heera* . . . The wheelchair? For the Arthur Rank Hospice? Yes, I'll keep it ready for collection this afternoon . . . Yes, I'll remember what you said earlier . . . No, it won't happen again, Mrs Wellington-Smythe . . . Goodbye.'

Heera returned to the Staff Area and brought out a wheelchair from behind the curtain to park near the till. She noticed a video cassette lying on one of the smaller sorting tables.

'My little nephew loves *Thomas the Tank Engine*,' she confided amiably, 'but I'd better check the tape first. Those Korean girls sold *Snow White and the Seven Dwarfs*, and that *eediot* customer complained after a whole week that it was an adult video. She bought it for her toddler's birthday party, she says, and the children saw some hot Russian babe called Nikita with seven LittleJohns. What does she expect? This is not Block-buster. But she kept the video a whole week, so how many "children" watched the Russian babe Nikita "by mistake" is what I'd like to know. *Arre*, I also found a video once, and it was called *Birds in the Bush*. So I nicked it from the shop for a day, and it really was about some rare Australian birds, but I didn't com-plain,' divulged Heera with a chuckle. 'Anyway, girls, sad news. Meera Patel's husband died last week. Massive heart attack. He was watching *Jerry Springer*. Don't tell anyone, all right? Meera told me she's telling everyone he was watching *Newsnight*.'

Looking shocked, Swarnakumari moved to a table to arrange children's books. 'Poor Meera,' she murmured sadly. 'Who will colour her hair for her now? Terrible, *na*.'

Discovering a second pair of trousers and a tweed cap in another black bag, Heera continued, 'Her sister Madhuri was mixed up in some dispute with her English neighbour fifteen years ago. There was a common blocked pipe, and they wouldn't decide who was going to pay for the repairs. Anyway, things got really bad between them and the neighbour called Madhuri a "black bitch" in front of her in-laws from Surat — can you imagine, during the Diwali days, that too! And then Madhuri said that during the night this *angrez* woman's dog had done a wee over her rangoli pattern on the ground near the garage. She said it must be on purpose, naturally, because English dogs are so well-trained, they never do their business just anywhere, so how else can it happen? But of course, who knows the truth? The English neighbour may not have been to blame, but anyway, one thing is clear. I would not like to be called a "black bitch", either,' concluded Heera firmly.

'Nor "fast colour",' added Durga, enjoying Eileen's puzzlement.

There was a twist to the story: Madhuri had garnered her children's support during Diwali to enthusiastically etch traditional Diwali rangoli patterns using white powder on the path near the garage. The English neighbour's elderly father was visiting that year, and took an evening walk with his terrier in the fading light. The moon was already visible among the bare branches of the tree-lined street as he noticed what appeared to be a ghostly white Nazi swastika shining on the ground. A war veteran, he returned unsteadily to his daughter's home, incoherent and disoriented. Convalescing on his bed, he pointed wordlessly with a trembling finger in the direction of the window. Later that night there was a sharp passing shower, and the rangoli patterns were washed away, leaving the ground dry by the morning. The rest was history.

'Look, girls, how is it that all the manky trousers and tweed caps in England land up at Lady Di's posh shop only? The more she wants to impress her friends, the more rubbish we get. Funny smell in here.' Heera sniffed. 'Smells like cat pooh.' She thrust her hand into the bag. 'It *is* cat pooh!'

Swarnakumari wailed. Heera dragged the offending bag away and commanded, 'Give me your soap dispenser, Swarna!'

Swarnakumari removed it with reluctance from her handbag. 'I will also go and wash my hands,' she said. 'Dirty, dirty shop. Much better for me to go and help in the old people's ward at Addenbrooke's Hospital. When I see those poor helpless people I tell myself, I am not staying in Cambridge when I am old, but Your Uncle has got so used to life here, he likes this English law and order. Just the other day he showed me the Cambridgeshire County Council blue library van. It had stopped outside old people's flats so that elderly people could climb into the van to borrow books. Your Uncle told me so proudly, "See, Swarna, this is why I like this country. I can see where my tax money is going." No, Your Uncle will not leave England.'

At the precise moment when Heera marched towards the telephone to do battle with her employer, 'Your Uncle' folded away his newspaper. Two hours earlier, Mr

Chatterjee had embarked upon his daily trek to the newsagent next to the Methodist Church, bought his Bengali newspaper and savoured the headlines. As he walked away from the till, he sneaked a ritual glance at the covers of the girlie magazines that Mr Patel, a family man, placed on the highest shelf and always upside down.

Peering sideways, Mr Chatterjee wondered about Newton's law of gravitation and whether the falling apple could ever have remained suspended in mid-air.

CHAPTER FOUR

All cats are grey in the dark

MR CHATTERJEE TWITCHED the net curtains at the bay window of his semi-detached home and peered outside. It was 8.13 a.m., and as always, Mondays to Fridays, the woman emerged, wheeling her bicycle out of her doorway. A freckled toddler sat stoically on the child seat, and the woman bent over the strap, displaying exposed breasts to an expectant Mr Chatterjee. With a flash of black fishnet tights and the twirl of her skirt, she was gone.

Every weekday morning, the sight of the woman was as wholesome as a portion of tropical fruit in a breakfast of toast, juice and tea. Growing up as a boy in Calcutta, as the city of Kolkata was then known, he had been accustomed to the British legacy of thick white bread, and as a creature of unswerving habit he rejected new-fangled wholemeal, wheatgerm, organic, rye, poppy seed and barleyseed varieties. The white slice emerged every morning, lightly browned from the toaster. The popping sound soothed his waiting ears, and, thick and respectable, the bread stared up at him from the white and green patterned Johnson Brothers plate, waiting for the corners and edges to be carefully buttered. Thin-cut marmalade came next, followed by a single slice of mild Cheddar cheese and his cup of Earl Grey; not for him the nostalgia-inducing vapours of ginger tea laced with cardamom.

Mr Chatterjee was a man of method, and order his only god and guru, although he dutifully accompanied Swarnakumari once a year to the Bengali community's Durga Puja celebrations in London. Mr Chatterjee surveyed his household with pride; everything was in its place, and all the clocks obeyed the same master, as did the weeds.

He had perfected a daily regime that started with the head, not the heart. Every Saturday he vigorously massaged coconut oil into his receding hairline. The oil seeped into every corner of his being, soothing away self-doubt and dandruff. It coated every thirsty, curious hair until it lay down satiated and limp. Yoga face massage followed, as he slowly pinched his sallow forehead, cheeks and nose to nervous life.

On Thursdays he walked from his neat front lawn to the Rock Road Library, reading the newspapers there for hours. Mr Chatterjee followed British politics closely, and was informed, if conservative in his views. On Wednesdays he strolled to the city centre and spent the afternoon at Heffers, Waterstone's and Borders, often browsing through the old books outside the Fisher Hall. Once a month he accompanied Swarnakumari to the Sainsbury's at the Coldhams Lane roundabout, and every Tuesday he drove her in their white Vauxhall to the local Tesco at Fulbourn. The trolley always carried the same brand of soap, detergent, juice, cornflakes and honey.

On Mondays he wrote letters of complaint to the

local authorities and sent readers' views to the newspapers. He always wrote each note in a neat, rounded hand with a blue Parker fountain pen. *Respected Sir/ Madam*, he would begin, drawing attention to the overflowing bin in the park, the litter left by school-children walking on Queen Edith's Way and the pupils smoking in the quiet lanes.

He wrote to the heads of various schools, accusing them of moral turpitude. In his view, despite their school uniform, their female pupils looked like young women of dubious character. He listed a number of suggestions: skirt lengths well below the knee, stockings thick and opaque, shoes flat and sensible and the hair neatly tied back with school ribbon. No cosmetics or jewellery, nor smoking in uniform or 'mingling' between boys and girls outside the school gates.

Overhanging boughs on Trumpington Road were a danger to cyclists and walkers, he wrote to the City Council, and the bus service down Queen Edith's Way was disappointingly irregular.

Peering through the net curtains, he hurried to the door. Habituated to Mr Chatterjee's simmering excitement, the postman ceremoniously handed him the post on an imaginary silver salver. The sight of the buff envelopes filled Mr Chatterjee with nervous suspense; he opened each letter with care. Those from the Inland Revenue were sharp and advisory, others from the credit-card companies and retail outlets relentlessly unforgiving. It was the latest stern summons from the DVLA local office for repeated road offences that captured his attention. He penned an immediate response:

12 Newton Square
Cambridge

Respected Sir/Madam,
I have received an envelope containing Summons Section 29 – Unlicensed Keeping – requesting the defendant to appear at 10.00 hours on 25th November at the Magistrates' Court to answer the information that on 23rd August at the A14, a mechanically propelled motor vehicle was kept on a public road for which a licence was not in force, contrary to Section 29 (1) of the Vehicle Excise and Registration Act 1994.

I have noted there is an accompanying document, which outlines the full nature of the offence concerning the expiration of driving licence and continued driving of the vehicle without displaying trade licence plates. I have noted that despite being told the offence would be reported, the offender made no attempt to respond. This indifference is not surprising. It comes from the man Langley Tonner, who repeatedly uses this address for reasons I cannot fathom. He has never resided in this house, of which I have been the owner for the past three decades, and he is completely unknown to my family and myself. I do not know why he continues to evade the long hand of justice and the law in this manner, causing such inconvenience and harassment to my family and myself. I receive Inland Revenue tax bills and summons to bailiffs' courts at this address on a regular basis because of this man.

I have repeatedly contacted Royal Mail, urging them not to deliver mail to him at this address, but have been informed that it is not possible to take any action in the matter. Apparently, a letter with an address and stamp must be delivered. I urge you to find the offender without delay and prevent him from using this address henceforth.

Yours faithfully,
Shyamal Chatterjee

Despite his failure to convince the DVLA and other authorities of the misdeeds of the elusive Langley Tonner, Mr Chatterjee had engineered a more recent coup of which he was proud. New kitchen units had been ordered from a leading local DIY firm; they were delivered with five items missing, including the new sink tap. Incensed, Mr Chatterjee telephoned the company.

The girl at the other end loved her vowels less than her nail extensions, but he understood that Customer Services could do nothing, for Customer Services was not the same as Sales, and Sales Orders were at a Norwich number. After listening to Vivaldi's *Primavera* four times, he was transferred to a queue with Westlife easing the pain. Sales had little contact with the factory near Basingstoke that delivered the items, and the factory recommended he try Customer Services instead.

Mr. Chatterjee wrote an irate letter to the company director, sealed the envelope and carried it to the post office, where the friendly woman recommended 'recorded delivery'. His further purchase of a weekly stamp booklet was a secret indulgence, producing the excitement generated in lesser beings by a lottery ticket.

Seventy-two hours later, the missing units had arrived safely, although Customer Services had been unable to specify a time of delivery.

Mr Chatterjee took the new items of unsolicited mail to his garage with an air of quiet achievement. Tying a fresh bundle, he placed it on the existing stack. It was thirty inches high and consisted of five hundred and seventy-one letters and leaflets and brochures, weighing sixty ounces. Ever since he had heard of a retired gentleman whose photograph had appeared in the *Daily Mail* displaying seventy ounces of junk mail, Mr Chatterjee had been determined to compete, ambitiously setting his sights on a two-year record. Swarnakumari never visited the garage, and it was yet another of her husband's secrets of which she was unaware.

Having completed the important business at hand, Mr Chatterjee turned to the *Victoria's Secret* catalogue that arrived with regularity in the post, requested by the rascally Langley Tonner at Mr Chatterjee's address. He stared at the bold eyes of the models on the pages, their flirty posture as they slung their fingers casually over a bare hip or a bikini strap, bronzed bodies sheathed in tiny garments of lace and crochet. He felt unease tinged with self-disgust meeting the gaze of the young girl with the golden beach skin. She looked fourteen.

Shortly after his retirement, Mr Chatterjee had begun to surf the Internet. Reluctantly discontinuing his subscription to the *National Geographic*, he now attempted to find material online on the tigers of the Sundarbans. His search for 'wild animals' led him directly to a website of girls clad in faux fur bikinis. Surprised but not unappreciative, Mr Chatterjee decided on further explorations with a click. He was confronted next by a *Teen Lusties* live video with free sound and chat, no credit card, no hidden charges, and was to regret his mistake once he was flooded with regular offers on *Beach Babes* and *Barely Legal Sluts* along with guaranteed breast and penile enhancements. Puzzled over his automatic transfer to an *Asian Babes* Home Page, he was annnoyed that his ethnic origins had become public knowledge on the Internet. The pneumatic images of a girl called 'Shonali' were particularly disturbing; the name sounded Bengali, and he wondered why an Indian girl would bring such shame upon her community. Disgusted, he resumed his search for a heater for Swarnakumari's conservatory, which, in turn, led to a flood of intriguing adult inducements ensuing from the word 'heat'.

World news occupied centre stage several times a day; he listened to the radio and watched television until the headlines were as familiar as a shloka or mantra. He hastened to share the information with Banerjee, who made clucking noises of disbelief, shaking his head at the evil in the world that had so narrowly missed Cambridge and the Banerjee and Chatterjee households. Together, they mourned the old days, each tragedy serving to highlight and underline their present wise life choices. Banerjee began listening to the news himself on his new digital radio, ahead by two additional bulletins while his friend took a nap. He was thus able to refer to items in the afternoon bulletin of which Mr Chatterjee was as yet unaware.

Mr Chatterjee took his constitutional twice a day; the benefits of regular exercise were balanced by the opportunity it provided as the Neighbourhood Watch Co-ordinator to observe his neighbours, their homes and their habits without embarrassment. Mr Chatterjee firmly believed that a Bengali man's home was his castle, and he its commanding military officer. Mondays to Fridays, Swarnakumari served him macher jhol, corchori, posto, sukhto, macher tok, mutton kosa, begun baja, chingri macher malai curry, amer chutney, dal, chapattis and rice. On Friday evenings, he had a gin and tonic.

On Monday evenings he and Swarnakumari visited the Banerjees on Nightingale Avenue for a game of bridge. He drank malt with Gaurab Banerjee, who had made the mistake of nominating his wife the commanding military officer of his castle. A fiery woman with a stentorian voice, Mrs Banerjee always glared menacingly at her husband as he poured a second whisky and announced, 'That is enough.' At this, Banerjee would subside without protest into his leather sofa. Mr Chatterjee, who never had a second glass, watched the public humiliation of his friend with disapproval; a woman should know her place, and if she did not – well, it was up to the man to firmly escort her there.

Gaurab Banerjee's daughter Madhumita had married an Albanian classmate at Columbia University and now lived in San Ramon, California. That was like losing your daughter forever, thought Mr Chatterjee sadly; how often in a lifetime would and could the Banerjees meet Madhumita in San Ramon without the Albanian son-in-law in tow? At least, ventured Banerjee in hesitant defence, Heinz would learn Bengali. Madhumita had promised. Their children would have a fair complexion, he added.

The Albanian son-in-law from Tirana went by the name of Gjynejt. His parents called him 'Gjelosh', while his friends called him 'Haxhi'. Madhumita called him 'Ferrok'. Banerjee was bewildered. As Gjynejt-Gjelosh-Haxhi-Ferrok was addicted to ketchup, he had been nicknamed 'Heinz' by his American classmates. Banerjee was relieved. Heinz was a German or Austrian name; it could even be Swiss. It sounded respectably Western and European. San Ramon was full of Indians,

63

added Banerjee; there were plenty of temples and Indian restaurants all over California. The latest craze was for Chinese-Indian food, he said – spicy Chinese food with a touch of Punjabi. Mr Chatterjee shuddered.

Shyamal Chatterjee had always been of a serious bent of mind. As a boy, he had preferred books to the company of other children and adults; as a teenager, he profited from the hours spent at Durga Puja, Shivratri and Saraswati Puja learning logarithms instead of flirtations with his doe-eyed cousins. Like several young men of his time, he was sent to London to study law, a subject for which he had no interest but much aptitude. He spent his years and money wisely as a lodger with his landlady Rosie on Tottenham Court Road and complained about the biting winters before returning home carrying both the china teapot for his mother and his virginity intact.

Swarnakumari Mukhopadhyay had lived a sheltered and exemplary life in Calcutta as the youngest of four children. The family doctor had been convinced it would be a boy; her father concealed his disappointment over a fourth daughter, and Swarnakumari rewarded him with sweet renditions of 'Rabindra Sangeet' in gratitude. A product of Brahmo Girls School, she was shy and reticent; her sisters Devika, Menaka and Madhulika were the fiery rebels who married wealthy landowners and heirs to tea plantations. Swarnakumari liked needlework.

Her father consulted the senior Chatterjee in all his legal affairs and for advice in a wrangle over the eviction of tenants. Barely home from London, Shyamal Chatterjee was despatched with papers to the rambling Mukhopadhyay mansion. Swarnakumari's father was impressed by the manners of the earnest, neatly dressed young man who refused to share a glass with his host. Work and drink never mixed, he asserted firmly, also politely declining the sweets brought to him on a silver salver by Swarnakumari. Padding gracefully across the room, she sent him a shy glance, one that he intercepted and took back with the dusty legal files he carried that evening. Swarnakumari's father needed no further persuasion; Shyamal Chatterjee's honesty and humility would be suitably rewarded.

If Swarnakumari found Mr Chatterjee dull, she would have been incapable of expressing those sentiments as she settled into life in England. They moved to Cambridge, where he commenced employment with a reputed solicitor's firm. He was always sensible, never spontaneous but always reliable, and Swarnakumari had few complaints after the renovation of the kitchen with its stainless steel double sink, the building of the conservatory and the landscaping of the garden. Swarnakumari had nevertheless received the news of her husband's retirement with alarm and discovered her spiritual guide and mentor Guru Ma at the moment when Mr Chatterjee discovered mould in the bathroom. For Swarnakumari, Guru Ma was the equivalent of headphones.

Swarnakumari firmly believed that a prayer recited with increasing frequency became a living truth. Guru Ma's little book of homilies for daily happiness was a clarion call to right action and non-action, resistance and endurance. Truth stood naked, but physical intimacy was no longer an option for Mr Chatterjee; his wife's permission and participation had been withdrawn years earlier. Swarnakumari had taken a private

65

decision under the influence of cloudy sandalwood incense and pious prayer; he sensed a steely resolve in her that would not be easily challenged. Battling her resistance silently, he was annoyed that he had not been consulted on a matter of such importance. He could not be certain, but he suspected that Banerjee was in a similar situation of choicelessness. Women had their secrets, their eccentricities and unfathomable rituals, Banerjee had once intimated with an air of such resignation that Mr Chatterjee had clung gratefully to his words as evidence that he was not alone.

Swarnakumari had been an exemplary wife and mother, he thought; she had been content to settle in England, displaying a quiet support of his every suggestion. Conscious of her sheltered upbringing, Mr Chatterjee had ensured her protection from the evil influences of British society, endorsing her reluctance to venture out of the home.

Her desire to work in the charity shop was applauded by him as a noble, altruistic effort. The impulse purchases were another matter; he was somewhat unhappy with her gift of a grey Marks & Spencer cardigan from the charity shop. Englishmen appeared to be of an entirely different build, even if the size was S. It was difficult to ascertain whether it was the shoulders or the chest or the sleeves that were the problem, for no full-length mirrors were to be found in the Chatterjee household, a move initiated by Swarnakumari after she had read Guru Ma's homily on vanity. A mirror reflection, decided Swarnakumari, was merely an illusion, not reality.

They did not need any more bone china cups, saucers, plates and bowls, egg slicers, rattan magazine racks, vases, recycled pencils or lampshades from the shop, thought Mr Chatterjee. The small television set she acquired for the bedroom had, however, been useful, and after Swarnakumari fell asleep he turned down the volume and watched until late into the night. His dreams were lurid, and, feeling revulsion and distaste, he wrote letters of complaint to the television watchdog protesting against explicit programme content.

Swarnakumari was garrulous every Thursday evening as she recounted the day's events, described the customers and the arrival of new items. Mrs Wellington-Smythe was a fine, aristocratic woman, with a strong sense of authority and command, decided Mr Chatterjee. He mentioned her name several times in conversation on his walks with Banerjee, who in turn narrated Heinz's stories of barbecues in the San Ramon backyard and a trip with Madhumita to Yellowstone National Park in their black BMW five series car. Banerjee had somehow formed the impression that Swarnakumari and Mrs Wellington-Smythe were good friends.

Mr Chatterjee had noticed an increasing yearning in Swarnakumari for India, for Kolkata and for her relatives, but he deliberately refrained from comment. He was of the view that the past should remain the past. There was no future in the past, and as for the tense, it was present perfect. At an early age, Mr Chatterjee had learned the wisdom of the haiku he had read: *When sitting sit/When standing stand/Above all, don't wobble.*

Mr Chatterjee never wobbled, although the breasts of the woman in No. 32 opposite the quiet square did. He had noticed them and their owner from the moment she had moved into the house with the blue door on 24 June 1997. She lived alone with two cats that were entirely house-trained and remained indoors. Two days after her arrival at Newton Square one of the cats had leaped out of the window and was seen wandering disoriented and distraught over the lawn like a blindfolded inmate released at midnight from a high-security prison. By a happy coincidence, Mr Chatterjee was tweaking the net curtains at the time. Despite a strong aversion to cats, he gallantly gave chase. Rachel Chesterton explained that she had lived in a London flat and was obliged to relocate after her divorce. She expressed her gratitude with an offer of tea, patting his arm gently with rose-pink nails to propel him into her kitchen. He had stared in wonder at the wooden flooring, the cosy bright curtains and the cheerful furniture of an IKEA world.

Rachel was lonely; she had recovered from skin cancer three years ago, but it was her divorce that was her undoing. Her chronic alcoholism led to a court decision awarding custody of the child to the father. She found Cambridge provincial and dull, as dull as her little Indian neighbour, who looked at her with inscrutable eyes and transparent thoughts. Conscious of the proprieties, he had declined further offers of tea, choosing instead to chat on the street. If he passed her in the company of Banerjee, he merely nodded briskly from afar.

On his Neighbourhood Watch rounds one winter's evening he saw a twisted bicycle abandoned near Rachel's house. He knocked on her door, noticed it was unlatched and waited. He knocked and rang again before gingerly calling out her name. He found her crying on a sofa in the living room, wearing only a dressing-gown, an empty bottle of vodka by her side.

Between sobs she told him that her ex-husband had moved the courts to prevent her visits to her child on the grounds that they were disruptive.

Absorbing the impact of her words, Mr Chatterjee found the sight of her gown open to the waist even more disturbing, as she leaned across and rested her head on his shoulder. He patted her reassuringly, but suddenly felt warm, naked skin instead, as the gown fell away. She began to kiss him with urgent, desperate passion. Then a furry living snowball scratched his arm and landed with lightning speed on Rachel's bosom. The sight of her ballooning breasts swinging under the weight of a clinging cat clawing them in jealousy was one that Mr Chatterjee never managed to erase. He fled, remembering to shut the front door firmly behind him, and on reaching home rang the local police station about the twisted bicycle. He was a good Neighbourhood Watch Co-ordinator.

Rachel Chesterton had moved home shortly after the incident, carrying no recollection of her last encounter with Mr Chatterjee, a detail sadly unknown to him. For years thereafter, Mr Chatterjee had suppressed a thought couched in rhyme that gnawed at his insides: what would he have done, with the dress undone, had the cat not won? Searching for the answer, he drove solitary in the silent winter dusk down Lime Kiln Road to gaze at the city of spires below. The branches of the bare trees were wagging, censorious fingers in the sky and the frost on his neat patio garden was the ice in his heart.

Over the years, Mr Chatterjee slowly convinced himself that he was not to blame, that her breasts were, in fact, thorny, wrinkled pineapples that should have

69

stayed on the stem, and that encounters of this nature were as much an occupational hazard for a Neighbourhood Watch Co-ordinator as for the engineer called out to inspect a gas leak.

Mr Chatterjee had recorded a private image of English life in the neighbourhood with his customary powers of observation; the women who gave their husbands a peck on the cheek before the car backed out of the driveway; those who never came out; the men who regularly cut the lawn and washed the cars and trimmed the hedges; the women who put out winter pansies in garden centre terracotta containers and planted aconite, snowdrops, anemones, grape hyacinth, tulips and daffodils along the path to the front door; the children who greeted the neighbours and those who stayed up late; those who had cats and those who had dogs; those who left Dairy Crest milk bottles outside their door and those who were disabled; those who left the black bins out too long and those who took them in early; those who recycled and those who did not; those who swept up the autumn leaves and weeded the flowerbeds; those who read the broadsheets and those who read the tabloids; those who bought DIY furniture and those who entertained; those who had attic conversions and those who had conservatories – and those who led happy lives.

Mr Chatterjee believed that the years devoted to the study of law and human nature had sharpened his faculties, and it was thus evident to him that Mary and David were a cultured elderly couple and ideal neighbours for the adjoining side of his semi-detached house. Even the dull, muffled sound on the stairs stopped after some years; David moved downstairs once he contracted Parkinson's disease. Mary was devoted and uncomplaining; she wheeled him out into the sun, a blanket over his knees, to cheerfully water the petunias. She began to suffer from migraine, a condition that made it difficult to tend to an ailing husband. Their two sons, who lived locally, made infrequent visits. Mr Chatterjee pursed his lips at their lack of filial devotion, while Swarnakumari wordlessly added Mary's Tesco and Sainsbury's shopping lists to her own. Soon David no longer left the house, and the sons no longer visited.

Returning from an afternoon in the Central Library, Mr Chatterjee was met by an excited Banerjee outside the lane. The neighbour, David, was dead. That was not all, said Banerjee, falling into step with Mr Chatterjee as he began to walk towards his home; it was murder.

Mr Chatterjee paused. *Murder*. The word reverberated in his head, growing louder until it was a horn blasting over the treetops and chimneys in the quiet square, flew over the Cherry Hinton Park, past the swans and over the railway and onto the speeding track, returning over the fields of Grantchester and along the ripples of the River Cam to the police car parked outside the house on Newton Square.

Arriving at his home, he noticed that an over-zealous police officer had extended the cordon to include the Chatterjee entrance, erroneously giving the impression of multiple crimes. Mr Chatterjee stared up at the house next door in disbelief as Banerjee narrated the succession of events. He felt betrayed. Had he not been reading the pages of the *Telegraph* at the library, he would have been at home; *he*, as Neighbourhood Watch Co-ordinator, would have been the one the police would have approached for assistance.

71

Perhaps it was still not too late. Striding up to the officer in the police car, he introduced himself, declaring himself ready for a lengthy interview on the neighbourhood and its inhabitants, but the officer merely had instructions to stay outside the house for a further hour. He knew nothing other than that there had been a murder, that the elderly lady had been taken away and that she was unharmed.

Mr Chatterjee walked up past the front lawn to his home along with Banerjee. Swarnakumari had little to add; she had been praying in her room, unaware of the commotion outside, and Mallika was away in London for the day. Mr Chatterjee sat still and small on his favourite leather armchair. He was afraid, and wondered whether he should write a note to the neighbours, but lacked the words. The motive for murder had to be burglary; the cold-blooded assassin had evidently noticed a helpless invalid and an elderly lady who stayed indoors and rarely received visitors. The man would have stood behind the privet hedge to observe the house at close quarters; indeed, he was lurking in the neighbourhood, waiting to strike again, and this time the target could be the Chatterjee household.

The presence of the police car was initially reassuring, but the officer drove off an hour later. Mr Chatterjee bolted every door and window in his house, placing chairs and tables and heavy objects against every exit. He wondered whether he should leave the lights on, but the electricity bill during Durga Puja and Diwali had been high, and prudence prevailed.

Long after Swarnakumari was asleep, Mr Chatterjee continued to sit upright in his bed, a torch and the cordless phone at his side, the cord from his pyjamas

72

dangling nervously as he trembled. He felt the warmth from Swarnakumari's soft folds touching his thigh. How peacefully she slept! The last words she uttered before she closed her eyes were that God and Guru Ma had taught her to fear nothing. He marvelled at his wife's composure; she squealed at the sight of a cockroach, but could be as steady as a lighthouse in a storm. Her faith in her mentor had been an irritant until this moment; perhaps it was time to test her Guru Ma's wisdom.

He leaned over and felt his way to the prayer book that he knew lay on her bedside table. Shining his torch low, he stared at the first page. Under the picture of a woman with streaming black hair was the blueprint for a spiritual life. He read Tagore's words from *Gitanjali*, and, inspired, decided he, too, would make his life simple and straight like a flute made of reed for the Divine One to fill with music.

Mr Chatterjee continued to read with increasing respect, discovering the philosophy of life that his wife attempted to adopt; it included purity of action and heart, compassion for those less fortunate, and a homily on health. The consumption of vegetables and fruit such as apple, pear, pineapple and melon was advocated to reduce the *tamasik* destructive forces in the body. Mr Chatterjee grimaced as he read the word 'pineapple'. He put away the torch, as worried about the life of the battery as his own, and lay next to Swarnakumari, inhaling her healing softness again. He extended a hesitant arm, his body cupping her back. Then he remembered; he had forgotten to find out what Guru Ma had to say about sex. As he groped in the dark for the light switch, there was a sudden thud and a crash. Mr

Chatterjee leaped out of bed in alarm, forgetting his arthritic knee, reached for the telephone and shakily called the police. A moment later he heard his daughter's incredulous voice calling. Mr Chatterjee had forgotten about Mallika's return that evening.

The police car he had summoned to his house woke the neighbourhood; those who had cats and those who had dogs; those who were elderly and those who were young; those who went to work and those who did not. The same officer emerged from his car. The Neighbourhood Watch Co-ordinator had been shamed.

Sitting upright on his leather sofa the next day, Mr Chatterjee answered the policewoman's questions about his neighbours Mary and David. When had he last seen David and Mary? How had Mary seemed to him? Had he ever overheard any disagreement between the couple? Did he know the nature of David's medication?

Prefacing his every reply with the words, 'As the Neighbourhood Watch Co-ordinator . . .' Mr Chatterjee proceeded to display his powers of observation and his legal competence to the young WPC. He inquired whether he should send a letter to the neighbourhood about the burglary. She raised her eyebrows. 'This was no burglary, it's fairly straightforward.'

Mr Chatterjee was perplexed; he decided to write a letter on the following Monday to Cambridgeshire Police on the public's right to know. A day later he had the distinction as the Neighbourhood Watch Co-ordinator of hearing the news first. Mary had killed David. She had poisoned him and confessed, ringing the police herself. She was in a low-security prison, and her lawyers felt that a reduced sentence could be

74

obtained on account of the blinding headaches she had been suffering and for which she had received no medication.

Mr Chatterjee was appalled. Calculating the time of death, he realised that David had been murdered a few feet away from him at the very moment he was watching an adult film on the 'Mute' button. The body had lain in rigor mortis until the morning. It was said that Mary was clearly not in her right mind. She had told the police that she drew back the curtains to let in the sun, and brought David his morning cup of tea, placing the tray by his bedside. She had drunk her own before ringing the police to say that David did not want any more.

That evening Mr. Chatterjee felt nauseous and, for the first time since he could remember, was unable to eat Swarnakumari's macher jhol, dal and rice. He looked at his wife's plump form without comfort, and a dry fear invaded his being of ageing, waning life force, sense and faculty slipping away invisibly like the dew with the first warm rays of the sun, of burden and loss. It had been easy to be young, and it might be difficult to be old. The unformed questions hovered, taking voluminous shape as he looked at Swarnakumari's placid face. What were her unfathomable depths? Could she one day take on the aspect of Kali in a mood of vengeance, slashing his world with a word, a swoop, a sword? Could she dismember him in his sleep? He imagined the sheets covered in blood, his blood; afterwards, she would lovingly apply bandages to his body to stem the thickening flow.

He considered the large chopping knife lying in the kitchen drawer. Mrs Banerjee, after all, had been given to menopausal moods and had thrown objects in threatening rage, her large kohl-lined eyes flashing. Banerjee had told him so. It had happened almost fifteen years ago, he had added reassuringly, but Mr Chatterjee remained discomfited. Banerjee said he had simply stepped out of the way as an object whizzed past, and retirement had brought its own prudence; she would never hurl glass again. Men who had already lost their hair lost the last shreds of dignity at this age, mourned Banerjee. It was best to let women have their way; the alternatives were too dangerous, he joked seriously. His cousin Bikash's wife had trashed an entire collection of Matchbox Dinky cars painstakingly acquired by Bikash over thirty years. They would have been worth a small fortune, his son-in-law Heinz had lamented. Afraid he had revealed too much, Banerjee hurriedly changed the subject to the lack of kidney donors among South Asians in Britain.

Mr Chatterjee listened to Banerjee without his customary attentiveness. He was still deeply affected by the deaths of his neighbours, for Mary had died of natural causes in prison two weeks later. He could no longer be certain of his judgement, nor of his observations of human nature, but of one thing he was convinced: devotion came in several forms.

A year later, Mr Chatterjee was still deeply affected – by his new neighbours. Prior to Mary's funeral, there had been a flurry of activity from the two sons, who arrived in two matching self-drive vans and dismantled the home, piling the furniture and other items in the front garden as if for an auction. Peering through the net curtains, Mr Chatterjee witnessed the efficiency that

76

could be produced by the equal distribution of blue and red sticky labels.

A *For Sale* sign had been stuck by a careless estate agent in the hedge on Mr Chatterjee's side of the house while he sank unsuspecting into his favourite armchair with his Bengali newspaper. The doorbell rang, a young couple brushed briskly past Swarnakumari, and Mr Chatterjee glanced up from the riveting results of the Mohan Bagan football game to find himself in the midst of an unorthodox inspection of his living room brick by brick, wall by wall. The woman even leaned over to examine a small discolouration in the paint on the wall directly behind his head. She wrote on a pad, noting the paint and the woodwork in a professional manner and stared disparagingly at the ceiling; the couple then proceeded through the conservatory and into the garden.

Mr Chatterjee followed, bewildered. The woman turned her gaze from the rock garden, the tinkling water fountain and goldfish to observe sternly that it would not do, it was not suitable as a play area for a young child. Mr Chatterjee meekly agreed, but demurred when she suggested the water fountain and goldfish be removed, and the rock garden covered. The couple returned to the hallway, sniffing appreciatively, their noses following the smells as they peeped into the kitchen and nodded at Swarnakumari with her floury hands.

'Can we go upstairs?' asked the man.

Tearing his gaze from the man's muddy boots poised on the first stair, Mr Chatterjee finally found his voice. 'Why?' he asked.

Three months later, as Mr Chatterjee was writing a

letter to the City Council about dog fouling at the lamp-post at the corner of Fendon Road, a large removal van drew up, followed by a car. Mr Chatterjee's curtains twitched. His new neighbours had arrived.

Mr Chatterjee heard the sound of laughter as he drank the tea that Swarnakumari had prepared for him that Thursday morning. It was that boy again, he thought angrily. That boy and Mallika together. He peered through the net curtains. They were outside his front gate.

The new family had bought a house where a life had been snuffed out, where memories swirled and fires of devotion still burned, and although he had refrained from comment he agreed with Swarnakumari that the new occupants should have performed a little ritual of prayer for the gentle departed souls of David and Mary, who might still want to linger. Perhaps even at this moment, their spirits were straying, seeking refuge in the Chatterjee side of the house, tinkling the Japanese wind chimes, swaying the curtains and dimming the lights.

The African family had spelled mystery. What business could possibly have brought the three of them all the way from Australia to Cambridge? wondered Mr Chatterjee. The talk of the Science Park and the Napp Laboratories was nonsense. What did the African man really do for a living?

Applying the strategies of deduction he had developed over the years, Mr Chatterjee concluded that, as his neighbour appeared to have unlimited funds for renovation of the house, there was an unambiguous trail of involvement in the illegal export of ivory. He knew that Portobello Road in London was awash with ivory of indeterminate age. Under British law, ivory had to be older than 1947 to be sold. The man had escaped to Australia from Nigeria, but when he found the police were on his heels he moved his family to the modest semi in Cambridge to provide a cover for his clandestine activities until he was exposed, for capture meant a maximum sentence of seven years of imprisonment. Mr Chatterjee was so convinced of the truth of his own speculation that he instructed Swarnakumari and Mallika to avoid contact with the family. Invited by his neighbours for an evening drink on a number of occasions, he had politely declined, recommending to Swarnakumari that she, too, find a suitable excuse. No member of the Chatterjee household was to be implicated in the trafficking of tusks.

Loud music, parties, overnight guests, carelessly parked cars, the slamming of doors and conversations in operatic tones next door obliged Mr Chatterjee to resort to longer daytime naps, and he spent waking moments in a state of roadside recovery, his wellbeing severely tested and threatened. He envied Swarnakumari her ability to sleep soundly.

Compounding his worries was the adverse impact he feared his new neighbours would have on the value of his property. He arranged a free annual valuation by a different Cambridge estate agent to proudly remind Swarnakumari of the wisdom of a profitable investment. He would have erupted in prickly indignation and incomprehension at the suggestion that his own move to Newton Square thirty years ago might have been a matter of similar concern to his neighbours.

Mr Chatterjee looked at the Nigerian teenager's

loose, fluid limbs, his low-slung jeans and hooded top and the grace rippling through his feet as he twisted effortlessly on his skateboard. Joseph was dangerous, even if he was only seventeen going on eighteen, he decided. He had caught Mallika listening to something she called 'gangster rap' and 'garage', and she had turned defiant. She no longer sang 'Rabindra Sangeet'. Banerjee was saddled with an Albanian son-in-law; who could foretell the frightening fate that might befall his own household?

Mr Chatterjee studied his neat list of errands for the morning. Driving out onto Queen Edith's Way, he stopped for Banerjee, who was rubbing his hands against the cold at the corner of Nightingale Avenue. They were on their way to buy fresh fish from the Bangladeshi shop off Mill Road, to make their selection from rui mach, ilish mach, koi mach, tangra mach and chingri mach. Mr Chatterjee believed that it took a Bengali to truly discern the freshness of a catch. He was not alone in this assumption.

As they loaded the fish into the car, Banerjee suggested they visit the charity shop. Mr Chatterjee looked surprised, but Banerjee was insistent; his wife had heard about Swarnakumari's legendary bargains, especially Mr Chatterjee's splendid grey Marks & Spencer cardigan. Banerjee's own maroon Debenhams cardigan had sprung two asymmetric holes, and he had been directed by his wife to procure an immediate and inexpensive replacement.

Mr Chatterjee would not be persuaded to visit the shop, and, loath to admit his reluctance either to Banerjee or to himself, he mumbled an excuse, but to his amazement Banerjee remained firm. It was either the charity shop or a confrontation with his wife. Any man in his situation would have chosen the former without a moment's hesitation.

Mr Chatterjee had no alternative but to acquiesce. It was his first visit to IndiaNeed, and he wished he were not attired in the ill-fitting grey Marks & Spencer cardigan, which made him appear meekly round-shouldered and small. He wished he were not smelling of fish, wished he could be alone and without Banerjee at the time of his introduction to the Honourable Mrs Wellington-Smythe.

CHAPTER FIVE

Charity begins at home

DIANA WELLINGTON-SMYTHE LIVED in England and dreamed of Tuscany. Summers were spent in their grape-laden villa outside Florence with her insolent daughter Imogen, silent son James and reticent husband Rupert. The Scrabble, draughts and chess were never unpacked, and returned to England in pristine condition during the last week of August. Imogen was growing breasts and James was growing restive, but Chianti at lunch and supper restored Diana's partial tolerance of Rupert, pale and city pink in short sleeves. As tall as her husband, she was imperious in classic Armani, her blond hair, too intimidated by its owner to be curly, swinging straight down her neck. Her features struggled between boredom and equine haughtiness.

Father and son, mother and daughter strolled in silence to the village piazza in the evenings as the sun glinted on the window shutters of the white-walled houses, setting the red geraniums ablaze. They stopped for ice cream at the local gelateria overlooking a narrow cobbled street. Human nature was like gelati, the elderly man told the signora; at its best when it had more flavours than one, the mellifluous pistacchio melting into the earthy brown of cioccolato, creamy vaniglia surrendering to the spicy strawberry red of fragola. It was the only counselling Diana would ever have.

On their way back to England from Florence, the family had dallied in Rome. Diana had shopped at Via Condotti; at Missoni, she abandoned the struggle into a size ten. Imogen, with her size six hips, swinging blond hair and pout, moodily twirled an orange and red flame-twisted scarf around her neck and stared challengingly at her mother in the mirror. They made their way to the Trevi Fountain. It had been drizzling, and the steps were wet as James and Imogen watched the scurrying tourists and their squealing slide toward the fountain, slippery peas posing in a pod. Imogen's lips curved mockingly as Diana impulsively asked Rupert for a coin.

'Euro or British, darling?' he asked, reaching into his trousers as an Asian man offered him a dozen roses *'per la bella donna'*. As Diana watched, Rupert waved him away indifferently. For one brief, mad moment, there was nothing in the world she wanted other than a single red rose.

Diana had recently joined a private class of Intermediate Italian learners who shunned the courses offered by the Sixth Form Colleges of Cambridge and met in an elegant home on Grange Road instead. 'Non parlo bene l'italiano,' she began with uncharacteristic hesitation, placing the mandatory bottle of Barolo on the table in front of the teacher, an Englishwoman who had lived in Florence as an artist for many years. The man next to Diana leaned over and smiled a crinkly, warm smile of wealthy cologne. 'Ma, Signora, non è vero,' he murmured. Diana had found a man to contradict her at last. Afterwards they talked of Tuscan painters' light, and the next evening they walked along Quayside, continuing into Midsummer Common, past the cows flicking their lazy tails, along the water and past the houseboats, returning to an Italian café and its red-checked tablecloth.

'Basta così stare insieme con te,' Philip had declared soulfully. Being with her was all he wanted, staring into her grey eyes after the macchiato. Diana melted quicker than the chocolate mint the waitress had placed on the saucer. Romancing in Italian in Cambridge led her three mornings later to perch among several Chinese vases in the living room of a Newnham home as Philip poured out the tea.

'Do you take sugar?' he asked.

'Don't you think I'm sweet enough?' was her arch reply.

The tray rattled. He trembled at the fires rising. 'Non c'è nessuno come te. There's no one like you,' he said unconvincingly, brushing her fragrant cheek and neck. She smiled faintly. He nuzzled her ear and drew closer. She was as soft as a giraffe on eggshells and smelled of lavender and a linen cupboard. Philip had warm memories of Wendy Barton's house in Hampshire. At seventeen he had stood with Wendy in her dark, fragrant linen cupboard lined with wooden shelves and piles of crisp white sheets and embroidered duvet covers. Wendy of the pert, round, shiny breasts; one silken orb had looked larger than the other in the dim golden light. He had wanted to ask her about the irregularity, bounce the weight of one and then the other, but her mother was laying out the tea and shortbread in the kitchen below, the radio rising in a ghostly murmur. Wendy must be all grown up out there somewhere in London, gym-slim, married to a banker, two children, St John's Wood, golden retriever, thought Philip, and he kissed Diana forcefully, sweeping her of all resistance.

The thought of wicked Wendy in London, still asymmetrically desirable, fanned his ardour. He continued to hold Diana in his arms, breathing endearments into her ear as he kissed her with increasing passion. He licked her earlobe and they subsided backwards onto the sofa where she was directly underneath his grandfather's portrait, which admonished the easy abandonment of Philip's green-checked boxer shorts.

Philip attempted to lift her, but she was rather more heavy-boned than he had anticipated, and they sank deeper into the sofa. As they kissed, Philip nibbled her earlobe again. Diana's skin felt warm and yielding. She unbuttoned herself swiftly out of her purple cashmere twinset and was in the act of unzipping her brown Italian boots when her mobile phone began to ring. It flashed the IndiaNeed number. Adroitly gathering her belongings and her control, she answered; she had never liked losing either.

Back in the shop, Swarnakumari hovered expectantly as Heera spoke. 'Oh, good morning, Mrs Wellington-Smythe, it's Heera from the shop. I'm sorry to disturb you, but it's important. That's why I'm ringing you. You see, we were just sorting the bags and we found—'

Heera turned to the others as she replaced the receiver. 'D'you know what that Diana ki bachi said?' She mimicked a clipped upperclass accent. 'I'm sorry,

Helen, shop matters will have to wait. I'm on my morning canter.'

'Lady Go*di*va,' murmured Durga.

Diana had returned to Philip waiting unclothed and expectant on the sofa. He lay there patiently like a painter's sylvan Adonis sans woodland wreath. At the hint of steel in her voice as she spoke on the telephone, he had hastily draped his boxer shorts over his upper thighs. His grandfather's stern portrait relented, but the moment had clearly curdled. Philip had once been a King's College chorister, wearing the Etonian collar, singing in a pure, high voice at the Service of Nine Lessons and Carols on Christmas Eve. Then he sprouted hair on his chin and lost his voice, never to regain its power.

'You look ridiculous, get dressed!' Diana commanded in nursery nanny tones, and Philip obeyed, recalling his own nanny's reign and rein of terror. Philip was resigned; he knew when he had been given his marching orders.

Diana's grandfather had been given his marching orders after the Raj crumbled, and when he returned to England and to the impressive country manor in Berkshire, he had surrounded himself with antiques and artefacts acquired from India; a giant punkha fan of rosewood pinned to the wall, a peacock-shaped inlay table, figurines from Southern India, and the stuffed heads of tigers as sporting trophies. Diana's father had joined the Foreign Service and travelled with his wife and without his child to Nigeria. It was left to the grandfather and nanny to instruct and educate Diana, a task they performed with admirable resolve.

Diana travelled to India when she was twenty-four. She had originally planned a visit to Brazil, fired by a previous encounter in London with a man of mixed German and Amazon-Indian blood, who smoked thin, twirled cigarettes of dubious origin, brushed his teeth with bark and wore no underwear. She soon tired of his caveman looks, halting English and neat bottom shaking to the samba beat.

India and a people's raw display of emotions left her wary of the depths of dark, warm eyes. A hurried coupling with the Rajasthan tour guide would have been a mistake, and she had been wise to ignore his boyish charm and reject his gift of a sandalwood elephant, as she did the advances of the suave, handsome businessman at the Taj Hotel bar overlooking the Bombay harbour.

She had strolled out one evening from the air-conditioned splendour of the hotel lobby and into the world outside. A sticky blanket of heat had clung to her bare arms and legs as she walked under the arch of the Gateway of India, where King George and Queen Mary had once been welcomed with pomp and ceremony. Assailed by postcard-sellers, chattering footmen behind a queen's train, she finally sat on a parapet overlooking the harbour with its bobbing boats and grey water that never turned blue. Beside her was a family of Indian tourists, and the children chattered excitedly, pointing to various landmarks. A toddler in a woman's lap entwined his fingers into Diana's scarf, imprisoning the tassels in his little fist, and she stared solemnly into his brown eyes before disengaging her scarf. She rose and walked back to her air-conditioned room. Diana had learned at an early age that attachment, especially to pets and parents, led to heartbreak. IndiaNeed was born twenty years later as Diana's apology to the country of her father's birth.

'How many times have I told her my name's not "Helen",' stormed Heera, after Diana had abruptly terminated their conversation. 'You know, girls, I don't understand – what's this English problem with names? I have a cousin, Ashok Binani, who lives in Edgware. He's become quite fat now, but anyway, he used to be in the British Army – he was in the Falklands War – and d'you know what those English Army blokes called him?' She paused for dramatic effect. 'Bill.' She repeated, 'Bill. Now you tell me, d'you see any connection between "Ashok" and "Bill"?'

'Well, Army Bloke Ashok didn't have a choice, but what about the Asian population in Cambridge? Half of them call themselves Bill or Barry, Jill or Jane, and the other half's like me, putting up with ridiculous versions of our names. I'm Der-ger, Dugga, Dooga or Dergay, take your pick and mix,' laughed Durga, as she offered the other women a bar of Cadbury's.

'I just realised your husband's a plumber, Eileen, and his surname is Watts. He should have been an electrician,' teased Heera.

Eileen put away the basket of assorted skeins of wool and muttered as she munched a piece of milk chocolate, 'He should have been a lot of things.' She did not elaborate further on what might have been, nor on what might have been left.

'Except for Lady Di, no one has problems with my name. How about you, Swarna?' asked Heera.

'People usually call me "Sara"' admitted Swarnakumari. 'But what to do? If they can't say my name, they can't, *na*?'

'Or won't?' said Durga, licking her fingers. She loved chocolate with the passion that some women reserved for lipstick.

A name was nothing, thought Durga. She herself was nothing like her namesake in Hindu mythology – the Goddess Durga, protector of the good and the pure, and destroyer of the evil demon Mahishasura. According to legend, the combined energies of the gods created the feminine form of a ten-armed yellow-clad woman riding a lion. They hastily supplied her with weapons of destruction against the demon and she became Durgashtini or a mother goddess who destroyed evil and offered her devotees protection.

Names could be misleading; Durga's aunt, whose skin was the colour of milk with a spoonful of honey, had been superstitiously nicknamed Kaali, 'The Dark One', as the first surviving child after three stillbirths. Was a name an identity, an anonymous cloak or a terrifying emptying of self? The extra 'a' that her Gujarati neighbour Anal Shah had hastily inserted between the 'n' and 'l' of his name after receiving a scholarship to Harvard was the linchpin between respect and ridicule, but Ajay Dikshit at Trinity, a Cambridge friend, had succeeded in solemnising a marriage with Emma Cockburn in front of an audience too solemn to titter during the exchange of vows.

Durga said, 'So you mean Ashok is told, "Shoot the enemy, Bill!" and when the job is done and Ashok gets a medal, it's "Well done, Bill!" and pat, pat on the broad back.'

Heera continued, 'Exactly. I don't think I told you

about Seema Tipnis; she was a receptionist to an eye specialist called Ramsbottom. Poor thing, she was so embarrassed to say this man's name. After all, she's Hindu – how could she refer to Lord Rama's bottom fifty times a day? She told us his name was Dr Ramsey, but I found out, anyway.'

'Naturally,' said Durga.

'Talking of names, funny how Asians born here just can't pronounce Indian words the way we do,' remarked Heera. 'I once challenged a young Punjabi fellow to say "Pandit Ravi Shankar". And do you know – each and every word sounded so strange from his mouth. I said to him straight, "If you can say the 'a' in 'another', why do you have to say it like 'ant'?" ' Heera paused, puzzled. 'But *you* don't talk like that, Durga, and you have lived here all your life,' she remarked. Distracted by the sight of Eileen carrying a pair of longjohns, she continued, '*Arre*, I thought I asked you to throw this pair of men's thermals away. Why are they still here?'

'But they are new. Someone can use them, *na*,' protested Swarnakumari reasonably.

'Who do you have in mind? Darling Rupert? Have you seen how long the fork is? It can lift a truck,' observed Durga.

'I have a funny story to tell you about thermals, girls. My cousin Viju came to stay with us. Smart chap, he cracked the ticketing system of the London Underground by the second day, so he stopped buying a ticket. When his wife smiles, you see her large pink gums first, then her teeth. Anyway, you know how many of these first-time Indians are: he wore sweaters here even in the summer. Such a smell of mothballs! White thermals under his shiny suit on a Sunday, can

90

you imagine, and we went to the Natural History Museum. I think the thermals had a very long fork, because it was looking so bunched up under his belt, I knew it couldn't be natural. Oh, and one trouser leg of his suit was longer than the other, so I asked him why. He said the Indian tailor told him he should continue wearing the trousers and it would be all right in time. *Arre*, what a funny thing for the tailor to say!' roared Heera.

Durga interrupted, 'Viju could grow a longer leg. It's never too late.'

'Anyway, we saw specimens of those reptiles in the museum, and then his thermals started itching, so we couldn't go to the Imperial War Museum. We had to come back to Cambridge. I finally told him straight, "Enough of this nonsense!" I made him change into a white kurta pyjama and Bata rubber flip-flops, and he was so happy. I saw his suitcase later. My God, so many Ludhiana Mill woollies, strips of Saridon, Vicks inhaler, cough drops, Johnson's turmeric bandaid, Madhiwala ointment, clove oil for toothache, Amrutanjan pain balm, Jeevdaya Netraprabha for sparkling eyes, safety pins and a bandage, even that anti-flatulence stuff, you know, Havabaan Harde. I just couldn't believe it. Was he preparing to go into an English jungle, or what? And when he was leaving to go back to Delhi, he gave me five packets of rose incense sticks. They are so strong, I get an instant headache.'

'Then you should have kept his Amrutanjan pain balm also, *na*,' advised Swarnakumari.

'What to do? I usually get very boring gifts from India,' shrugged Heera.

'Like oil-shedding mango pickle,' contributed Durga moodily.

'Or twenty sandalwood paper cutters. I tell you, I have some strange guests in my house, and where they all come from, God only knows! I once came home to find strangers waiting outside my front door. He was a software consultant from Birmingham and his parents had just arrived from Delhi. They knew a friend of mine in Hyderabad, that's how they'd heard of me. They made themselves comfortable, drank my tea, ate my biscuits, but his ma was so tired, he said, jetlag continuing from two days ago, could she lie down somewhere for a few minutes, so I showed her to the guest room. Then he said, Ma and Baba must be so hungry, not used to this cold, could I suggest some place they could eat, but Ma was a pure vegetarian and already tired of eating bread. After her nap, Ma suddenly sprang up full of energy like a toddler with a dry nappy, and got busy in my kitchen, helping me cook rice and *dal*. Then the son announced he was on a carbohydrate-free meat diet to control his diabetes without medicine, did I have any lamb or chicken, and look how Ma is shivering, how is she going to make it back to Birmingham, it is already so dark, and she had wanted to see Cambridge. As soon as he said that, his mother immediately went all floppy. So they stayed the night. On top of that, I had to lend the whole family their nightclothes. The son is a little taller than Bob, and he complained, "Oh look, these pyjamas of your husband are too short for me." *Arre*, was he waiting for designer Burberry made to his size, or what? I told him, "As long as Bob's pyjamas cover your bits, that's all that should matter." Then he asked if I had thought of breakfast, because Ma liked apple juice, orange juice was too sharp for her teeth, and Baba liked white bread for toast, and did I have enough milk? Ma awoke at five and started moving around noisily, so I had to get up too. She asked me when I went downstairs, *bete*, how do you boil the water here, I want to make chai, and can Baba do his yoga asanas on your carpet – no hurry, whenever you are ready. Can you believe this behaviour? And no Diwali card, no thank you letter from these strangers afterwards,' concluded Heera indignantly as the shop bell tinkled.

A toddler on a leash dragged his mother towards a Lego helicopter that he instantly dismantled while she looked apologetic. An expensively dressed woman entered a moment later with a tiny shaggy dog clinging to her bosom.

'Where's Diana?' she demanded sharply.

'Mrs Wellington-Smythe is not here, she has gone riding,' answered Heera. 'I'm sorry, but no pets are allowed in the shop.'

'Don't be ridiculous. Phoebe wouldn't hurt a flea or a fly. She stays right here with me, and you may tell Diana I said so,' the visitor retorted firmly. 'Well, I haven't driven all the way from Latham Road for nothing. I'll give her a ring, but if she isn't going to show up, I'd better look round the shop myself.'

The woman advanced, tenderly stroking the pet with her red nails. Swarnakumari froze as she met the creature's penetrating eyes. Guru Ma's prayer book had contained no references to pets.

'I'm the manager. Why don't I show you around?' suggested Heera.

'Not much to show, is there?' said the woman.

'Who do you get in here, or daren't I ask? Let me guess
– dear old ladies with their knitting needles, dirty men
in raincoats, impecunious students, mothers looking
for next year's Christmas presents in January?' The
woman smoothed her hair thoughtfully. 'I'm amazed
Diana has kept this outfit running so long. About two
months, isn't it? She's right – it does need a complete
makeover. She can't keep asking Board members to
send in the stock and buy it back, too. What do you get
in here?' She stopped at the window display. 'I mean,
really! An assortment of Wedgwood teacups and saucers, Indian trinkets, wine glasses, Jane Shilton handbags, Crabtree and Evelyn bath salts, lavender-scented
candles, a china plate, the Queen's framed photograph.
What is this, a shop for geriatrics?'

She looked disdainfully at the shelves and the racks.
'Where is your designer collection? Jaeger, Betty Bar-
clay, Krizia? Handbags, shoes? Prada, Gucci, Fendi,
Burberry? I thought not. Absolute rubbish in here. I'd
say those Indian beaded necklaces are pretty, and the
scarves and bags too, but this shop needs quality. It has
to be trendy, chic.' As she turned, she tripped on a piece
of Lego that had detached itself from the child's fingers.
She ignored the mother's hasty apology and wagged a
stern finger at the boy. 'That's very dangerous, young
man! Your mother should really keep you – oh, I see,
you already have a leash.'

She turned to Swarnakumari. 'Well, clearly, even if
you did run an upmarket charity shop, it's in the wrong
location. Ideally, you should be somewhere like Rose
Crescent. And it is absolutely pointless having Postman
Pat and hot-water bottles in here; you are simply
turning away the well-heeled clientele you need.'

Swarnakumari agreed, nodding her head in bewilderment.

'Did Diana tell you about the new animal charity she wants to set up here? We are going to protect a rare species of Indonesian fox. It really is a most amazing animal, and it is being hunted for its fur, but anyway, I'm trying to convince Diana that this place would be just as marvellous as a trendy little French coffee shop instead. Monet, Manet, Matisse on the walls, croissants, pain au chocolat, café au lait – that sort of thing. It's a good size of room, bigger than the Salvation Army shop,' she said consideringly. 'It would be an excellent place for the school mothers to meet. Parking is such a chore outside Browns – I'm always afraid I'll get my wheels stuck in those ridiculous gutters of Hobson's Conduit. It's an absolute nightmare. Not that you have a great deal of parking here, either. None, in fact, as far as I can see. Anyway, I suppose Diana will explain it all to you. Now I simply must give her a call.'

The woman rummaged in her handbag for her mobile and placed the dog on the floor. 'Di? Vicky Bartlett. Where *are* you? I thought we were meeting at your shop. Anyway, I'm here, and I'm through, so if you want to meet up after lunch instead ... Not Browns again, sweetie ... Oh well, all right, I suppose we could collect the children directly afterwards. See you in twenty minutes? Ciao.'

It happened very quickly. The dog, unaccustomed to exercise away from Victoria Bartlett's sedentary breast, took a wobbly step forward. The child stamped on its paw. The dog yelped, Victoria Bartlett screamed and bent to scoop up the dog and glared into the child's eyes, and the child screamed back and threw up over

95

her Prada shoes. Victoria Bartlett left holding her dog and her temper.

'What a time we have had, *baba*. That naughty child, the dirty vomit, cleaning,' sighed Swarnakumari, a quarter of an hour later.

'*You* didn't clean up the mess, Eileen did,' contradicted Heera. 'And I could have kissed that child, if he hadn't thrown up. I gave him a free lolly from the till,' she confessed.

'I slipped him one, too,' confided Durga. 'Three, actually. I hope he does throw up again; that child will go far. If his mother gets rid of the leash first, that is. He's a strategist displaying precision timing.'

'How come I never see *you* doing any cleaning up, Durga?' Heera asked suddenly. 'Too many posh madams in this shop?'

'Forget it, *na*, Heera. The truth is the truth: we all know that Indians from good families are not used to cleaning up the vomit of strangers,' appeased Swarnakumari. 'Now tell me, what was the friend of Mrs Wellington-Smythe saying about the fox she was carrying?'

'She wants to save it. Lady Di, not the friend. The fox, not IndiaNeed. The friend wants a coffee shop, not a charity shop, and it was a dog she was smothering like an asp to Cleopatra's breast, not a fox,' explained Durga.

'It was not a fox,' confirmed Eileen. Negation came easily.

'Oh, I was wondering, because of course I knew it was a dog, but then I started thinking maybe it was a fox, because otherwise why would the poor child be so scared, *na*?'

'*Arre*, dog, fox, does it matter? That La Di Da woman is going to shut this place down and doesn't have the courtesy, the decency, to tell me?' raged Heera.

'You don't have to believe what the friend says,' said Durga comfortingly. 'She could be as truthful as her blond streaks.'

'What is going to happen to those villagers?' asked Eileen, turning to the photograph behind them.

'They're so last season, darling! Not in fashion any more. Next, please,' said Durga.

'The friend wants a coffee shop here. For what? As a meeting place for private school mothers to chit chat and find out if the other brats are doing more classes after school than their own. Ballet, martial arts, piano, swimming, drama, tennis, chess and Kumon Maths aren't enough, you see,' informed Heera. 'Don't think I don't know about all these things just because I don't have any children. I know many of these independent school mothers who drive up and down in big four-wheel-drive cars; they are on duty even on weekends for more lessons and sleepovers. On top of that they bake cakes for the school fairs and sew costumes for the plays. *Arre*, the poor things are so slim watching the League Tables and their own diets of ambition through the windscreens of their shiny cars, they live in a different world.'

Italian opera soothed Diana's nerves as she drove into Cambridge every morning from the countryside surrounding Haslingfield. Imogen was hunched, silent, on the seat. She would go clubbing and stay over at Izzie's, and she didn't care what her mother said about Izzie's brother David not being a Perse or Leys or King's boy. She was fourteen and old enough, and he was seventeen and old enough. Her silence grew, swelled until it was a crashing cacophonous wave, beating a plaintive crescendo of rage. It was the hormones, soothed Diana's mother.

Rupert stared out of the first-class window as the train sped past Stevenage to King's Cross. He took a sip of Perrier to calm his dry mouth, dabbed at the tiny egg stain on his crisp Paul Smith shirt inside his navy Paul Smith suit and arranged the papers in his mono-grammed leather briefcase. A knot of tension gathered in the pit of his stomach and spread down to his brown Hackett shoes as he thought ahead to the takeover bid and the auction in the afternoon at Sotheby's, but instead of the old surge of excitement all he felt was dread. Each day hammered the same dull beat of predictability.

She had sentenced him to slow torture more surely than pins bludgeoned into his extremities or slivers of wood slid under his nails. He was disintegrating into chalk and dust, severing his life force against the sharp, hysterical edge of her voice. The bloodless holidays with her were the worst; every year he wanted to tell her he was going to trek in the Brazilian rainforest or in the Australian outback, free to roam while she stayed at home alone.

Soon it would be Christmas and they would play charades, gaze at the roaring fire and roast memories and chestnuts, and jingle, jingle the bells until the blood rushed out of his head, leaving him a dry riverbed caked with cracks of longing. Unwrapping the decor-ated present, he would find last year's past; pulling the silent cracker, he ached to leave before he choked, spew-ing the miles of gold and red ribbon from his engorged lungs. Santa never came down the chimney, the partridge had never liked being in the pear tree, the world wasn't joyful and triumphant even when it snowed with eight milking maids, he never went to church in the silent night, and his mother-in-law would come up from Berkshire to stay and treat him like a little boy and insist he ate his Brussels sprouts, but his mother didn't when she should have, and would stay away.

He would grow his thinning hair into a ponytail and sideburns, wear flared studded jeans and a shirt unbuttoned to his waist, a black leather jacket, heavy leather boots, smoke pot, ride his Harley Davidson into the wind and not only to Harston village on Sundays past the church and the graveyard; there would be a girl waiting on the highway to heaven and she would ride pillion to San Francisco in a leather jacket with flowers in her hair and she would ask for nothing. Everybody had a hungry heart. He would be a rider on the storm.

Rupert was going through mid-life angst; it was the hormones, said Diana's mother.

CHAPTER SIX

Fools rush in where angels fear to tread

THE MID-MORNING TRAFFIC dawdled through narrow Mill Road, past the solicitor's firm, the bakery, the Indian curry houses, the Internet café and the grinning drunk lurching against the windows of the Chinese supermarket. A young man in T-shirt, jeans and black slippers pounded the pavement with urgent steps past the fish shop at the moment when Mr Chatterjee and Banerjee passed through its entrance. He looked over his shoulder in panic. The wind tickled the banner proclaiming *The Lord is Your Guiding Light* outside the church at the corner, before whisking away the hat of an elderly man and crushing it under the wheels of an indifferent car.

The young man continued to run, desperately seeking refuge. Only minutes ago he had been sniffing his mother's fragrant saffron rice, wondering how many of his annoying cousins would stay to lunch; now he was a fugitive, lungs bursting, legs racing for life. Too late, he saw a large woman in a blue sari leave a shop door to bend over a black bag on the pavement.

He collided with Swarnakumari, and the impact lost him a slipper, but he dashed wildly through the entrance. The young man's breathless tale as he was hustled behind the curtain to the Staff Area at his request was garbled: his sister had eloped with her English boyfriend to get married in Ireland and was on her way to Stansted. Although the rest of the family was distraught, it was his uncle who had exploded in rage, swearing retribution. His own father had been placatory; such a violent response was hardly appropriate. His son would follow the pair, he soothed, and use his powers of persuasion to prevent their departure. The apoplectic uncle nevertheless insisted on accompanying the young man, who quailed at the words; he had been his sister's confidant, assisting in the online ticket reservations. A sly, fat cousin sounded the alarm as he fled down the stairs. Three burly young neighbourhood thugs, eager to teach him a lesson on cowardice, followed in vengeful pursuit.

'Durga, quick, bring out that Roman robe and the woman's veil!' commanded Heera. 'They're both in that old cupboard there, along with the kimono that those drama students gave us.'

The young man was hustled into the shapeless robe, and a lady's veil of indeterminate cultural origin placed over his head. Durga suggested kitten heels. He stared at his feet in dismay, increasingly agitated as he realised he had lost a slipper in his haste to find refuge.

Heera was soothingly maternal as she imparted her instructions. She had taken command, driven by compassionate empathy to aid the fleeing pair. He was to remain in the main shop area and act like a customer, she warned. Durga suggested crutches to lend authenticity to his veiled and robed disguise. Eileen was directed by Heera to retrieve the telltale slipper from outside the shop, but she was blocked at the entrance by the elderly customer returning from Catnap.

Outside, the three burly young men giving chase met in simultaneous impact, subsiding in a heap of arms and legs. They plucked themselves free, straightening their collars with a scowl. The slipper lay humble and telltale, pointing truthfully towards the shop. A thug wordlessly held it aloft as he entered, and like gangsters in a film, the trio moved warily sideways through the clothes racks, awaiting the bullet that could whistle through the thermal socks and teddy bears or even the net curtains at any instant. The leader ordered his companions to their hands and knees to search under the clothes racks and in the wardrobes.

'Oh, hello there again,' twittered the elderly lady to Swarnakumari at the till. 'Oh, these poor wee cats, someone has to look after them! I couldn't have any cats in me own home, my Arthur said . . . Sorry I've popped in again, but I've remembered what I'd forgotten. I still have to get Dorothy a birthday present, you see! It's her eightieth; she's as spry as anything, still lives in her own home, you know. I'll just have a little wander and let you know if I find something, dear.'

She headed for the commemorative china plates as a chic young blonde turned to Heera. 'I was in the shop yesterday, and I think I lost a diamond earring in here,' she cried. 'Did you find it?'

Heera moved away with the blonde customer at the moment when Mr Chatterjee and Banerjee entered. Javed arrived a moment later, pausing to look at the golf set near the window, momentarily delaying the

102

desire to see the love of his life as he flexed a golf club and tested its quality.

'Nice big place,' said Banerjee.

'I do not see Mrs Wellington-Smythe,' Mr Chatterjee fretted.

'Oh, there she is!' said Banerjee obligingly.

Mr Chatterjee straightened imperceptibly.

'Your wife, over there,' said Banerjee.

As he followed Banerjee's pointing finger, Swarna-kumari emerged from the Staff Area, wet and flushed from repeated handwashing. It was Eileen who had noticed the bird droppings on the sari. Swarnakumari had already spotted her husband, but the sight of the shapely young blonde on her knees had initially distracted Mr Chatterjee's attention from his wife. Like bunnies in a china shop, the blonde and the three thugs hopped by on all fours, searching under the voluminous dresses trailing to the floor from the clothes racks. Eileen stood, arms folded, lips pursed, surveying the steady destruction of order.

'Nice big shop,' repeated Banerjee. Swarnakumari approached her husband, who remained taciturn.

Javed looked past Eileen at Swarnakumari, and at Durga, his gaze moving to settle on Heera and registering shock. He reminded himself fiercely that she had changed, but not beyond recognition; she had aged, but not to his dislike; he would be Hafiz, the Persian Sufi mystic seeking beauty of the soul, not of the flesh.

'Can I help?' asked Heera.

Javed continued to stare without speaking.

'I'll leave you to it,' she shrugged, and walked away.

The elderly customer approached a shelf of hats while the young man draped in robe and veil stared at the wall. 'Ooh, isn't that china plate nice! Dorothy likes the Royal Family, she does, got the Jubilee collection, too. If it's not too difficult, luv, could you use one of your crutches and pass me that pink hat on the shelf? The one with the flower, luv, that's it. Mebbe I could give her a hat instead of the dictionary, though she loves doing the crossword, she does.'

The young man obliged, and the robe fell away, revealing a hairy wrist. Mr Chatterjee stared, while his friend Banerjee was still absorbed in a book on German baking in ten easy steps. Javed followed Heera with his eyes; Mr Chatterjee watched Javed watching Heera.

'Ooh, wool and made in Italy, too! That's posh. Dorothy will like that. Poor Edith, went to Italy, quite rude and nasty they was with her, poor thing, but I like Italians, so friendly, never heard of anyone's bottom being pinched, have you? Come to think of it, I wouldn't have minded someone whistling at me or pinching me bottom, but they never did. I knew a nice Italian family on Neville Road, can't remember the name now. You looking for something special, dear?' asked the elderly customer kindly.

Heera rushed to the defence of the silent young man. 'She's deaf-mute, poor thing.'

'Oh goodness! And crutches, too! Some people have such rotten luck, don't they? I mean, look at poor Edith. She had that cancer scare, then the heart and the pacemaker, and going so quickly, too. Oh well, that's life for you. Oh, there aren't any electric ones, if you're looking for those, dear,' said the elderly customer helpfully, spotting one of the pursuers. 'I already been in here half an hour ago, and I was looking for electric

104

blankets, and I didn't find any, but this nice lady here said there were some new Edinburgh ones. The thing is,' she leaned over confidentially, 'my Arthur used to say—'

The thug pushed her roughly aside, tripping over the blonde making a desperate bid to find her earring. Shocked, the young man in disguise moved jerkily forward with his crutches, inadvertently knocking Heera on her thigh. She tottered and Javed rushed solicitously forward, helping her to a chair.

Eileen was silently observing the wanton destruction of a morning's work. She disappeared into the Staff Area, returning a minute later carrying the toy gun partially concealed by an apron. She stood in front of a thug, her grim face a terrifying, shadow-ridden mask as she recalled an assailant's attack on her brother in a Belfast alleyway. There could be no doubt that she would pull the trigger, and a silent agreement passed between the thug and Eileen. The three men vanished. There had been no witnesses.

'The coast is clear,' announced Eileen, satisfied.

The young man flung back his veil. 'Phew, that was close!' he exclaimed. Mr Chatterjee scrutinised his face in stunned silence.

'Wait, isn't he one of them, too?' Heera, struggling to stand, pointed at Javed.

'Who?'

'Him,' accused Heera. Everyone turned to stare at Javed in suspicion.

'Who is he?' asked the young man, bewildered.

'I don't know. I thought he was one of your chaps,' replied Heera.

'Who is this person?' scolded Swarnakumari in a

loud voice for her husband's benefit. 'Who were those three men?'

'Looking for a man,' supplied Durga.

'Aren't we all?' contributed the chic young blonde sourly on her way out. 'I was hoping I'd find the earring, but it's not here, or maybe it's just too busy on the shop floor today.'

'Yes, there were three men looking for something they could never find,' agreed Heera hastily.

The blonde left. Banerjee was gazing speculatively at Javed's maroon Pringle pullover. Javed glanced at the motley group. He had not been expecting privacy, but the presence of so many staring Asians at the shop was intimidating. Blotting them out of his vision, he whispered tenderly to Heera, 'I'm Javed.'

She looked at him in disbelief, and her eyes changed first, turning moist, brimming as her chin and lips trembled, buckling under a torrent.

'Javed?'

He was wordless.

'My Jav——?' She recovered swiftly. 'I mean . . . Javed. I didn't recognise you!'

'I would have recognised you anywhere,' he murmured. 'Still the same Heera, not a day older, you look just the same.'

Mr Chatterjee hovered within earshot.

'I found just the thing for Dorothy. She'll love this vase, but mebbe I should have got her a cardie instead. She feels the cold through her bones, poor thing, not much hair on her head now, you know, but she'll still get her hair done on Wulfstan Way every week. Wants to look her best, and why not? A woman's got a right to look her best at any age, but between you and me I

106

wouldn't bother any more if I were her. I mean, it's not as if anyone visits her, is it? It's not right when children abandon their old parents like that, is it?' quavered the elderly customer to Mr Chatterjee, who did not respond.

'You look shocked, Heera. I'm sorry I frightened you by landing up like this,' apologised Javed.

'I'd better be off. I need to make sure my sis is all right.' The young man absently surrendered the borrowed disguise to a startled Banerjee and commenced a search for the missing slipper. Eileen's tart observation that he ought to be grateful he had survived to wear the one he still owned led him to tearfully thank Heera and the others. Immediately after his departure, Banerjee asked Swarnakumari for assistance in the search for a leather jacket and a Marks & Spencer cardigan.

'Where is Mrs Wellington-Smythe?' was Mr Chatterjee's renewed query.

Heera stared up at Javed. The tumbling waters foamed and crashed into cliffs and crevices of worn memory; her heart pounded as she gazed into his warm brown eyes.

Javed could never have imagined a reunion in a charity shop amid customers whose motives would remain a mystery. There were two men smelling faintly of fish, and why was one staring at his cardigan and the other at his face?

He had cherished a burning flame, but time had flown; he was no longer the moony, besotted youth of three decades ago penning poems to her eyes and hair. Her hair was a shock. He remembered long, luxuriant black tresses in which he had buried his head and entwined his fingers, not the henna-tinged hair limp around her neck.

Guilt-ridden and ashamed of his abandonment of Heera, he had swallowed his cowardice and carried his unease to his relationship with Shabana, finally surrendering to the forces of darkness pinning him into inaction and a dull acceptance of his fate. All he needed to know was whether she echoed his own yearning and longing, and if by some wild chance she was as unhappily married as he had been. Middle age was not so ridiculous that it precluded desire and spontaneity, banishing impetuosity. Passion did not belong only to the young, who knew not the value of what they held, and the mature vine glinting in the mellow autumn rays and burdened with the sweetness of ripened grapes was no less worthy than the young fruit that awakened eager and early to greet the morning sun.

Javed was suffused with poetry amid the clothes racks and shelves of the charity shop; it had become a rosy-hued paradise in which Eileen, Durga and Swarnakumari were the houris as he and Heera strolled in gardens of scented blooms. Heera, too, had forgotten her surroundings, transported back to the tiny bedroom in her parents' old Hyderabadi haveli overlooking her neighbour's mansion. As she leaned her arms over the rail, face upturned amid the garden scents of jasmine and rajnigandha, Javed would appear on the terrace a few feet away, unfold his latest poem and bequeath it to the dying rays of the sun, persuading them to linger until he had declared his love. She had laughed at the more extravagant phrases; surely she was not to be likened to a graceful swan, her face no rising moon, her

108

powdered arms no more perfumed than the scent of a thousand petals?

A single candle glowing on his terrace and the mandolin strings spoke eloquently of his love, and on her eighteenth birthday she had returned to her room to behold a hundred winking candles ablaze on his terrace; lit by their flame, he had placed a thumping hand on his heart as he fell to his knees.

Did such a love last, she wondered, and did the flame burn brightly only because it never lit the darkness but for an instant? Was it better to have loved and lost, but then why was he in the charity shop, was it a sign? Was there a divine design to which she should surrender, recalling the countless times she had whispered his name across the oceans?

She must look ridiculous to him in her black work trousers and shabby blouse and with her sagging bosom and chin, big hips and hairy arms and unplucked eyebrows. Her hair needed a wash and her roots showed, age showed. What was she thinking, sitting here with him in front of all these people, and she had not even offered Swarnakumari's husband and his friend a cup of tea. All this love-shove business she had harboured all these years was silly, like the disguise she had given the young man – it was time to discard it without regret. She rose with determination at the moment when five middle-aged women entered the shop.

'Guten Tag, wir wollen nicht stören, aber dürfen wir . . . ?' A woman apologised in German for the interruption, switching to halting English; they were a delegation of German charity officials on a visit to Cambridge to observe the functioning of an English hospice. After an additional round of other charity shops in the area, they had been directed to IndiaNeed. The woman was apologetic; they had arrived unannounced. Durga stepped forward, introducing herself in fluent German to their delight, and they followed eagerly as she led them through the shop to describe the various village projects in Rajasthan.

'Swarna, Eileen,' hissed Heera. 'Help me make tea for everybody.'

'Allow me,' offered Javed gallantly, following her behind the curtain into the Staff Area. They found tea-cups with matching saucers as the kettle boiled. Heera darted quick, shy glances at him – they were making tea together. The vapour from the kettle rose, warming her heart.

The German women chatted companionably while sipping their tea, and Frau Inge Hartmann proudly displayed a handbag photograph of her son, Thai daughter-in-law and their two children. Banerjee was emboldened. It was time to come out of the closet; he had a son-in-law of German origin called Heinz, he confessed shyly. The women squealed and pumped his hand vigorously.

The shop emptied as the elderly customer left clutching a hat and a vase for Dorothy, followed by the German women crying out a fond 'Wiedersehen'. Banerjee had been defeated in his quest for a Marks & Spencer cardigan; he would now commence a search for Diwali cards. Swarnakumari showed him the cards produced by the Rajasthan project; Banerjee knew instantly his wife would appreciate neither the upturned faces of the villagers on the cards nor the price, and desisted from a purchase. Her disappointment would be difficult to bear, but her wrath would be far worse.

After her initial dazed and delighted response, Heera had appeared withdrawn and tense. Javed gathered that her husband was away. He wondered if there was something amiss despite her ready acceptance of his invitation to dinner, but as he left he had a spring and bounce in his step. He felt only release and liberation. So this was what it felt like to be born again, to be given another chance. Life wasn't supposed to send in a second monsoon shower moistening the baked, cracked earth, and if it did, surely it meant that he had to dare to be different, leap where he never would have trod. If he tripped and tumbled, dived and drowned, what would it matter, for he would have heard his heart as surely as if he had kicked the camel hard on its bottom, and if the camel wouldn't move, why then he would be fanciful, think he had laughed with the crowd, confess he was sitting on an obstinate, scheming creature as wilful as a new wife, and did they know what it felt like to please a wife who wouldn't be moved, and what could he do if cajoling and pleading didn't work, and begging only made her more obdurate? What could a man do but sit there, wait patiently until the new moon had made his young wife mellow and pliant? And then the crowd would have laughed with him and understood and melted away.

He stopped impulsively at the florists; the blonde woman appeared wistful as he ordered a dozen perfect red blooms to be sent to the charity shop to Heera. He penned an Urdu couplet; the words had reappeared from thin air, were perfectly timed and rhymed. He signed dramatically on the card, an elongated 'J' distinguishing the drab white envelope. The florist was impressed by his Porsche fountain pen.

He bought a packet of roasted peanuts from the shop next door and inhaled their nutty, salty smell. The crowd had sent peanuts whizzing past his nose at the camel that day; now it was time for the fizz, to celebrate as surely as if the peanuts were the glass of champagne from which he would abstain.

The four women rearranged the shop; clothes hangers had unhooked themselves from the racks, long dresses and coats had been flung over the rails, and everything that had lain in the storm path of the three thugs overturned in callous haste. A pile of blankets lay in a crumpled heap on the floor, and Eileen mumbled under her breath as Banerjee glanced at his watch and exclaimed at the lateness of the hour. His good humour had deserted him; he would return empty-handed except for the fish, still lying in the boot of the car, that would no longer be as fresh as when first purchased. There might be trouble ahead.

Mr Chatterjee had questions queuing in his head, bursting like a thousand noisy firecrackers. He was uncertain of what he had witnessed at IndiaNeed, the shop where his wife worked every Thursday as a volunteer. Swarnakumari's sari had been wet, clinging to her back, and she had looked like a curvy Southern belle emerging from a waterfall in an Indian film, stepping out in embarrassment from behind the curtain. His curiosity had led him to wander into the Staff Area. The sight of a blond wig, handcuffs, transparent lingerie and a pair of tiny white knickers with *Punish Me* embroidered in black lying on a table in the back of the shop was unnerving. It was the note pinned to the knickers, however, that was by far the most disturbing:

MRS W-S, WHAT DO YOU WANT TO DO WITH THESE? The query had been penned in capital letters; his legal training had taught him that, without further evidence to the contrary, he could not preclude the possiblity, however unlikely, that the note had been written by his wife.

Preparing for departure, Mr Chatterjee attempted for the last time to garner information on Mrs Wellington-Smythe's whereabouts. She was out on her morning ride, supplied a brusque woman with an Irish accent. He hid his disappointment well. He had always known aristocrats were thoroughbreds.

CHAPTER SEVEN

Birds of a feather flock together

BOB HEARD THE gushing of the bathwater; it was a gurgling, luxurious sound. Soon he would hear a light swish, a slap of water against a yellow rubber duck before a Beethoven sonata slipped teasing and seductive under the door. Resistance was no longer a choice, and he undressed reluctantly, his clothes falling in a heap outside the bathroom door as he walked inside to join Adam.

Cleverly concealed lighting shone softly on the gleaming chrome taps, glass basins and the rails with their fluffy black and cream towels; designer toiletries were arranged next to a DVD and CD player, and the Jacuzzi bubbled invitingly. Bob paused to look at himself in the Italian mirror of Adam's marble-tiled bathroom. He felt utterly ridiculous.

That was not the way it had started with Adam. *Adam* – he had been consumed by that name, until it became as natural as a breath; without it he gasped for air, strangled by guilt and shame. As he slowly lowered himself into the slippery bathtub, Adam handed him the rubber duck. Bob dutifully squeezed until it squealed. Its red beak bobbed in the foamy lather in which Adam floated. Bob looked at the duck; unlike him, it would never drown. When Adam indicated he was ready, Bob reached for the loofah, scrubbed his back and exfoliated his feet with peppermint scrub.

'Do you think the merger will go ahead?' asked Adam lazily above the music. Bob nodded.

'Hard day, wasn't it? We'll go to Papa Donatello's for a bite, or do you prefer Thai?' Adam shrewdly never suggested an Indian curry, and in any case it gave him indigestion – and Bob guilt.

Adam went organic when he cooked; everything, from the salad to the dressing and the nuts and the wine, had to be sensitively grown. The kitchen gleamed with a silver Smeg refrigerator and French copper bain-marie and casseroles, Skeppshult cast iron pans, Yatagan knives, an Au Nain mezzaluna, Piazza ladles, Alessi kettle and Rowlett toaster. Adam tossed the salad with his home-made vinaigrette only seconds before serving. The trick, he explained, was to prepare it in French style; the dressing was poured into the bottom of the bowl and the freshly cut salad leaves arranged on top.

The glass-topped dining table for ten was immaculately laid out for two; a blue Kosta Boda candleholder swirled the light into shimmers of gold. There was seduction in the salad as Adam turned up the volume on the Bang & Olufsen speakers. Bob had found the Scandinavian influence on the house intriguing: Holmegaard and Royal Copenhagen, Ittala glassware and crystal, Poul Hennningsen lamps, Arne Jacobsen chairs and Aalvar Aalto sofa. Adam explained casually that it was Anders Pedersen who had left those behind. Who was Anders, and what had he meant to Adam? wondered Bob, jealously aflame. It could only be the act of a

115

generous lover; he would find out more about the Great Dane, or go quietly insane.

Bob sensed he was the new concubine as he surveyed the bedroom inspired by the Far East. An enormous Chinese fan was pinned to a brocade wall-hanging behind the bed, which had a black satin coverlet embroidered with dragons; the bedside tables were carved red wooden boxes, and tasselled lamps lit the way to a delicate bamboo wardrobe. Adam had gifted Bob a pair of embroidered Chinese slippers. As his feet sank into their plush softness, he did not dare ask whose memory still lingered there. He padded obediently in the slippers, which were a size too small, obliging him to take smaller steps. He would not mince, he muttered fiercely to himself; he did not want to mince.

Searching for clues became Bob's magnificent obsession, self-revulsion oozing a boil in every pore as he scoured Adam's home for former loves and past lives. There were secrets in the engraved wooden box for Havana cigars and in the collection of Cuban music and books on New Zealand. The music in the bedroom was Brazilian, with Milton Nascimento, Maria Bethânia and Gilberto Gil given pride of place. A bold hand had scrawled *Beijos* and lipstick marks on the cover of each CD, and Bob's tortured dreams were now mocked by men with black locks and bronzed Latin skins. He was lying on Copacabana beach, suffocating in a black suit and tie, while their string-ringed bottoms shook moist sand onto his face. Adam towered over him, a caipirinha drink in one hand, the other skimming the sleek twisting hips. Bob looked up to see the Corcovado Christ figure, arms open wide. He tumbled down Rio's hill and was lifted into the statue's concrete embrace.

116

On Bob's first evening in the house Adam had prepared a celebratory meal accompanied by Bollinger champagne. Listlessly picking at the lettuce, Bob had played hockey with the porcini mushrooms and pushed the puy lentils to a corner of his plate as Pavarotti ascended a scale. Bob was nervous of the step he had taken, his boldest since proposing to Heera in Hyderabad. Submission and surrender to another man's choice of toothpaste, wine and medium roasted coffee was not easy, and, although the fact was well hidden from Adam, he never slept soundly away from his own bed. As Adam bent his head to look quizzically at him, Bob met his eyes and smiled, displaying an assurance that he did not feel.

Bob entered the room of Chinese dragons to the accompaniment of a loud squawk. It was his introduction to Noddy, Adam's yellow nape Amazon parrot. The bird had olive-green wings, a yellow patch at the back of his neck, a dark grey beak, light grey legs and orange eyes. A native of El Salvador, he had been sold to Adam for a thousand pounds by a pet shop. Noddy, who weighed four hundred grams, sat in a cage with perches, toys, an avian gym and food and water bowls. The cage was hung in the Chinese boudoir.

'You never told me you had a parrot,' said Bob wonderingly.

'Shhh ... don't say it aloud. Noddy doesn't like being referred to as a parrot. He's human, aren't you, my love?' teased Adam.

There was another squawk and Bob stared, hypnotised, into little orange eyes on fire.

'Aren't you going to do something about the pa—

117

about Noddy?' protested Bob, trying to ignore the flames of distrust emanating from the bird.

'Noddy loves to watch,' replied Adam.

That night Bob sought his teddy, Charlie, but dreamed instead of a jungle filled with hanging vines and snake-like gnarled roots that he blindly pushed aside, escaping marauding humans with piercing beaks for mouths as he stumbled helplessly towards the light.

He awoke to Noddy's raucous shrieks and stared at the bird, engaging the beady, venom-filled eyes in battle. What a ridiculous name for a parrot, he thought. There was soon going to be trouble in Toyland, but for the moment Adam had arrived with shelled sunflower seeds, fresh sprouts and fruit for Noddy, who attacked his breakfast with relish. Bob wondered whether both the seeds and fruit were organic.

'Stay absolutely still! Don't move!' commanded Adam. It took a moment for Bob to realise Adam was talking to *him*. Adam opened the cage. 'Step up, spit spot!' he ordered, and Bob froze. Noddy hopped onto Adam's wrist, attempting to jump onto his shoulder. Adam coaxed the parrot down onto his wrist again and stared firmly into his eyes. Bob relived the image of a head teacher thundering to a thin boy in shorts.

'Good boy, Noddy,' said Adam approvingly and scratched the bird's head as it obeyed. 'Now get on the stick!' Noddy hopped on. 'Sing, my little songbird!'

As Bob watched in amazement, Noddy cocked his head adoringly and trilled in a man's voice, 'You are the wind beneath my wings'.

'You are an angel.' Adam rewarded him with another head scratch, and gently nudged him towards the cage.

118

'Got to go now, my little singing nun, or I'll be late for work.'

Noddy hopped in, as he sang in drunken-girls-night-out-karaoke-style, 'I will survive'. Adam peered into the cage and pleaded, 'Please understand, my featherbunch!' Noddy sang, 'Leave right now', and was silent.

Matters escalated that evening. Bob had been shopping, and as he unlocked the front door he heard a woman's voice coming from the direction of Adam's bedroom. 'Adam, darling, not now. Ooh, that tickles!' she said huskily. Black jealous rage overtook Bob as he dropped the carrier bags, hurried upstairs and burst, incandescent, into the bedroom to find Adam sitting calmly on the bed while Noddy was strutting on the floor. As soon as Noddy saw Bob, he made a guttural sound; his tail feathers flared and his pupils dilated menacingly.

'Stay!' said Adam firmly, his palm turned upwards.

Noddy stared at Bob, then suddenly flew at Adam and bit him hard on his arm. Bob stared helplessly at the sudden patch of blood forming on Adam's shirt.

'Bob, leave the room for a mo and shut the door, will you?' requested Adam.

Bob overheard Adam's murmured endearments to Noddy while he sat on the Aalvar Aalto sofa. Adam emerged calmly from the room half an hour later; he had managed to stem the blood and tie a clumsy bandage on the arm.

As they drove together to work on the A14 in Adam's car the next morning, it began to rain. Bob looked out on the dismal flat landscape near Huntingdon that he had passed every day for years, feeling he would be consumed by flatness his entire life – until he had met Adam, that is – but he realised Adam had tweaked the truth when he said he was not in a relationship. There were three of them now: two men and a parrot. A very dangerous, jealous parrot.

Adam patiently explained: the yellow nape Amazon bird was one of the best talkers in the bird world; it could learn tricks as early as four months. It could sing opera, whistle, and memorise whole songs, imitate the young and old, male and female, rollerskate, go down on a slide, roll over. It loved an audience. When it was around five years old – coincidentally, Noddy's age – the species became aggressive, especially in the breeding season. Noddy saw Adam as his mate, and would seriously harm anyone who was a threat, not afraid to teach its own carer a bitter lesson to boot. So, thought Bob, other men and women showed off tattoos, but Adam had love bites from an Amazonion parrot. All this was very entertaining and endearing, but what was he, Bob, supposed to do? Accept defeat and leave the parrot crowing in victory, squawking its little triumphs? Make way for Noddy?

The mystery of Anders was one no longer. Noddy had apparently flown at the Danish lover in bird wrath, and nearly gouged out an eye. Anders left in a hurry and flurry, but not before committing a wilful, cruel act, shuddered Adam, eyes turning moist at the memory. While Adam was in the shower, Anders had written a note in Danish beginning with the words *Øje for øje, An eye for an eye*, let Noddy out of the cage and escaped himself, without saying goodbye or why. When Adam emerged, fragrant from emollient and sensitive scalp detangling lotion, he found Noddy fly-

120

ing in shock around the house, and about to insert his beak into a wall socket. Noddy could have died, shuddered Adam. He could have bitten house wires, been poisoned from chewing house plants, hammered the ceiling while searching for the sky.

Adam advised Bob to be patient and read *The Companion Parrot Handbook* on parrot handling. *The Guide to a Well-Behaved Parrot* by Athan and Earl-Bridges was another useful reference for an understanding of the wonderful world of parrots. He should remember the cardinal rule: he was never *ever* to enter the room again when Noddy was out of the cage.

Adam took Bob to London the next day; it was a treat to obliterate the trauma of the introduction to Noddy. Bob felt like an East Anglian bumpkin as he was led through Harrods and Selfridges and New Bond Street, and accompanied Adam into bespoke tailor shops on Jermyn Street. Afterwards, they dined in a gentlemen's club behind the Ritz. Bob was bewildered. Adam was clearly a man of wealth, so why had he chosen to work in an architect's firm and live in the Shelfords?

They walked together into the lights of Soho and Madame JoJo's, and ambled arm-in-arm to their hotel on Shaftesbury Avenue in the early hours of Sunday. Returning to King's Cross Station that evening, they made their way to Platform Nine for the Cambridge train which, to their surprise, was nearly full. Adam spotted the last two empty seats and as they sat down Bob realised he was caught in the midst of a Cambridge group of Women Working for the World members – a few of whom he recognised as Heera's acquaintances. Bob wanted to flee, Adam wanted to stay, the train doors slammed shut, and they were on their way. The numerous tunnels darkening the carriages as the train sped toward Stevenage and the arrival of the refreshments trolley initially shielded Bob from discovery. It was in the vicinity of Hitchin Station that Janet Hewitt noticed Bob.

'Bob?' she asked tentatively, leaning over her neighbour. He straightened uncomfortably; there was no way out as the other women began to nod and smile. The questions fell thick and fast. Why had Heera not joined them on their outing to the Bramah Museum of Tea and Coffee? They would not forgive her for staying away, and could he tell Heera to call? She was to arrange the next guest speaker. As Bob searched for a response, Adam chose the moment to publicly cement their relationship. He leaned against Bob and dropped a casual arm over his shoulder, drawing him close.

Mrs Chakraborti's eloquent fish-shaped eyes grew even fishier; there was silence as the group turned away from the unmistakable intimacy on display, commencing an animated discussion of English teapots. Adam continued to rest his hand on Bob's thigh or arm as he chatted. Leaving the exit at Cambridge Station, Mrs Chakraborti hissed, eyes flashing, 'Shame on you, Bob. Shame on you!' She disappeared into the crowd and Adam threw back his head and laughed.

They had their first argument as they drove out of the station car park.

'How could you?' spluttered Bob.

'What?' countered Adam coolly.

'You know what I mean! In front of those women . . .'

'You'd better get used to it, Bob. Either you're with me, or you ain't. There's no two ways about it, you know,' said Adam calmly, as they drove over the bridge, past Homerton College and onto Hills Road.

'This is all too new. It's going to take some time. You're pushing it,' snapped Bob.

'It was those women who got to you, right? Because they know your wife. You wouldn't have minded if they'd been strangers on a train to Newcastle, or if we were cavorting in Ibiza.'

'It's not just that. I'm not comfortable yet. I don't know whether I ever will be. The physical stuff is not something to put on display. I didn't even do it with . . .' Bob paused.

'With your wife? Poor boring Bob,' mocked Adam. 'It's all right when there isn't anyone looking, is that it? You do like your dark closet an awful lot, don't you? Are you sure you've come out of it?'

'There's no need for sarcasm. I said I wasn't comfortable, so just drop it, will you? Can't you see I have a lot of issues to deal with, inside me, with the people who know me, who know me together with my wife? Do you know how difficult it is for me not to think about her at all? That woman just used the word "shame". Do you know what that means? Yes, I am feeling shame. I'm not ashamed, but I do feel shame. Does that make any sense to you at all? You don't know, do you, what it feels like to be split in two, down into your very guts, wanting to be true to what you feel inside but not knowing exactly what or why that is. I like you, Adam. I like being with you a lot, you know that, but there are big issues here. You've got to understand, be supportive, give me time.'

Bob glanced at the other man's hard profile as they drove round the Addenbrooke's roundabout. 'You really

123

don't understand, do you?' he continued quietly. 'I can't figure you out. Who are you, Adam? You're suave and sexy. Why are you with a miserable git like me? I've got to know.'

'Can it wait until we get home? We're almost there. Let's do this properly. And I've got to meet Noddy first, sorry. It's very important to interact with these birds on a daily basis. They misbehave so easily if one doesn't. So can we talk afterwards?'

Bob waited impatiently on the Aalvar Aalto sofa for Adam. The image of the fiery ball of a woman spitting those words at him was indelible; he deserved every word, he thought. It was punishment for following his inner self; would he now never cease to be haunted by what he had done? The temple of Apollo at Delphi carried an inscription: *Gnothi seauton – Know thyself*. The familiar feelings of guilt took control, emotions that he tried desperately to erase, and when Adam emerged from his chat with Noddy it was to discover Bob holding his teddy, Charlie, fast asleep.

By the next weekend, Bob had begun to unravel the mystery surrounding Adam. The bell rang insistently, and Bob opened the door to find a solemn little girl and boy on the doorstep, as a woman moved forward. She was slim and blonde. 'You must be Bob. I've heard so much about you. All good things,' she smiled. 'I'm Saara, and I've come to drop off the children.' Before Bob could respond, she looked at her watch and jumped into her car and sped away, shouting instructions to the children. They looked at him without interest, moving past him into the home with an easy familiarity.

'Where's Daddy?' asked the girl.

'Where's Noddy?' asked the boy.

As Adam explained later to Bob, he had two children, and the blonde Finnish woman was Saara. They were not divorced, only separated. Under Bob's watchful gaze, Adam changed. Gone was the cool, sophisticated exterior; stripped, he was a father.

He asked Bob to join them in the park at Cherry Hinton overlooked by a row of houses. They walked past the ducks onto an open patch of green and Adam unpacked a large duffel bag. Bob thought his lungs would burst as he raced after the ball and tossed and caught the frisbee. Claire remained mutinous and refused to look at Bob, rejecting his offer of a sweet.

It all made sense. Saara and the children lived in Cambridge, and that was why Adam hadn't moved away. He needed to see his children, and still referred to Saara as his 'wife'. It was as simple as that. Bob watched him as he sprinted after Mark, hoisting him in the air, pummelling him until he squealed in delight, pushing the swings and pumping the see-saw, his arms ready to catch the little boy as he slid down the slide.

That night Bob lay on his bed staring at the ceiling, ignoring the parrot although Noddy did his best to engage him in battle. Adam with his hands full of flour, pounding the pizza dough, bathtime and the bedtime story . . . who was Adam?

Adam had explained later. He had wanted to be the perfect father to his children. His own father had died when he was two, and he had grown up with an indifferent stepfather. Bob thought he understood now why Adam had sought him out, and it was not flattering. He didn't want to be reassuring, responsible or

125

reliable; he wanted angels to sing of passion, feel Adam's desire for him burn his flesh and soul. The years suddenly yawned ahead. Was he being groomed as a grandfather to Adam's children, to read a bedtime story every other weekend and tackle their future teenage tantrums?

He had thought he knew Adam and his essence when they first met; now he realised he didn't know him at all. Was he the ogre in the tower or the angel in the skies? Adam had become more and not less, and Bob less and not more than when they first met. Why did it feel as if Adam was the rising sun, and he the setting orb?

That night, the telephone woke Bob and Adam instantly. As Adam dressed hurriedly in the dim light, he explained. Saara was being taken to hospital with terrible pains. It was appendicitis. Could Bob take charge, look after the children while he was gone? Bob observed with petty satisfaction that Adam had omitted to mention Noddy.

It was three in the morning, and Bob wandered into the kitchen, pouring a large whisky before entering the room where the children lay sleeping. He looked down at Claire, at her rumpled sleeve, the brown hair framing her face, her drooping lips.

Bob was swept by a surfer's wave on a sandspun beach as he bent over the child. His shoulders hunched, preparing for an engulfing torrent as he stood, a timid boy of thirteen in a white shirt and grey school shorts while his father paced angrily. His mother had averted her face as his father's cane came crashing down on his knuckles, her mousy hair undone. His stern father had withdrawn into a dark silence and his classmate Peter

126

now avoided his gaze under the watchful eye of the teacher.

As he turned away from the faces of Adam's sleeping children, the first sob contorted his stooping frame; his tears pitied the bewildered schoolboy beaten until he bled into denial of realms he could not fathom, the mother who had long passed into embarrassed, early oblivion and a father whose deathbed remained unflinching tombstone.

He fled to Adam's bedroom in anguished rage at his own foolish arrogance, at the years of confusion, for the children he would now never have, that *she* would never have. The tears welled and swelled, spilling into the bathtub until the duck began to bob merrily, flowing over the tub's sides onto the dark marbled floor. The flood seeped under the door into the rest of the house, gushing over the designer furniture and the crystal, dousing the light of the Swedish candles, quelling the rhapsody until there was only hollow silence in the darkness.

He held his head between his hands; a quiet, dull man perched on the edge of a satin-covered bed next to a shabby one-eyed teddy, watched balefully by a parrot. Perhaps he could only be the one or the other, black or white, and the shades of grey could never be his. He envied Adam his several worlds. He himself was solid and stolid, boorish and bookish. He was no Latin lover in the Chinese boudoir, and he hated tasselled slippers, organic broccoli and whitening toothpaste.

Noddy squawked warningly as Bob continued to weep. He hopped down from his perch and his tail flared. The low growl came again. Bob had forgotten about Noddy. He looked at the bird, approaching slowly, rapidly gulping his whisky.

'Now listen, you little birdbrain!' His steely voice startled him as well as the parrot, which emitted a loud screech of protest. Bob stood his ground. He stared eyeball to eyeball with Noddy. Volcanoes erupted from the parrot's eyes; molten lava of hate spilled over the slopes of his wings as he flew in anger at the bars of the cage.

'Shut up, bird. You'll wake everyone. Do you want to do that? I think not. Yes, bird, that's what you are, only a silly old bird. Did you hear what I said? Old bird. Old bird,' repeated Bob.

The whisky was taking effect. Bob jumped shakily, clumsily, onto the bed to peer into the cage. He executed a wobbly jig. 'Look, I've got a bird's-eye view up here! "Fly robin, fly, up, up to the sky",' he sang tunelessly, squashing the embroidered satin cushions without alarm. The bird bristled, shooting fire through the cage.

'You think you're a singing nun in Salzburg, but you are nothing but a mean green bunch of feathers and you'll end up on an Ascot hat, without the sound of music,' warned Bob. 'There's no old age pension for birds, you know. Tough mean parrots don't even get eaten; they just get tossed into the bin along with the . . . er . . . potato peel.' Bob was inspired, viewing his glass through pleasantly blurred edges and his life with clarity. 'And, you little birdie dum dum num num, however much you may want Adam, he's not yours. He's *not* yours. He's not mine, either, I can see that now, but he's certainly not yours, so just eat up your sunflower seeds like a good bird. You are not *his* bird. You are only a *bird*. B-I-R-D.'

Noddy glared balefully but made no sound as he paced his cage.

'Shall I tell you something else? You have a really silly name. "Noddy". Ha! Noddy's not only the dumbest character in Toyland, he sings terribly out of key.' Bob took another large sip. 'I'm surprised you answer to it. No self-respecting yellow nape Amazon parrot from El Salvador would ever accept "Noddy". Where's your Latin machismo and pride? Speedy Gonzales. Guantanamera. "Yo soy un hombre sincero" and all that. Olé! Arriba! Paella! Marbella! That's all the Spanish I know, sorry. I'm English. Not supposed to speak any foreign languages. And I'm in foreign country at the moment. Hang on, there's a Spanish phrase book somewhere!' Bob lurched towards a bookcase and found an *AA Essential Spanish for Kids*.

'Ah, here it is. Now let's see. Yes. *Tengo novio.* Now that's a useful phrase. That means I have a boyfriend. *Vete a la porra!* I'm sure you know what that means: Sod off! *Buen viaje!* Have a good trip! So now you've heard it loud and clear in your own language, I'd suggest you shape up – spit spot – or ship out. If you're good, I'll put in a word for you to stay, El Salvio. If not, well, I just might want to find out what it's like to kill a bird with a stone. It would be a shame, wouldn't it, if someone left your cage unlocked for the second time? Pure accident, but this time you would be alone, all alone in this beautiful house. What could happen next? Ooh, I fear for you! You might swallow the poisonous sap from the dieffenbachia growing in the patio, or your beak could get stuck inside a socket and this time you would get electrocuted, but never mind, you'd still have the best parrot perm and stringy bottom this side of Latin America.'

Bob was exhausted. He felt an urge to talk to Heera. He reached for the telephone and passed out. The next morning, Adam returned home. He rushed to Noddy's cage.

'Hello, my love, my Noddy. Sorry I wasn't there last night.'

Noddy turned his back on Adam.

'I said I'm sorry. Noddy? Darling? Listen, let me get you some breakfast. Some fresh fruit and sunflower seed, how does that sound?'

The parrot remained silent.

'Say something, Noddy darling. You know I couldn't help it, I just had to go, but I did come home as quickly as I could. Saara was ill, and you know these things can happen.'

'El Salvio! El Salvio!' shrieked the parrot.

'I know I should've been there for you, darling, but do understand. I'll buy you a new perch, would that be nice? And I'll let you out of the cage for a whole hour tomorrow, how about that? I'll come home early if I can.'

'El Salvio! El Salvio!'

It took two days for Adam to understand. His parrot's new name was El Salvio. El Salvio had started singing 'La Bamba'. In an English accent.

CHAPTER EIGHT

Faint heart never won fair lady

AT THE MOMENT when the young man had been racing down Mill Road, hurtling into Swarnakumari's ample, bending body and slipping into IndiaNeed, a man in his mid-thirties embarked on a leisurely walk from the College Backs towards Mill Road. Dressed in brown chinos, a cream crew-necked pullover and a beige overcoat, he strode, a man who loved the out-doors, across Coe Fen. He was American, and his name was Roman Tempest.

Looking back twenty-four hours later on his casual expedition to Mill Road that morning, Roman was reminded of Horace Walpole. Reading the tales of *The Three Princes of Serendip*, Walpole had deduced that an accidental discovery by sagacity of things one did not seek was 'serendipity'. Serendipity as happy chance, accidental good fortune and wordless wisdom, then, had charted Roman's course when he might otherwise have visited the Sedgwick Museum and greeted the reconstructed iguanodon skeleton or an ichthyosaur or two. Perhaps it was Teresa who had impelled his steps away towards Mill Road.

Teresa was a helpful English colleague who blushed

rapidly, embarrassment staining her pale throat and cheeks. He imagined the nervous redness spreading through her until she was a blazing tomato, and had stared at her skin in amazement as the flush spread down her neck, a glance she had coyly misinterpreted. She unbuttoned her blouse further, retained a fluttering hand in the region and punctuated her conversation with high-pitched giggles. Actively seeking his company, she alternated between Pouty Pop Queen and Ice Maiden, a combination he found disconcerting while discussing Steven Greenblatt and the New Historicism of American literary theory. Once he had idly formed an image of her as Britney Spears in academic garb, it was far too entertaining to banish.

Early that morning he had explored a path beside the river with a view to the back of the Wren Library and of the Gothic New Court of St John's College, wondering if Wordsworth had wandered lonely there as an undergraduate at St John's, moody in the mellow autumnal moment. Roman then made a ritual visit to the Peterhouse memorial to Rev. Godfrey Washington bearing the Washington coat-of-arms, the precursor to the Stars and Stripes flag. He had returned to the river, and as he stopped to trace the veins of a russet leaf on the Fen path before continuing on his way, verse flooded his being. He, like Whitman, was free and healthy and light-hearted on the open road; the long brown path beckoned and he would choose where he would go. A man in an oilskin coat and wellingtons nodded politely at Roman as he walked by with his poodle on a leash. The poodle paused, and the man paused to remove a little plastic bag from his coat, and soon they were on their way again.

Roman halted to admire the majestic horse chestnut trees on Trumpington Road and the autumn foliage of the Botanic Garden before continuing up Bateman Street and into Station Road, turning left onto Devonshire Road. Teresa's directions to Mill Road had been hurried and not as the crow flew; he suspected that she had deliberately chosen a long and winding route, hoping to offer herself at an opportune moment in the role of tour guide. A student distracted her attention as they had talked outside the Porter's Lodge, and Roman had slipped away in relief.

He stood at the corner where Devonshire Road met Mill Road at the bridge. Teresa had informed him that Mill Road was 'an exemplification of the ancient quarrels between the townspeople and the University' that led to the coinage of the phrase 'town and gown'. The 'town' was still smarting from the insults of Henry III in 1231, when he forbade it to exact high rents from scholars, and at the same time gave the University powers to license the alehouses and supervise the markets, fairs, weights and measures. It was not until the Act of Parliament in 1856 that old disputes were settled, she had added knowledgeably.

Roman entered Mill Road through the tumbling October leaves, recalling Thoreau's autumnal sun and autumn gale. Roman experienced life through poetry, and effortlessly memorised large passages for every occasion. It impressed the students, was useful to tease women like Teresa, but he nevertheless genuinely loved great poetry, chiefly as he was unable to write any of his own.

At the moment when Roman Tempest set foot on Mill

Road, Durga was checking the new deliveries of puzzles. If the cover stated 250 pieces, but a piece was missing, the volunteers were not permitted to proceed with a sale; typically, a missing piece was usually the motive behind the generous donation to the charity. Fortunately, 'Sir Puzzle' offered to take away the incomplete puzzles and still pay full price.

A tall, hawk-nosed man in a grey woollen overcoat and felt hat entered, followed by a short middle-aged man. The tall man asked to see the collection of watches, and as Eileen unlocked the shelf and brought out the tray, he lifted his arm to reveal four watches on his right wrist; none showed the correct time. He scowled and pointed to two with broken dials, strapped them around his left wrist, paid and departed.

Swarnakumari was staring through the curtain at the short man inspecting the lingerie. 'Durga, go and help him. Your Uncle would not like it if I do such things.'

Pretending to check the window display, Durga strolled out to the front of the shop. The bespectacled man in his sixties resembled her neighbour Mr Beescroft, who tapped his cap every time they met with their rubbish at the communal black bins. The man rummaged through the undergarments and thrust his hands inside a blue brassière, brushing it against his chest before returning it to its original place. As Durga approached, he hastily chose a red brassière instead, producing a brown paper parcel he was carrying to bundle his purchase under his arm. As he left, a third customer emerged from behind the rack of nightgowns. 'Don't worry, luv, he's harmless. He goes to every charity shop down this road and does the same thing,' he bubbled.

'Your Uncle would not let me come here if he saw what that dirty man did, *hanh*' was Swarnakumari's comment afterwards.

'*Arre*, c'mon on, Swarna, tell the truth. You complain loudly, but actually you enjoy this khichdi pot of life bubbling in here, don't you?' teased Heera.

The florist's assistant crossed the road with Javed's bouquet; he was a freckled lad miscast as the happy bearer of floral tidings. As he darted in front of a speeding car, Javed's card fluttered away into the traffic. The assistant stood outside IndiaNeed with his flowers, intent on his mobile, his fingers working furiously. Roman Tempest was standing outside the shop, peering at the window display. The lad dropped the bouquet and Roman dived, catching it neatly, a baseball in his waiting glove.

'You nearly lost that bunch. Hold on tight, man!' warned Roman.

'Thanks, mate,' replied the lad without looking up. He jerked his thumb towards the shop. 'Got to do this delivery and me girlfriend's waiting down the road. She's going to kill me – says she won't be waiting longer than five minutes. Got to send her a message now. Can you help, mate? Just go in with the flowers, say they're from the Sunflowers Florists down the road, all right? She's going to kill me. Gotta run. Cheers, mate!' He sped away.

Roman entered the shop with the flowers. He paused, searching for a note from the florists among the blooms. As he slowly approached the counter, he saw her, slim in a cream turtleneck and denim jeans, her black hair untidily bunched around her shoulders, noticed the droop of her neck, the curve of generous lips as she mocked and teased a large Indian lady dressed in a sari. He paused again, considered for a brief, mad moment saying the flowers were from him, but was intercepted by a grey-haired woman.

'Sunflowers Florists delivery from across the road,' he revealed hastily.

'Who are they for? There's no card,' she accused as she peered into the bouquet of a dozen red roses. He shrugged apologetically.

'They couldn't be for me. They must be for one of them.' The stern woman carried the bouquet to the counter. He waited uncertainly.

The large woman in the sari gushed, 'Let me see! Let me see! Lovely roses! For whom?' Her curious eyes devoured the flowers. 'For whom?' she repeated. Not for a moment did she entertain the thought that she might be the lucky recipient. Mr Chatterjee was not given to frivolous gestures.

'If you think they could be yours, take them, there's no card,' suggested the grey-haired woman.

Another Asian woman looked at the blooms and declared, 'Must be for you, Durga.'

Durga. He memorised the name, sliding over its unfamiliar edges.

The large woman looked at her, avid eyes snapping. 'Who is this admirer of yours, *hanh*, Durga?' She wagged a finger. 'Trying to keep secrets from us, *na*?'

'They can't be for me, either. No one sends a rose to a cactus,' replied Durga. Her voice was attractive and low. He hated shrill voices. Kathy's had become very shrill in the end. Cactus. Had she just said '*cactus*'?

'Then for whom are these flowers? Durga says they

can't be for her, Swarna says they can't be for her, you say they can't be for you and I'm saying they can't be for me,' wondered Heera, turning to Eileen.

'Blimey, that's women for you. If you don't send 'em flowers, they complain. If you send 'em flowers, they complain. What's a man to do? What's all the fuss about? Share 'em three apiece and get on with it,' advised the customer who had previously been buried in the rack of nightgowns but had since moved on to the inspection of old record albums. He winked at Roman.

'Phone the florist,' suggested Eileen. 'That's the logical thing to do.'

Roman continued to stare at Durga. Instant attraction didn't happen in real life, it was the stuff of the chick films Kathy had dragged him to watch with a popcorn bag in one hand and a large Coke in the other. He couldn't remember the last time he had felt silly and weak at the sight of a woman, flames leaping, sending incoherent thoughts and snatches of poetry to his head. San Francisco, Kathy and the Arizona retreat were a fading drumbeat; he was mesmerised by the curve of a stranger's lips.

Heera returned to the group, embarrassed.

'Well?' said Eileen.

'They're for *me*. They're from Javed,' acknowledged Heera shyly. She stood holding the bouquet, lost in the perfection of the flowers, sniffing their fragrance and gently caressing the petals. With brimming eyes she hugged the blooms to her face, returning to breathe deep of their scent.

'Flowers from Javed?' There was a world of inflection in Swarnakumari's voice. A flame once extinguished was best forgotten, she brooded. Even if Javed had been Heera's young love, it was a long time ago. Her parents should have kept a strict watch, and then it would not have happened at all. Now that Heera was happily married to Bob, after saying, 'Hello, how are you?' there should be nothing more for her to say to another man who was not a blood relative, she decided, convinced Mr Chatterjee would not approve, either.

He had not spoken during his visit to the shop other than to inquire after Mrs Wellington-Smythe, she realised with a jolt. She did not understand why he had arrived there unannounced; he had appeared preoccupied and tense, giving her no opportunity to properly introduce her shop colleagues.

In truth, Mr Chatterjee's face as he wandered through IndiaNeed had registered not only incomprehension but also the unexpected entry into a brave new world that had made him feel irrelevant, as if the life he had lived had been revealed as no life at all.

'Heera, when you've finished, could you take a look at those old cigar boxes I found?' called Eileen.

Heera accompanied her behind the curtain, carefully holding the bouquet, as two burly men entered the shop, dragging a large, heavy object. 'Afternoon, got a delivery. Could you sign for it?' said the taller of the two, drumming his thigh impatiently. Swarnakumari was curious; the shop rarely took delivery of large items. 'Dunno. Just did what I were told. Cheers,' drawled the man on his way out in reply to her question.

As Roman watched, the group of women slowly encircled the object abandoned in the middle of the shop. Durga stood a few feet away and he stared at her, at her dark hair and eyes; she was a stranger who felt a mere breath away. He paused, overcome by self-irony; it was too soon after Kathy. He was already running from Teresa, and he should continue to be cautious and prudent, but once he had seen Durga, delicate as the leaf he had examined earlier, he sensed the image of her would be forever his to own and pin on the wing of a Petrarchan sonnet.

It had been different with Kathy. Kathy was not to blame, nor he; perhaps they would blame it on San Francisco. If they'd never moved to the Bay Area from the New England small town, why would he be here, in wind-swept Cambridge on a chill autumn day? It had been a Faustian bargain, unlike any at Macy's. A rueful smile chased his face, as he remembered his enthusiastic endorsement of Herb Caen's Baghdad by the Bay in the early days. No longer would he gaze up for the moon and settle for those towering confections of steel, enough of the cable cars and fire sirens, the plaintive foghorns and the Pyramid. No more eclectic bookstore, rollerblading in Golden Gate Park, mingling in the crowds on Labor Day weekend on the ferry to Angel Island or the Halloween party in the Castro, the sweating bearded Cinderellas and Tinkerbells at the Moby Dick or Twin Peaks, the lighting of the Christmas tree at Union Square. No more *Nutcracker* at the Opera House or envious amble past Neiman's and Saks, poetry at St Paul and Peter's Church, jazz in North Beach. No more cherry-tree blossoms in the Japanese Tea Garden; no longer would he allow himself to think of the Wharf and chowder and sourdough bread, Red's Java diner, nor the Anchor Steam beer straight from the source and the Farmer's Market at the Ferry Building. Nevermore did he want to read another *Chronicle* arts critique, nor a restaurant review, nevermore scurry for seductions by wine and books and food and the conversations of strangers.

Caught in the dance, they had failed to see they had toppled off the floor. When she argued for a new French-designed pre-heated toilet seat and ordered pre-wrapped counter pick-up presents for his friends, he should have seen that together they had already staled their infinite variety. He had wanted to read, write, teach, recite poetry, and Kathy, now as slim and indispensable to her interiors firm as dental floss to her teeth, hair burning brightly from lunch, talked with animation only of her therapist and wax, both Brazilian.

Her hysteria was timed to December, so inconvenient in the run-up to Christmas that, when she bravely continued to arrive at work, her employer increased her benefits package in gratitude. Roman obligingly timed his own less dramatic breakdown to the end of the semester, moving to a Buddhist retreat in Arizona.

'I go to the back of the shop only for two minutes and there is a problem already. Swarna, you should at least have asked what these men were delivering! What is this big thing lying here right in the middle?' asked Heera in exasperation as she poked at the object's edges. She tugged a lever, and with a loud groan it opened like an accordion and settled amicably with four spindly legs folding out underneath.

'Looks to me like a bed,' volunteered the customer, peering over an album of Diana and the Supremes. 'You know, one of those collapsible ones.'

'But what's this on the mattress? Some fool's written in ink, *Pamela and John forever*,' cried Heera, vexed.

140

'What are you going to do with it? It doesn't look new at all,' scoffed Swarnakumari.

'No, it doesn't. Pamela and John have spent forever on foam. And it will collapse if you sit on it,' warned Durga. 'It *is* a collapsible bed, though,' she added reasonably.

'Those are the same two names as on the sorting table,' said Eileen.

'That's so naughty,' admonished the customer, uneducated on either plot or characters, but keen to appear enlightened.

'Naughty'. The word smacked of the nursery and the smack, thought Roman. He would use it one of these days; shuffle from one foot to another, a leg crossed over the other, and with a pained expression on his face and clasped hands he would concede, confess, 'I'm naughty,' and await his punishment. He was also waiting for an opportunity to add 'Oops' to his vocabulary. After a year out in the West where men were wild, and the saguaros grew tall and strong, where the giant cactus lived for two hundred and fifty years and grew to seventy feet, where time and space rolled out into the desert, there had been no opportunity to say 'Oops'. Now he was ready. He would learn about civility and tea, crumpets and horses, rain and tweed, the grumble and apple crumble, ale and Britannia, conservatories and the colour magnolia, country rambles and brambles.

As Durga turned, her dark brown eyes met warm hazel eyes. 'What's so funny?' she demanded.

'It's unreal. I'd heard about English charity shops and sweet old ladies, but this place is weird,' Roman spluttered.

141

She looked at his springy dark hair, fresh, open face and rangy frame, at his mouth and tanned skin. Her smile widened and deepened, somersaulting over the collapsible bed, tumbling in the mattress, bouncing high on its springs and vaulting gracefully back.

'I'm Roman Tempest,' he said, offering a hand.

'Then I must be Indian Storm,' she replied, feeling the firm warmth of his grasp spreading into her own. 'Why Roman?'

'My parents loved *Roman Holiday*. Isn't it a cool name?'

'Yes. But it's also cheesy – Mills and Boonish. Like a tall, dark, handsome stranger in a romantic novel.'

'I *am* a tall, dark handsome stranger,' he replied. 'And romantic.'

'I'm Durga,' she said.

'I'm Visiting Faculty, teaching an MPhil course in American Literature. Who are you?'

'I'm a Townie now, but I did an MPhil in Modern Society and Global Transformation, Social and Political Sciences. Starting a researcher's job in television in London in a fortnight,' she answered.

'Aren't you the florist?' interrupted Eileen suspiciously.

'I'm Hermes at your service, madam. Messenger of Zeus. Or rather, of Sunflowers Florists, Mill Road. Behold my invisible cap, winged boots and caduceus. It's a long story,' he continued, but it was too late. Eileen shook her head dolefully and marched away.

Turning to Durga, he chuckled gleefully, 'She thinks I'm nuts, doesn't she?'

'She thinks everyone is nuts,' replied Durga. 'What is a caduceus?'

'The rod that Hermes carried, entwined by two serpents. He received it as a gift from Zeus when he invented the lyre. He used the shell of a tortoise for the lyre, by the way.'

'Now *I* think you're nuts,' she confessed.

'But nice? Please say I'm nice. You British love the word "nice", don't you? It covers everything, just like a tablecloth, or should I say "sari"? Hey, do you think I'm "interesting", too? Because that's not good,' he said, reprovingly. "Interesting" is dangerous,' he concluded.

'Are you like this all the time?' she asked.

'I wasn't before. Now I know it's as important as carrying a dozen red roses.'

She laughed, and he felt he had always known the sound.

'I get the feeling folks around here think Americans are brash and pushy, but I'm acting on impulse – I don't usually do this – could I take you out to dinner and tell you all about the florist? It's a riveting story, I promise, and will last until dessert,' he pleaded.

She was silent. Sensing her hesitation, he retreated, 'Okay, got the message. Step back, Roman, step well back. Naughty, naughty boy. That was too brash, too pushy. I'll back off before I do something stupid. I've already been stupid, haven't I, but I've also been nice, so there is something you could do for me, now that I'm here. Could you direct me to an old bookshop that's supposed to be on this road somewhere?'

'You must mean Browne's,' she said, trying to suppress her smile. 'Turn left when you come out. It's a few doors down, you can't miss it.'

143

He was forced to move closer to her, as Swarnaku-mari brushed past, intent on fetching a measuring tape for the bed. 'Do you have a picture of a desert, or a cactus?'

'In here?' she asked incredulously.

'Well, why not? If you can have a collapsible bed, why not a cactus? Sounds reasonable to me.'

'Why don't you just go to a garden centre and buy a real one?'

'The sensible solution. Of course!' He smacked his forehead in a mocking gesture. 'Why didn't I think of that? Sure, I can do that, but I want a picture. Is that too much to ask? Can't I have a look, no, what's the right word, can't I take a "little peek" among these cups and saucers, anyway? How about a guided tour of Buckingham Palace?'

Pausing in front of the men's winter coats, he con-fided, 'Have you ever felt so lonely for what you think you might lose that you think you need something tangible to remind you of it?'

'You mean like crutches?' she asked.

'Crutches?' He looked startled before recovering. 'Never thought of it that way, but if you desperately want to talk about crutches, then I guess I need them, or maybe I just think I do. I'm from the East Coast. A smalltown boy who singed his soul in the big city, born again. Sounds very Jehovah's Witness, doesn't it? How interesting! My life was deadlines and dates and pub-lishing papers. I was Icarus, flew too close. I also lost Kathy. We went to the School Prom together, that's how long I've been with her. She told me in the end that I made her unhappy every single day, and I thought all I was doing was loving her. That was the

144

shock that shook the pear tree. Something was very wrong with my life, and I had to take it apart. I spent a year in a Tibetan Buddhist retreat in Arizona, and I found silence and space. Sounds very New Age-ish, and it was only a year, but it *has* changed my life. Anyway, back to Cambridge. It's driving me crazy. I want a desert outside. I need those crutches – a picture, something, anything that helps me meditate on the colours of the desert. Do you understand?'

'Yes, I think I do, but I'm not sure I can help. I don't think you will find anything in here.'

They wandered through the clothes racks, unconsciously distancing themselves from the others.

'A picture of an *Echinomastus erectocentrus var. erectocentrus* would do just fine,' he said humbly, enjoying the bizarre intimacy of standing close to her next to a shelf of leather handbags while the rest were discussing the bed resting like a sleepy pregnant elephant in the centre of the shop.

'That sounds obscene. Is it?'

'That's a needle-shaped pineapple cactus,' he continued with a pained expression. 'Me? Obscene? Haven't you ever seen a barrel cactus? It's an amazing flame of orange. Or a fish-hook, hedgehog, rainbow, the prickly pear and cholla, the night-blooming cereus, Arizona Turk's head, golden beehive, pima pineapple, the organ pipe?'

'I think that's called showing off.'

'I'm trying to show you that a man so desperately homesick for a cactus can be a safe dinner companion,' he wheedled as they passed the china plates. 'And scintillating company, too.'

145

'That's it, tour over. As you can see, no desert, no cactus.'

'I thought you said you were a cactus.' He regretted his runaway tongue.

'What? Did I say that? When?'

Roman decided not to pursue the subject. There was something about her softness surrounded by prickles that *was* like a cactus.

'Do you think they need some help?' He watched Heera attempting to fold the bed, and strode forward. 'I guess no one wants bedtime stories just yet. Where's this Sleeping Beauty going?' he asked, as he pulled the lever.

'There is really no space in the shop,' observed Eileen disapprovingly.

'Precisely. We'll put it outside,' decided Heera.

'Outside the shop?' asked Swarnakumari, alarmed. 'Someone might take it away.'

The idea had crossed Heera's mind, and was in fact part of a plan. It was an easy – if illegal – way to dispose of unwanted items, for even the charity shop did have to reject and eject on occasion. Roman called on the male customer to assist in the removal of the bed; together they placed it slyly to partially conceal the Catnap window next door, and leave the IndiaNeed display visible. Unlike the vinyl-loving customer, Roman felt this was his cue to leave, but it was no ordinary departure; he no longer felt like the same man of the morning. He had something urgent to say to her, but it was too soon. He was reluctant to have her eyes spell a cool goodbye to the cactus-crazy American searching for a bookshop on Mill Road. Her indifference would be hard to carry away in the wind.

Roman noticed it was a changed wind, giving direction, no longer scattering the leaves into the cracks in the pavement. Pablo Neruda knew what he was feeling, and had said it so much better than he ever could. She and he were together in the autumn. He could not merely vanish; a tempest did not go quietly. 'Tempest' was 'tempestas'; 'tempus' was time, and he would be Prospero, stirring up a storm into something 'rich and strange'.

Durga wondered why she had agreed to go out with Roman Tempest. He had returned after propping the bed along the wall outside the shop. Running his fingers uncertainly through his hair, he waited for her response to his invitation, his eyes soft and warm, the accidental brush of their hands leaving them both awkward. They had arranged to meet the next day; she would accompany him to the American Cemetery at Madingley, and show him the Eagle pub, where wartime American pilots waiting for sorties had etched their names with cigarette lighters and their girl-friends' lipsticks on the ceiling. Then they would go out for dinner. Another time they would visit the Samuel Pepys library at Magdalene College, the Whipple Museum of the History of Science, the Scott Polar Research Institute and the Fitzwilliam Museum. In the spring, they would visit the Botanic Gardens and walk in the Backs to admire the crocuses, daffodils, tulips and bluebells.

There was an important detail she had omitted to mention, did not see the need to mention: she was married.

CHAPTER NINE

Home is where the heart is

DURGA STOOD RUEFUL after Roman had left, a quiet tempest brewing. It had been stardust and shooting stars, she had met the stranger whose locked glance she had coveted in her dreams like a romantic fool, but he had been a pleasant interlude, nothing more. She would retreat.

It had been a spring day in South Kensington; the magnolia blossoms in the communal gardens were bursting into velvety bloom, and Durga was thirteen. Her parents informed her over lunch: her father, the manager of a leading Indian bank, was being transferred back to Bombay. The move had been premeditated; Durga was being whisked away from the temptations of drugs, cigarettes, sex and rock 'n' roll in time for a dose of roadtested middle-class Indian values.

At the age of twelve Durga had sung and pirouetted in her room in their South Kensington flat overlooking the French café, reed-thin arms and legs, gawky in a short skirt. Pop would ruin Durga's voice, argued Durga's mother; Indian classical singing came from the pit of the stomach. Soon after their arrival in Bombay, Joshiji had been summoned for Hindustani classical music lessons. He waddled in every week, his dhoti revealing smooth, hairless calves. Fondness for paan led him to clear his throat often as he transferred the sodden red wad to another cheek in order to teach Durga a simple taan. Reaching for her father's old Time-Life books on the coffee table, he would dictate notation and hum the unfolding of a raag. Durga observed his fascination with the page displaying Sophia Loren in the famous black and flesh-striped transparent garment. She would deliberately pause and ask a question as his little eyes feasted and fastened on forbidden flesh, returning with reluctance to the musical composition.

A few months later, Joshiji was knocked down by a taxi during an act of worship at a roadside temple, and, shocked by the inexplicable interruption of his prayers, he became a recluse within the four walls of his Borivli home. Durga was merely relieved at the cessation of lessons, and the tanpura's strings broke over time.

Mishraji was recruited to teach Hindi, and he arrived every Wednesday wearing a worn but spotless white shirt and trousers, travelling from his home in Kurla, high on a hill near a buffalo milk dairy, to leafy Malabar Hill for the tuition. Durga hated the lessons, demonstrating her contempt for her circumstances, the language and the country to which she had been unceremoniously transplanted by blotting the seat of his pristine trousers with ink. He merely smiled and proceeded with the lessons. Over time, his son and daughter-in-law commandeered his rooms in the humble tenement building, feeding him meagre leftovers; it was a cruel fate for such a mild-mannered man.

Miss Noronha, Year Nine teacher, was the school's unofficial guide to puberty and adolescence; between lessons there had been homilies on the evils of sitting on the floor and eating bananas during menstruation as both affected the flow, as well as the optimum angle of hygienic suspension over a public seat. Good things came to girls who waited before marriage, but Miss Noronha omitted to mention to her class that she had waited far too long. Durga's marriage invitation to Miss Noronha was returned as *Addressee Unknown*. She heard two conflicting stories: Miss Noronha had left for Australia, and Miss Noronha was dead.

Miss Sathe was hired for Marathi lessons. She wore starched Finlay saris and lived in a tiny flat behind a temple ruin at Walkeshwar. A mousy, diminutive woman, she puckered her lips and emitted kissing sounds to denote assent and consent. It was one of life's little ironies that she herself remained unkissed, although it was rumoured there had once been a middle-aged suitor in her life, a Hindi teacher called Mr Doot. On his first visit to her home he had found her ministering with clicking, puckered sounds to a cantankerous mother. His ardour cooled rapidly, but he tenderly left her his copy of a story by Munshi Premchand.

Durga's new friend Anita was dismissive about the extra tuition, urging her to focus on the development of the body instead. She enjoined flat-chested Durga to follow a daily regimen of throwing her arms wide to the front and back to the accompaniment of the rhyme *I must and I must and I must and I must, I must and I must increase my bust.*

At thirteen, Anita was already buxom in her too-tight PE shirt, drawing sly glances from the school caretakers. She loved erasers of every kind. The Indian ones were boring, had no smell, so she bought imported Japanese ones by the dozen; her favourites were square and white with a green border carrying a letter of the alphabet and a picture. She perched them between her nose and lips to sniff their scent during lessons as she rocked on her chair. Anita had merely laughed when Durga asked if increased bust size was linked to the sniffing of erasers, making no denial. Anita did not attend Durga's wedding either; she was erasing a messy divorce.

Durga remained unresponsive and sullen; on her aunt's advice, an astrologer was summoned to her father's executive flat near the Hanging Gardens. Poring over her horoscope, he had turned silent. Whatever the stars were planning for her future, champagne corks weren't going to be popped.

'But what about marriage?' asked her mother, an academic, who had bestirred herself reluctantly from a scholarly essay on Vinoba Bhave to await the verdict on her daughter's destiny. Displaying a deep scepticism towards astrologers, she demanded from their findings a scientific approach far more rigorous than they were willing to display.

'Difficult. *Beti*, your life is a struggle. You will encounter bad luck after bad luck all the way through,' he had announced to Durga between greedy slurps from the saucer of ginger tea. 'You will also suffer from women's problems,' he pointed vaguely in the direction of Durga's abdomen, 'but later, much later, maybe at thirty, thirty-five.' His baleful owl eyes gleamed as her mother slipped him an extra hundred rupees toward the dilution of planetary harm to the refined Maharashtrian family.

151

A stern, scholarly woman, she was happiest among her books. Durga remembered her seated at a little desk, head bowed nightly in a lamp's glow, an avid expression on her face as she turned the pages, her tongue darting between her lips in fierce concentration. She ceaselessly fed her daughter the texts of the Vedas, Sri Aurobindo, Ramana Maharshi, Vivekananda, Mahatma Gandhi, Sant Tukaram and Sant Gnyaneshwar, demanding nothing short of excellence from Durga, who dutifully collected the form's silver badge every year. The school badges soon began to be made of a dull tin-like metal, evidence of the school's declining moral standards.

Durga witnessed violent arguments between her parents as her ambitious father rebelled. Entertaining at home was an essential part of climbing the corporate ladder, he protested, but Durga's mother stayed firmly on the ground. The only exceptions, she said, were relatives, whose frequent interruptions had to be borne with equanimity.

Under her mother's influence, the family embraced asceticism; it was the poor and downtrodden who would receive its compassion. The modest approach of 'simple living and high thinking' was at odds with the new residences on Malabar Hill, where sprawling old bungalows and tree-lined grounds were being rapidly replaced by luxury high-rise duplex apartments overlooking the sea, and whose nouveau riche inhabitants roamed fearlessly in tooting cars.

Eighteen-year-old Durga took the single-decker bus from Hanging Gardens, rumbling slowly down from Malabar Hill past the dense trees of the Governor's mansion, the flame of the forest trees and their incandescent rain-drenched blossoms pierced by the rare shriek of a roaming peacock in the dense undergrowth. Reaching Chowpatty Beach, she would look across the bay and Marine Drive with its Art Deco buildings, and the Manhattan-like skyline beyond. Staring into the murky water, she wondered if she would ever return to England.

Durga had soon realised that her parents were loosely bound by convention in a relationship vitiating both as they struggled for independence. She came to the conclusion that they should never have married. In the meanwhile, her father watched the promotion of his colleagues with bitter dismay, convinced that his hermit wife was the cause of his own stagnation.

'You know what your colleague Verma does, don't you?' her mother erupted in self-defence. 'He is always putting an arm around the ladies, and there is also something going on between his wife and your boss, as if you didn't know. Did you think they were patiently counting bundles of five hundred rupee banknotes together every night?' As Durga's father remonstrated, she raged, 'Why should we adopt their pretence and loose morals? For a career? Money? Will you be able to live with yourself if we do the same? *Aho*, do you remember where you have come from?'

Durga's father was from a poor coastal Brahmin family. As a schoolboy, he had studied under the light of oil lamps; following a charitable system practised for centuries in the community, he was sent to a different household on a nominated day of the week for a free meal. A car once passed through the small dusty village with its magnificent mango groves, and an industrialist stopped to ask his way to a religious shrine. The boy had been concise and clear in his directions, his eyes snapping with intelligence without fear. The industrialist had him transferred to a city school and paid for the family to move to Bombay.

Verma was undoubtedly popular with the ladies at the parties. His compliments on their saris and jewellery led to coy giggles over the risqué jokes as he moved closer to drop an arm around a waist, lightly tap a neck, or lean over to inhale a favourite perfume.

'Well, well, what do we have here?' he asked interestedly, roaming Durga's small breasts and narrow waist with his gaze. 'You have grown into a real beauty.' When she failed to respond, he laughed, 'Don't you recognise your Uncle Verma? Come, give me a hug, *bete*!' He enveloped her in a tight embrace and guffawed as she fled.

The director, a balding man from Jullunder, asked Verma's wife to carry one of her husband's ties to every assignation. She chose a different one each time, but either Verma's collection was too modest or the trysts with the director too many, for Verma was obliged to hurriedly purchase a fresh stock of striped, checked and polka-dotted ties from the Akbarally's at Flora Fountain. So strong were the ties of the Verma union that he was subsequently promoted to manager at the Delhi office while she remained in a Colaba flat, but a year later he was found hanging from the ceiling – by a tie his wife had never seen.

Durga could not have been more ripe for rebellion, a tomato ready to spew angry seeded pulp, but while her female friends flirted with male classmates in the college library and in the chapel and smoked cigarettes in the canteen or perched on the benches under the college hostel trees, she remained protected by her mother's idealism and the fiery reformist texts of the thinkers and educationists who had been her spiritual guides. She had also inherited her mother's naiveté and trust.

At the age of twenty, Durga caught a chest infection. She visited a laboratory to collect an X-ray report. The grey-haired pathologist beckoned. Had she been examined recently? he asked. She should have a second opinion. The diagnosis was often wrong, he added jocularly. She should lie down, relax and let him reassure her. He asked her to undo her blouse, and stared at her small pert breasts, breathing noisily, his stethoscope dangling from his neck. He had straightened suddenly, and ordered her off the table. It was the equivalent of intoxication without the drink. It never occurred to Durga to complain; years later she heard the pathologist was under review for indecent conduct with a number of women.

Durga attracted the attention of several amiable young men; it was her classmate Vibhuti, striking a provocative pose in tight jeans and blouse, who told her about the 'Durga Virginity Challenge'. The rich son of a Bollywood music producer had even offered free canteen batata wadas and chutney sandwiches for all if declared the winner. Who would have thought a swot would be such a draw? spat Vibhuti grudgingly, leaving Durga bewildered and angry. Difference was a terrible burden. So was conformity.

She met a young British backpacker roaming the back streets of Colaba behind the Taj Hotel. Her nostalgia for London and untried rebellion led her to agree to accompany him to the Elephanta Caves on the island across the harbour. As she waited at the Reception of

155

the Presto Hotel while he changed for the trip, two large cockroaches scurried up the peeling, damp walls latticed with the stench of stale onions. He returned from his room clad in denim shorts. The sight of his wobbly pale pink thighs unleashed a rising, bilious wave as she imagined she saw the two cockroaches climbing his flesh instead. She fled, leaving a bus ticket fluttering to the ground, one that he collected and carried home to Nottingham as a souvenir to show his mates. She was a dark-eyed beauty, he had said with the air of a conquest over the Balti meal; she had sobbed when he left for England, begging him to stay and be hers.

The day she developed the mandatory infatuation for her French teacher at the Alliance Française, Durga met Vivek Thadani. An overcrowded bus had failed to stop; at the sight of another overflowing bus approaching, a young man suddenly detached himself from the impatient queue to lie supine on the road. The bus stopped. The young man winked at Durga as the passengers swarmed of single mind up the steps of the bus. He arose, nimbly joining the last eager passengers as they boarded.

'What's happening? Why have we stopped suddenly?' asked a woman anxiously, looking out of the window.

'Accident,' replied another succinctly.

'Who?' quavered a fearful elderly man, trembling as he held his newspaper and his breath.

'A young man,' contributed a passenger in the front seat near the exit.

'But I can't see anything,' sulked a plaintive voice from the rear. 'Can't you move your head?'

'Do you think this is the cinema?' another said reproachfully. 'Next you'll want popcorn.'

'*Arre*, she can't see anything because he's dead,' announced a peering passenger. 'He's under the wheels.'

'*Hai!*' screamed a few voices in panic, and a large, perspiring woman burst into tears that fell on her basket of spinach, giving it a fresh, dewy appearance.

'Calm yourself. These things happen,' murmured a stranger gently.

'It is in the hands of God. Time and place decide everyone's fate,' agreed a hard-faced woman in a snug salwar kameez.

'But what a place to choose to read!' exclaimed another woman.

'What? He was reading? In the middle of the road? These students of today . . .' The hard-faced woman clicked her tongue disapprovingly. Several passengers followed suit until the bus reverberated with a click, click, click.

'What was he reading?' inquired an eager voice.

'*Arre*, does it matter whether it was a book or a bus ticket? He has gone to heaven now.'

'I think he was lying down,' confided an elderly passenger.

'*Hai!* Suicide?' shrieked a woman attempting to peer over the oily heads of her companions.

'The driver is looking under the bus,' reported a man in a vantage position.

As several passengers rushed for a better view, the young man slipped into a vacant seat and winked cheekily at Durga. As she subsided beside him, he buried his face in the pages of a newspaper.

'He must be a jilted lover,' concluded the hard-faced woman. 'He must have decided to end his life in a dramatic way to show her how much he loves her.'

'But then she should have been there to see it, otherwise what's the use? His life will have been wasted for nothing. Where is she? Could she be on the bus?' asked an agitated voice at the rear of the bus.

Several sharp eyes roamed the bus, pausing momentarily over Durga's wooden face.

'Maybe his girl is under the bus, too?' suggested a new, unseen voice.

The women looked as if they would burst into fresh tears, until a calm voice in the front said that was unlikely. That only happened in television soaps.

'*Arre, chalo, chalo*, come on, we are getting late,' shouted a man impatiently to the bus driver.

The large woman had a renewed bout of tears.

'A young man has died, and you are bothered about being late?' yelled the hard-faced woman. 'He is someone's son, someone's brother, and now he will never have a wife, or bear children. Shame on you!'

The man subsided, embarrassed. The driver climbed back into the bus. He glanced at the tiny picture of Ganesha pasted to the corner of the windscreen and bowed his head in thankful prayer. He had been convinced there was a man lying on the road; now he could no longer be certain. 'It was only a goat, and it ran away,' he announced to the passenger in the first row.

The driver's verdict spread like bushfire. As the bus lurched forward, several passengers began to scramble for seats now as scarce as small change in the shops. A couple searched in vain, and the woman glared at Durga and the head buried in the newspaper. 'Look,

158

they are nicely sitting in our seats,' she grumbled, but her meek husband ventured, 'Never mind, at least no one died under this bus.'

Everyone agreed. No one wanted a ride in a chariot of death. Durga saw the newspaper shake, hearing little snorts. Soon she was giggling, her face red and puffy. The hard-faced woman nudged her companion. 'Look at these youngsters, no respect for death.'

The bus emptied opposite the post office near the Hanging Gardens. The driver hurriedly lowered himself from the seat to stand outside the bus, mopping his brow. Fate had saved him this time, but it was a sign: there was danger lurking on the roads. He would take up a job in an office canteen instead. At least he would not mistake food for anything else.

The newspaper was lowered and a cheeky grin emerged. 'Hi, I'm Vivek!' he announced. 'Did you enjoy the ride?'

'That was a really stupid thing to do. You could have been killed.'

'But you noticed me, didn't you? And now you'll never forget me.'

Durga never forgot. Vivek was inseparable from his motorbike, calling it Moody Baby, and unknown to her mother Durga had soon travelled the length and breadth of Bombay. The lights of the Haji Ali Mosque in the middle of the sea twinkled as they sped towards Bandra, her hair a pennant in the wind. Durga's mother frowned; who could have imagined bus rides to college could cause such damage to her daughter's hair? She prepared herbal concoctions using areetha and shikakai as shampoo substitutes, and oiled her daughter's hair with angry tugs.

Two years later, Durga's mother found out, and her first question, fearing much worse, was whether Vivek had held Durga's hand. Vivek made her laugh, said Durga. Her mother was sufficiently alarmed to discuss the matter with her husband. 'I think Durga should settle down,' she said firmly.

He protested, 'But she's only twenty-four. She's just finished the double MA and she's applying for the scholarship to Cambridge.'

'Let her get married and continue her studies. We should start looking now,' insisted her mother, lips sewing a thin line. 'She should not get into the wrong company.'

Vivek, the son of a businessman who manufactured matchboxes, was not the right company, she asserted, and the nonsense about him making Durga laugh was just that – nonsense. He was hardly going to set her alight. She should find a life companion with an intellect to match. Durga's mother awaited the impending visit of Mrs Kamath, friend of Aunty Sarojini and community matchmaker.

Mrs Kamath was a florid woman with a heaving bosom that moved like a rusty pendulum; her large gold earrings and prominently displayed mangalsutra, a gold chain with black beads and gold pendant, were not only a symbol of her married status but a calling card. She settled down comfortably to 'ladies' talk only'. As she bit appreciatively into the pohe snack prepared with reluctance by Durga's mother, she confided, 'I have "n" number of boys lined up for Durga. Just say the word.' She patted the sofa with a plump hand, inviting the mother to move closer.

'First of all,' began Durga's mother firmly to Mrs

160

Kamath, 'you should understand that my daughter is highly intelligent. She wants to study for many more years and we want a boy who understands that. We would like the two to get married first, and study together later. Durga would like to go abroad, so we are willing to wait until the right one comes along.'

'Of course, anyone who knows your cultured family would expect that only, no question. Best match will be found. Now can I have her horoscope?' humoured Mrs Kamath.

The family stood firm. Horoscopes would not be necessary. Mrs Kamath sensed steel; years of experience had taught her it would buckle and melt like butter.

Dressed in an orange silk sari for the occasion, Durga's mother stood uncertainly in front of her wardrobe mirror before dabbing *Chanel No. 5* on her wrist. The bottle had lain in pristine condition since they had left England eleven years earlier. It was a frivolous gesture for a serious business.

Sitting uncomfortably in the opulent living room, Durga and her mother were boldly examined by a middle-aged couple seated on a silk sofa across the room.

'Where is your son?' asked Durga's mother for the second time as a servant brought in silver glasses of rose sherbet on a silver tray. Ignoring her question, the man addressed Durga. 'As you know, we are a well-known industrialist family in Maharashtra. We believe that girls should be educated, of course, and it is commendable that you want to continue your studies, but our daughter-in-law is expected to look after this family first. It is a lot of responsibility, and she must be ready for this status and position.'

'How many in your family?' inquired Durga's

mother, directing the question at his wife. The husband answered proudly, 'We have three eligible sons.'

'But which princeling are we supposed to meet?' asked Durga's mother. 'You've seen my daughter, but not a single one of your sons is here. This is not a cattle fair.' She rose hastily to her feet. 'Enough of this nonsense! Come, Durga, let's go!'

Mrs Kamath meekly apologised as they drove away. Rich people were 'like that only', she prattled, but there was no need to fret, she had already found another, the 'best' match for Durga.

'The boy is from a good Saraswat Brahmin family. Engineer. Good-looking, tall, fair, very fair. Lives in America, New Jersey. Your Durga can continue studying there. These American universities are phirst-class. The boy has no sisters, no brothers. And on top of it, his parents live far away. Only slight problem and you know I am telling you honestly, I never hide anything, the boy is moody. You see, what happened is that he was married,' confided Mrs Kamath. She placed a warning hand on Durga's mother. 'No, no, just wait. I know what you must be thinking and what you are going to say, but he was married for a short time only. He is as good as new.'

'What was the problem, then?'

'Nothing much. He had a child, poor thing, dead at birth and then the wife had a nervous breakdown and she left him. These things happen, nobody's fault. Since a long time it is over. He is on his own. Only thing, he gets a little angry. Moody, shouts a little, but when he is married again, when there is another child, everything will be all right.'

Durga's mother terminated the conversation.

162

'Really, this Mr Fair-Very-Fair-Shouter needs professional help, not yours or ours. We send him our prayers and good wishes for his complete recovery.'

'Your mother knows what's best for you,' concluded Vivek when Durga described the meetings with Mrs Kamath.

'How can you be so sure?' she asked as they walked along Juhu Beach in the sunset. The sand was warm and sticky under her feet.

'Never mind that. When are you going to apply for the scholarship to Cambridge?'

'Soon, but what are you going to do with your life?' she wanted to know.

He grinned. 'Make bigger and better matchboxes, what else? You go ahead and do the fame thing for both of us. Remember, even if you do this marriage stuff, make sure you study and do something great with your life. Don't become a housewife buying brinjals in Dadar market, I'm counting on you.'

Durga had little time to pursue either the advice or the application; her father had a heart attack the next day. The doctor pronounced it mild, but Durga's mother abandoned her books and ministered to her husband with alternating panic and calm.

It was weeks since Mrs Kamath had successfully brokered a match; she planned her next visit to Durga's mother with care. Mrs Kamath was no longer her usual ebullient and persuasive self; her daughter's marriage had been under strain over a property wrangle, and she herself suffered from headaches and back pain. The doctor's diagnosis was bad for business; depression and matchmaking were an incompatible combination.

'I have come with five proposals, not one,' she

gurgled. 'This time you will not say "No", I know that. Your pretty daughter is in such demand, really!' Mrs Kamath shuffled the order of the 'proposals' with practised ease. 'See, the first one is a really good offer, but they insist the girl should be a computer engineer. That too, software, only. The second family wants blood tests after the boy and girl have decided, because nowadays, these modern people you know, they want to be sure the couple can have children. And healthy children, also. The third wants quick marriage, there are four brothers next in line. It is a joint family. The fourth is a college lecturer, he lives a little bit far away – in Mangalore.'

Mrs Kamath put down her teacup with finality. Satisfied with the results of her strategy, she said, 'So you didn't like the other four? Never mind. No problem, what is the hurry? Durga is young, beautiful and intelligent. We can wait two years, three years, five years, whatever you say. But I thought that with Bhausaheb's health problem, God grant him long life, but you know how these illnesses suddenly come upon us, you are so sensible, I know you will want to have everything settled at the right time. Now I have one last offer. Of course, I will have to see about this one if you like him, because the boy is very much in demand, but if you are keen I can give you the details. Chitpavan family. He is a doctor doing research in Cambridge. Parents and sister live in Pune. He will return after studies, that much I can tell you.' She paused. 'Also handsome.' It had been a masterstroke to pretend to gather her handbag in a hurry. Durga's mother asked her to stay for another cup of tea.

*

Dip dip. That was what the tea-seller at Nasik Station had said as Durga arrived from the riverbanks, the immersion of her parents' ashes over. She had asked for tea. 'Will a dip dip do?' He had mimicked the dunking of an imaginary teabag in the chipped white cup he slid under her nose.

Her cousin had unexpectedly found a quiet spot on the ghat behind a little marble temple and under a magnificent banyan, and he waded into the sunlit water with the urns. He had performed the last rites, accompanied by her silent resistance and welling anger; this should have been a daughter's right. There was also a distant memory of the same annoying cousin thrashing about in a Bombay swimming pool; he had caressed her teenage thighs before swiftly escaping in a noisy splash.

The tranquillity of the moment and the sweet chimes of the temple bell were replaced by the loud tones of a raunchy film song, 'Choli ke Peeche Kya Hai' (What's Behind the Blouse), streaming from a transistor held by a young man in an unbuttoned shirt and tight trousers ambling down the path above. It was a cruel, noisy requiem for the disjointed lives of her parents, crushed in a pilgrims' stampede. Durga's Aunty Sarojini offered consolation. At least the bodies had been recovered: other victims would be missing for ever.

Durga plunged into legalities and paperwork. Uncle Manohar shook his head sadly as he looked at the disarray of his brother's financial affairs. Still, there was a small retirement flat in Pune as Durga's inheritance; at least she had a roof over her head, and by God's grace it need not be his.

Mrs Kamath seized the opportunity to sway Durga's Aunty Sarojini; the girl was vulnerable to exploitation by unscrupulous sharks now that she was alone in the world. Besides, she added, embroidering past conversations without guilt, she could hear the mother's voice pleading: 'Only you can find me a good boy for Durga, I am counting on you.' Sarojini was moved as Mrs Kamath, dabbing her eyes, embellished stories of her visits to Durga's mother. There was no time to lose, said Mrs Kamath, with determination. It was in Durga's best interests to marry the doctor. He was also a gynaecologist, what more could a girl want? One way or another, exulted Aunty Sarojini later to her niece, she would be going to Cambridge.

When Durga and her husband returned home together after the wedding, his mother had greeted them at the door with a ceremonial thali for the ritual washing of Durga's feet, her silk blouse tight under armpits circled with sweat. The silver thali made a loud sharp *thak* sound as she placed it on the floor; Durga stepped into the thali, and her sister-in-law Archana reluctantly poured a few symbolic drops of water from a jug onto the bride's feet. The mother barked, 'Napkin, napkin, bring napkin!' berating the servant as Archana ordered him to take the 'dirty water' away, and Durga's feet left the thali cleansed for her new life. Both mother and daughter ignored the ceremonial coconut Durga was carrying, and as she entered the house the servant took it casually from her, as if she were a wordless postman expecting a Diwali tip. The family had green coconut chutney at dinner.

Atul's relatives were in attendance on her wedding night. A noisy card game coupled with intermittent desultory singing led the uncles to chorus their demands to Atul, who obligingly obtained whisky from his gynaecologist father, owner of Patwardhan's Maternity Clinic. The Johnnie Walker Black Label bottles were concealed behind the woollen suits smelling of mothballs in his steel Godrej cupboard with the cracked mirror. Atul's cousin, a fair, green-eyed woman with long, plaited brown hair, sent Durga a sullen, smouldering look. There was something proprietorial about the cousin, thought Durga. And his sister, his parents, the entire family. She was married to the mob.

The nuptial bed was bedecked with rajnigandha flowers and rose petals. Atul and Durga had made their way to his old bedroom accompanied by winks and jokes from the uncles. Minutes later, there was a knock on the door. It was his sister Archana. With only a token apology, she removed a hairbrush from Atul's wardrobe. Her sharp, satisfied eyes noted the couple's awkwardness.

'Didn't your mother teach you to cook?' reproached Atul's mother a week later. 'I have taught Archana everything. Studying is not an excuse. It is every woman's duty to learn these things, and you will be doing the cooking in Cambridge, anyway.' She placed the lid firmly on the pressure cooker. 'He loves vangebhaji, it's his favourite dish. You must learn everything about our style of cooking, although I must say he will still miss my special touch.'

As if on cue, Atul walked into the kitchen, placing an arm around his mother's waist. 'Yes,' he said simply, 'and if only I could, I would have you in Cambridge with me.' She looked as if she would cry.

Durga's moments alone with her husband were hurried rather than intimate; both waited for the knock on

167

the door. The days passed in the constant company of his relatives and friends, who saw little need for their privacy. Atul's light-eyed cousin Shreya developed a mysterious infection that she could only discuss in confidence, so they disappeared to talk in hushed tones on balconies with lush overhanging bougainvillaea, in rooms darkened against the midday sun.

Durga and Atul were awakened one night by a harsh, reedy wail from his parents' room. He hurried out, indicating that she should remain in bed, and did not return until the morning. As he explained to Durga later, his mother was suffering separation pangs again, as she had done when he had left for Cambridge for the first time. She experienced breathing difficulties, and complained of palpitations and impenetrable aches in the neck and limbs. He had stayed by her side, they had chatted late into the night, and he had finally lain across her lap in exhaustion. He would invite her to Cambridge next summer, he said; that would brighten her mood.

A professional family portrait was suggested before they left for England; there was excitement as Atul made an appointment with Patekar's Studios at Deccan Gymkhana. It was the equivalent of a family trip to Disneyland. His mother stood in front of her grey Godrej steel cupboard, searching endlessly among the piles of neatly folded saris, as his sister hovered to advise. Atul was handsome in his black wedding suit although it pinched at the elbows; he stole an appreciative glance at Durga in a purple and red Paithani sari that had belonged to her mother.

Atul's aunt and his cousin Shreya arrived unannounced. His mother stood in front of her cupboard again, calling out to them to select two saris: they had accepted the invitation to accompany the family to the studio. Fifteen minutes later they were waiting, stiff and starched, for his father, who had been delayed by the slow progress of a patient at Patwardhan's Maternity Clinic. 'Are you giving birth to a buffalo?' he asked in desperation, glancing at his watch. The sweating, heaving woman cast him a pleading look. He relented. 'Push harder!' he commanded.

He arrived at Patekar's Studio along with his family to find it changed. The big cameras and black cloth and popping flashbulbs were gone, and Patekar Senior had retired; his fingers were too unsteady. The son, a smart young man, was courteous, but the Pune air in the studio was one of efficiency, of the instant one-hour passport photo service, the multiplex cinema and the Barista coffee shop. The magician's curtained lair of mysterious dusty props and the world of quiet, leafy lanes were gone forever.

Patekar Senior would have slowly arranged the family members around the Patwardhan patriarch seated on a grand velvet chair, but his son Ravi was more hurried, now habituated to digital commercial photography. He had snappily assigned everyone their places, but there was a cousin who hovered unhappily on the periphery. With an intuition his father would have applauded, he subtly altered the arrangement; Atul now stood beaming – if a little squashed – between radiant cousin and wife.

Durga rang Vivek and her relatives from her new home in Pune; the conversations were stilted and guarded. Atul's mother and sister were watchful, displaying their displeasure at her continued links with

169

her old life. Durga had clung to her surname fiercely, unwilling to exchange 'Prabhu' for 'Patwardhan'. Atul's anorexic aunt, who lived in Florida and organised classical music soirées for visiting artistes from India, intervened with the persuasive vocabulary of a Sicilian warlord to announce closure on the matter: Durga was no longer a 'Prabhu'.

'Do you have any idea what a well-known family we are in Pune?' challenged Archana. 'Or is it because you think you are too good for us that you didn't want to change your name?' She had waited until Atul was out strolling with his parents in the University Gardens. 'And forget about all those fancy friends. Who is this Vivek I heard you phoning?'

'An old friend.'

'Oh? Does Atul know about this? What is the need to ring this friend from here?'

Durga had remained silent, unsurprised by the hostility, unwilling to talk about her loneliness, and Archana was satisfied she had found proof of Durga's guilt.

A week before her wedding in Pune, Durga had perched on Moody Baby near the quiet, leafy Afghan Church in Colaba.

'You will stay in touch, won't you?' asked Durga.

'What do you think? Who else is going to make you laugh out there in cold Cambridge?'

'I'm serious.'

'*Arre*, I laid down my life on the road for you once, and I would do it again, but don't tell anyone, it's bad for my reputation,' said Vivek with a tremor in his voice.

She looked at him, choked by a new realisation. 'Why didn't you say . . .'

'Not good enough. Not for you. Do great things with your life, Durga, as you were always meant to. Now enough! Moody Baby will cry in a minute, and you know how she hates ruining her mascara and leaving those black streaks on the road.'

Prior to her departure for Cambridge, Durga visited her parents' retirement flat for the last time. Standing in the hallway as the sun filtered through the rooms, her eyes lingered over the contents carefully transported from Mumbai. Her mother's books were piled high on a table, the reading spectacles neatly folded, the chair at a beckoning angle. Her father's liquor cabinet caught the afternoon light swirling in the wine, sherry, cognac and whisky glasses shipped with pride from England, the pub souvenirs, a model of a London bus, Durga's pop cassettes and teenage fiction spilling over the shelves, the broken tanpura and the Time-Life book so eagerly perused by Joshiji. She walked to the wardrobes, opening them in turn, burying her face in the soft folds of her mother's saris, as neat and fragrant as when last worn, running her fingers over her father's shirts from Marks & Spencer, labelled with lingering cologne. Durga wept.

Atul's mother wept until her son was no longer a speck in the private Pune luxury taxi bound for the airport. She leaned heavily on her husband for support, a cracked stalk in the wind. Rivulets snaked down her face, as her husband bravely blinked back his own tears. 'What do I have to look forward to, except my Atul's next visit?' she cried plaintively, prompting several female relatives to pull out tiny handkerchief squares in haste. Dab, dab, dab. Their sons and daughters, too, had

171

left Pune for the winking lights of the West, never to return. The green-eyed cousin Shreya wept pitifully in glandular gasps, but Archana remained dry-eyed. 'That is enough, *Aai* – you will make yourself ill. Do you want Atul to drop everything he is doing there and come back just for you?' she rebuked her mother, planting a seed for slow germination.

The rotund man sitting next to Atul in the aisle seat on the flight to Heathrow confided his diabetic condition within minutes of being airborne. 'So which fruit is the highest in sugar content, Doctor? Which vegetables do you recommend I should avoid? Doctor, any suggestion on exercise?' he asked humbly, whipping out a large notepad and pen. A gynaecologist was still a doctor, and the advice was free.

Durga looked at her husband's profile. The days in Pune had passed in crumbling suffocation, and black, hate-filled mosquitoes had bitten through her limbs despite the window mesh. She wondered at Atul's desire to have an arranged marriage; his cousin and sister clearly felt he and Durga were ill-matched, and slyly influenced his mother to concur. Atul's father was a mild-mannered man who spoke little. Surrounded by female nurses and patients all day, over the past twenty years his vocabulary had dwindled to the injunction 'Push harder!' at the Maternity Clinic. He was an unlikely ally, despite the apparent feminist sentiment behind the two words.

Faced with baseless suspicion from strangers, Durga was initially optimistic; she would turn the other cheek, douse fire with love. A smuggled surfeit of Mills & Boon romances had led to her muddled view of love and marriage, and she was horrified to find a rewritten script; she was playing the role of Cinderella *after* she had married the prince. Was he a prince who had turned into a frog, or a princely frog? Durga had taken a bite of the apple, but instead of a gentle awakening from slumber in a glass casket, she was learning to iron the creaseless shirt.

She glanced frequently at Atul during the flight. He was a handsome man, and perhaps it was too soon for disillusionment; they had left India and his family behind, the future awaited. It would be different once they were on their own and in Cambridge, city of spires.

Durga waited at the luggage carousel at Heathrow as Atul struggled to heave a second heavy suitcase onto the trolley. He looked down in dismay at the spreading oil stains on his beige chinos, leaned forward and sniffed. 'It must be mango pickle – oh God, it has leaked!' he exclaimed. He looked crushed, as a red stain formed a symmetrically large triangle on his crotch, coupled with two vertical red streaks on his thighs; his mother's blessings had safely accompanied him to England. Had Durga laughed, the echo would have sneaked into the terminal, into the waiting coffee cups and steaming ears of the passengers and out onto the tarmac with the planes, steering upward into the open skies.

'Do something!' he ordered sharply, aware of the smirks and stares of the other passengers.

'You mean do something about the suitcase first, or you?'

Before he could respond, a man approached. 'Atul Patwardhan? I thought it was you! We met at the New Hall dinner two months ago. Richard Cartwright, obstetrics.'

The two men shook hands and Richard Cartwright's gaze travelled downward.

'He's in a bit of pickle, can you help?' asked Durga. 'These suitcases are rather heavy, and I need to open one to get some wet tissues.'

Richard Cartwright obliged and as Durga dabbed Atul's trousers a passing passenger quipped, 'Mind the Crown Jewels there, luv!' Richard began to chuckle, but Atul looked thunderous. 'I'd say your best bet is to find another pair of trousers,' commiserated Richard as he left, but they discovered that the mango pickle had spread in spurts over the entire contents of the suitcase zealously fingerprinted on the outside by Atul's father with two large, handwritten, heavily gummed labels PROPERTY OF DR PATWAR-DHAN. The Cambridge address was prominently displayed. It was as legible as an optician's sight-testing chart.

Durga rummaged through the clothing and beheld the stained portrait. The eyes of the Patwardhan family were red blobs of sorrow. The packet of his mother's home-made sweets was coated in oil. Durga suggested disposal, but Atul was reluctant. 'We can't throw anything away. My mother has made everything herself. But I don't understand, how could you pack edible things with my clothes? You should have had some sense at least.'

'Who said *I* packed them?'

'Then who?'

'Mommy dearest? Sister dearest?'

He was about to protest when she waved a pile of baby clothes in indignation under his nose. They were all postmarked in mango red.

'Yours, I presume?' she asked coldly.

He stared sheepishly at the accompanying envelope addressed to Mrs Aparna Achrekar of Milton Keynes. 'That's my cousin Shreya's sister-in-law. She's expecting a baby. Maybe she asked *Aai* to send the baby clothes through us,' he mumbled, as she continued to display several packages at random.

'And who is Kishori Chavate in London? Lucky, lucky girl! A kilo of laadu for her sweet tooth. And who is Mr Mystery-Man Madhav Mhatre? Life will be one long party for him once he receives your mother's eight-cassette pack of Marathi devotional songs mailed direct by us to the American address attached here,' declared Durga with increasing flourish.

Durga would have been surprised to hear that she had begun to sound like her mother.

'All right, stop it now. I get your point. We are late for the coach. If we miss it, we have a long wait, so just put it all back and we'll have to sort this out later,' he said irritably.

It was a morose journey on the airport coach to Cambridge's Drummer Street. The driver had asked, 'What happened, mate?' in horror, for the trousers now appeared to be covered with dried blood, pointing untruthfully to the dismemberment of a vital organ. The other passengers politely averted their eyes, but a man walking quickly past had sniggered, 'Lost your lunchbox, did yer?' Atul scowled. His gaze returned repeatedly and hypnotically to the stains during the journey. 'They were my best chinos,' he complained. 'I bought them in New York when I went there for a conference. Dry cleaning costs such a bomb here, I'll have to wait and see if I can send them back with

175

someone. Actually, Nikhil is going to Delhi soon.' He brightened.

'You mean send them all the way to India?' she asked in disbelief.

'Why not? What did I tell you, every damn thing is so expensive in this country. Why do you think my mother was so keen for you to learn to cook? Who can afford to eat out at these prices? Listen, I really hope you brought everything you need, because we won't be running around in the shops as soon as we arrive.' He softened. 'See, it's not that there is no money, but it is not to be wasted on frivolous things. It is important to count every penny while we are here, and then we will have something to take back when we return.'

He had omitted to tell her that anything saved would be invested in Patwardhan's Maternity Clinic. Despite the future purchase of gleaming new machines, women would still have to push as they had through the ages.

Durga looked at the rain-streaked landscape and grey skies of her London childhood with increasing excitement. She was back in England, going to Cambridge and that was all that mattered. She would roam the colleges, see the fan-vaulted ceiling of King's College Chapel, the Fellows' Garden of Clare and Christ's, the Grecian buildings of Downing, the Wren Library, Trinity's Great Court. She was living a student's dream after years of crammed after-school coaching classes in rat-infested dank buildings, and nights of endless study leading to a single magical word: Oxbridge.

Atul shared none of the excitement she felt. He had not spoken to her on the flight or introduced her to Richard Cartwright, nor had he commented on her return to England after the long absence. He did not ask if this was home because it was the country of her birth and childhood, if home was what she had left behind in India, or was home wherever she was with him? On her first day back in England, Durga's suspicions were being speedily confirmed. It was about a boy, not a man.

As the taxi sped towards Hills Road from the coach station, Atul leaned over and asked the driver about the woody smell inside. 'I thought it was you, mate,' replied the driver sanguinely. 'Smells like an old lady with a cold in the back.'

Atul sniffed his way to the source of the odour and scrabbled frantically in his rucksack until his fingers made startled contact with a cracked bottle of Olesan eucalyptus oil and a hastily wrapped packet of incense sticks. As he searched further afield, he found a hot water bottle, herbal back-rub ointment and three pairs of thick hand-knitted men's socks.

'What have you been putting in here?' he asked in anger.

'Not *mea culpa*.'

'Then who?'

Durga thought it prudent not to point a finger in the same direction more than once, and did not reply.

As they entered the tiny flat, he snapped peevishly, 'What a bloody mess!'

It was not the welcome to Cambridge she had fondly imagined, but Durga could only concur.

CHAPTER TEN

All things come to those who wait

SWARNAKUMARI HAD DISCOVERED something far more important missing in her life than a mere dozen roses. 'Any of you have seen my Guru Ma's prayer book lying anywhere?' she asked anxiously. 'I had it with me when I came in this morning. I must find my prayer book, must find it. It has her photo on it. She has long black hair, and she is sitting in a white robe in lotus pose, with one hand up.'

'What's she doing with the other, I'd like to know?' said Durga.

'Durga!' warned Heera.

'Where did I leave it, where could it be? Girls, help me! What if it has gone?' Swarnakumari wandered distractedly into the Staff Area.

'Did you hear about the book by that woman who hadn't had you-know-what for thirty-five years, and suddenly she was having lots of it, so she wrote about it?' asked Heera, standing by the shop window. 'She was American, I think. Anyway, she was sixty-five or something and she put an advert in the papers, say-

178

ing all she wanted was you-know-what, and can you believe it, a lot of people answered.'

Eileen gave a disbelieving snort.

Durga turned to Swarnakumari as she returned through the curtains. 'Did you hear that, Swarna? This woman could be a role model for all those who think life's over at fifty.'

'Keep looking for the book,' urged Swarnakumari absently.

'Imagine, the youngest bloke to do you-know-what with her was thirty-two,' marvelled Heera.

'What?' mumbled Swarnakumari, barely listening.

'Why beat around the bush? Swarna, what would you say if a woman of sixty-five wanted sex? What would your Guru Ma say?' asked Durga.

'*Baba*, now you are teasing me again. What is there to say? At that age a woman should be thinking of nothing but spirituality, *na*. She should lead a simple, pure life. She must lose her attachment to all worldly things – all possessions, wealth, family, children. That is all,' concluded Swarnakumari firmly.

'Why not have fun in the years there are left?' suggested Durga.

'Is this the time to ask me such things?' barked Swarnakumari. 'Where could my prayer book be?'

'People do strange things at that age,' mused Heera. 'I know a woman called Sudha Barjotia. A little older than me, of course, she has a daughter-in-law now – they don't get along at all, in fact, they hardly talk to each other – but do you know what she puts on her face? That cream you get in India called Fair and Fine. As if it is going to make any difference to her now, after the age of forty-five. Both she and her daughter-in-

179

law use it, so at least they have something in common.'

Swarnakumari looked up with interest. 'What is this cream?'

'A cream called Fair and Fine to make the skin fair and fine. Honestly, Swarna, what else could it be?'

'If you are fair, you are fine,' observed Durga. 'Unless you mean the groom.'

'Does it work?' asked Swarnakumari, thinking of Mallika.

'Why don't you ask the men who use it?' countered Durga.

'You shouldn't make so much fun of her,' whispered Heera. 'Just help her find the book. She really believes in this Guru Ma, you know. These gurus are powerful people, and they can be quite inspiring.'

'That reminds me – when I was visiting Pune, I heard an amazing story,' Durga told her. 'There is a holy man, a baba, somewhere, who meditated in a pond for years. When he decided to emerge, his followers apparently discovered the fish in the pond had devoured his legs, so they carried him off on their shoulders. According to some reports, he's gung-ho about going back in again. I would fear for his arms this time, but then that's the power of faith for you.' She continued, 'And there's another baba who changes anything his followers offer him into something that tastes sweet. So let's say I give him a bitter veggie, it turns as sweet as honey.'

'What else does he do?' asked Eileen.

Durga looked puzzled.

'I mean, what's the point in trying to make other people's lives *taste* good?' Eileen persevered. 'The world needs other miracles.'

'Do you know, I heard a TV presenter the other day, who described Indian skin as mahogany,' interrupted Heera indignantly, still reflecting on creams and complexions.

'Are you sure he wasn't talking about furniture?' asked Durga.

Heera rushed to answer her mobile phone. 'Yes, Bob, it's me . . . I'm fine. Really . . . No, I don't think that's a good idea. I'm going out tonight. Can't we talk another time?' She silently returned to the counter, unnerved by the call. There was an unhappy edge to Bob's voice. He had been so insistent; was it about Adam?

No one spoke. Such moments were rare at India-Need, and did not last long. The shop bell soon tinkled, and a strapping young man entered, carrying a bulky shoulder bag.

'Hiya, Assistant Photographer, *Cambridge Evening News*,' he trumpeted. 'Which one of you is Diana Wallington-er-Smith?'

Durga mocked, 'Do you think any of us could be Diana Wellington-Smythe? Such a deliberate transposing of the postcolonial subject would not only be aesthetically unappealing but necessitate an inapposite dismantling of notions of self, ethnicity, race and class, thus bringing it into hybrid discontinuity.'

A faint smile hovered over Eileen's lips.

'Er . . .' responded the photographer.

'The director of the charity is out riding and won't be disturbed. And she won't like you messing with her name, by the way. It's Wellington-Smythe. Why do you want to know where she is?' asked Heera sharply.

The photographer turned to Heera, relieved at her

181

intervention. 'Well, she wanted to pose for the shop photo tomorrow afternoon with a toff, Lady something or other. It's some sort of Charities Special, but I've got to rush and do it now, or it won't get into the Saturday paper. Can't you ring her?'

Heera was emphatic in her refusal.

'Oh, all right then, why don't you lovely ladies line up there under the shop sign? Right there, yeah. Brilliant. Tell you what, display something from this shop, will yer?'

Swarnakumari and Heera both jostled for a central position, looking on in dismay as Durga mischievously slipped between the two. Swarnakumari held a teapot aloft, Heera a scarf and Durga a clock, and Eileen hovered uncertainly, displaying a child's mathematical set.

'C'mon loves, you can do better than that! Give us a smile, will yer?'

Durga murmured, 'Imagine Lady Di's face when she sees her little "Cambridge Curry Club" in the papers!'

'Yeah, that's it. Perfecto,' grinned the photographer.

As Swarnakumari coyly adjusted her sari over her shoulder, she spotted her prayer book nestling among a set of wine glasses in the shop window and leaned across the others, screaming, '*Who* put my Guru Ma prayer book for sale in the window?'

The photographer clicked. 'Lovely. Now ladies, if you'll excuse me, gotta rush, gotta get back to work. You'll tell Mrs er . . . Willington-Smith, won't yer? Any problems, ask her to contact me, she's got my number. Cheers, take care now, bye!'

Swarnakumari retrieved her prayer book, pressed it gratefully to her bosom, looked heavenward and mumbled reverently, 'How my prayer book landed up in the window God only knows, but I have got it back now, that is the main thing.'

'I thought the jolly Germans had nicked it,' said Durga. 'Come to think of it, we had so many odd characters in the shop today, it could have been anyone. Anyway, I'm off to get myself something to drink. I'll get the milk, too.'

'But Heera, what if Mrs Wellington-Smythe gets angry because we did not ring to tell her the photographer had come early?' asked Swarnakumari as the door swung shut behind Durga.

Heera inspected a lime-green cardigan lying on a chair. 'Let's have lunch first. She could still be riding that stallion of hers in a mucky field. I don't want her telling me off again. I'll ring later.'

Swarnakumari hastily discarded the prayer book. 'Let me see that cardigan. Oh, Laura Ashley. Good quality. My Mallika does not like that colour, otherwise I would have bought it. Give it to me, I will put a price tag and hanger. Oh, it's size eight, it would never have fitted her. We only have size sixteen and size eighteen hangers left. Never mind, who is going to notice in the window? Heera, you must tell Mrs Wellington-Smythe we must have correct size hangers. We are facing such a big shortage. It was so embarrassing last week, *na*?'

The previous Thursday had passed uneventfully except for an incident at closing time. A tall, broad-shouldered woman had approached Swarnakumari while the others were at the back of the shop.

'It says size fourteen on the hanger, but it's not a fourteen.'

'Yes, madam,' agreed Swarnakumari.

'No, it isn't.'

183

'Yes, madam.'

'Do you think I'm lying?'

'No, madam.'

The customer had raised her voice, and Heera ran out. Noticing the green stubble marks on the upper lip and chin, the broomstick eyebrows, and hearing a manly voice, Heera was flustered.

'Can I help you, sir?' she said.

'You may call me madam, or I am leaving this minute.'

'Yes, madam.'

The confusion over the customer's gender was never satisfactorily resolved, and Swarnakumari blamed it on the hangers. As she scribbled a price on a label and placed the lime-green cardigan in the window display, she continued, 'You know, my Mallika is very choosy about her clothes. She's put on a lot of weight, *na*. But what to do? She tells me, "Ma, I feel very hungry when I study." I think she is not happy about the way she looks, but she does not talk to me about it, so how to help her?'

Heera moved to the small table and chairs in the Staff Area as Swarnakumari followed. 'If you want Mallika to stop looking like a rosogulla, don't feed her rosogulla!' she said plainly. 'Stop feeding her so much food. Simple. Look, there's a story about Kabir – you know the famous poet, right? A woman asked him how she could stop her child eating too much sugar. He asked her to return after a few days for the answer. When she came back, he simply told her that she should tell her child to stop eating sugar because it was no good for her. The woman agreed, but was surprised, and asked Kabir why he hadn't said so in the first place. He told her he had to go away and stop eating sugar himself to see what it felt like before he could advise. *Arre*, what I'm saying is: practise what you preach. If you yourself are eating too much – of course, I'm not saying you are – but if you are, then how will Mallika stop?'

Mallika was battling more than the bathroom scales; she was breaking out, and not just in spots. Her parents had been indulgent, for Mallika had been prematurely born. Swarnakumari had desperately wanted a son, but once she had suffered two miscarriages after Mallika's birth, she had submitted to a humble acceptance of God's plan and turned to prayer. In the meanwhile, her culinary efforts had harvested happy results: the frail baby had become a plump, dimpled girl with stubby legs bursting out of her frocks. At school, Mallika was teased and bullied, and during PE lessons it was evident that forward and backward rolls would pose a grave challenge.

Coupled with the excess weight was the problem of hirsutism, leading to concealment of more than one kind. The hair on her head tumbled thick around her shoulders, her eyebrows met above her nose, the thick downy hair on her arms, back, stomach and legs triggered school nightmares. She squeezed her underarms together during gym lessons, tugged the swimsuit desperately over her thighs, but Swarnakumari appeared not to notice the severity of her ordeal. Her response was to buy Mallika a pumice stone, put chickpea flour mixed with turmeric in a bath bottle for application as a body paste, and instruct her to rub her skin harder. Fluffy English towels were discarded, and special thin white towels available only at the Khadi Gram Udyog emporium were sent for the purpose by an aunt from India. As time went by, Mallika developed a hairy upper lip and sideburns, too. She was eventually left to her own devices; experiments with the pumice stone left her in a dotted rash like a Madhubani painting, and she reached for her father's blunt razor instead.

Growing up on Newton Square, Mallika, like her father, had stared furtively at the covers of magazines. She longed to have the pale, translucent skin, pinched, aquiline noses, light eyes and long, fair legs, not only of the models but of her own classmates. Mallika stopped looking in the mirror; she was convinced it would crack. Black, black hair and skin, she wept as she contemplated a life of unremitting ugliness.

An English friend had once stayed the night when Mallika was eight. Swarnakumari had run the bath, and the two girls had splashed happily with their Barbie dolls. As Emma rose to dry herself, Mallika had stared at her friend's hairless, pale body and the velvet sheen of her skin, the golden curls of her shoulder-length hair clinging damply to her flushed neck.

Mallika's spots soon followed, dotting her face, competing with her eyes for size and luminosity. They never arrived singly, only in hordes, unannounced and inopportune, always staying the night, littering her forehead and both cheeks. If squeezed, an exposed spot like a lone student demonstrator resorted to angry retaliation, rallying support until it was a red army of protest.

While the boys were merely bullying Mallika, three of her classmates in Year 11 had become pregnant. To the proud approval of her parents, Mallika, the 'boffin' and 'swot', topped the school and Sixth Form College,

186

breezing into Cambridge University. She had dutifully followed her parents' advice and earned the respect of her peers; the rest, thought Swarnakumari, was best left in the hands of God, although of late she had been wondering whether Weight Watchers could accelerate the divine pace.

The arrival of the African family next door was the opening of a new world for Mallika, piercing the boredom of her cottonwool existence. Joseph had lived outside Sydney, and he described Bondi Beach and the surf, the Blue Mountains and the colours of the sunset, Australian dreaming and four thousand years of aboriginal history, the Great Spirit, the Wandjina and Ngalyod, the Rainbow Serpent, and the sun as a woman wandering across the sky spreading light and warmth. He told her of the legends of the lizards, wombats and emus, of waratah stems and watering-holes, of desert oaks and manburrangkali lily roots and the aboriginal belief that all life, whether human, animal, fish or bird, is deeply connected to a vast, unchanging web of relationship through the universe.

The discovery of a stubby funnelweb spider in his mother's slipper on a wet day precipitated the family's hasty departure from the continent. Mallika had listened open-mouthed in Joseph's bedroom decorated with boomerangs and aboriginal and African paintings and a didgeridoo and African drum.

It was an innocent friendship whose beat slithered its insistent way in colours of red ochre and white pipeclay into her modest, neat room a few feet away. A torrent of yearning to discover new worlds took hold, refusing to shake and fall to the ground like the graceful yellowed leaves of the lilac outside her window. Mr Chatterjee had been right: Joseph was a danger to Mallika; but not in the way he had imagined.

Swarnakumari was still lost in thought as Heera unpacked her lunch at the table and observed, 'You know, Swarna, every day we eat cold lunch just because Lady Di says the shop should not have food smells. We are not allowed to eat warmed-up Indian food in here. *Arre*, what nonsense! Such a bloody hypocrite, setting up this shop to impress her fancy friends like that Vicky woman and calling it IndiaNeed! Tell me, does India need her? What feeling does she have for India? The only connection is that her father was born in some cavalry cantonment in Shimla in 1933. So what? He's not bloody Rudyard Kipling, is he?'

Durga entered with the milk and flipped the shop sign to *Closed* as Heera continued, 'And why does she call her Siamese cats "Jaipur" and "Udaipur"? D'you think I will ever name my goldfish "Manchester"? Anyway, it's a big name discussion again, so forget it.'

'Raj nostalgia,' ventured Durga.

'You know, I was just telling Swarna, it's so stupid that Lady Di doesn't allow us to heat up our food here. All that nonsense about Indian food smells! I know I should have told her right away from the beginning, but from next week we'll use a hot-plate, all right? I'll tell her straight on her face if she says anything, "You call us your 'Curry Club', don't you, so then we *are* going to eat our Indian food." Let it smell, who cares? *Arre*, in fact, if we started serving Indian snacks in here, the customers would come running *because* of the smells.'

'Including those on crutches.' Durga set the milk on

the tea tray. 'The natives are getting restless. Mutiny. The subaltern speaks.'

'Where did you get the milk from? I hope you went to the Co-op. Lady Di knows it's cheapest there. I can see your guilty face – why didn't you walk that bit extra? Anyway, put the receipt at the till before you forget. Now have some samosas, girls. I got them from Sangeeta Chopra on the way here. I've not been feeling that well, but never mind, can't resist. Did you see her photograph in the paper yesterday? She was standing next to the Mayor at some college do, posing in front of the big samosa she had made. It was twenty-seven inches long. How she made it, I don't know.'

'Or why,' said Durga.

'She does the catering for many Cambridge colleges, and she makes those children of hers roll out the pastry – small kitchen. I think her husband has gone for good; someone saw him at Yarmouth sitting in a car with an English girl. Why are you not eating? There's chutney too.'

'I am fasting – my Guru Ma's birthday, *na* – but I am just thinking, could it be this Sangeeta has sold you some part of the same big samosa? It could be so stale, *na*?'

Heera considered the possibility while sniffing a samosa. 'Hmm, all right, don't eat it, girls, you never know. I tell you, no offence, but we clever Indians are like spring water in a well. The deeper you dig, the more you find. By the way, I was thinking we should meet outside the shop sometime. We should all get to know each other better. Durga, I know nothing about you. You never talk about yourself, and Eileen, you're always rushing about. So I was thinking, why don't we have a Diwali get-together? I would have invited you to my place, but it's in a mess. Shall we go out? Any suggestions?'

'What type of food? Indian?' asked Eileen.

'*Arre* no, are you mad, or what? What sort of treat would that be? D'you know, the other day some of us neighbours met for dinner at an Indian place near Castle Street. The food was not bad, I must admit, but I spent the evening thinking how much better my own cooking is.' Heera chortled.

'And cheaper, too,' Durga reminded her.

'You know how I am, girls. I have to talk, so I told the meek little waiter he must be shivering in his pants when he sees Indian customers like me, because he must know we won't like the dishes or the prices. Poor chap, what could he say – he just smiled politely.'

'I never eat out,' said Durga.

'*Arre*, you're not missing anything. I once went with the Essex wife of Bob's colleague, you know how these goras are – they always want to go for an Indian – we were in London and we went to a place called "Curry in a Hurry". First of all, what a name! *Arre*, how can you have curry in a hurry? And that in a place looking like All Bar One? I ordered special Kashmiri dal, and I'm not joking, girls, the waiter brought a huge white plate with dal put only in the middle – the same size as a doughnut. There was a big coriander leaf stuck on top, and paprika sprinkled all around the empty sides of the plate.'

'What did you do?' asked Swarnakumari, her curiosity aroused.

'I ate it, of course. Jacqui was tucking into her tikkas and korma, but I felt like a fool because I was thinking of my mother and my childhood. The pot of dal at home used to be huge, and my mother always made extra in case guests dropped in. She loved to cook lots of good food for everyone. That's the way we Sindhis are, you know.' Heera blinked furiously and her voice faltered. 'Sorry, girls, I'm just remembering my mother. I never knew the last time I saw her that it would be the last time.'

There was silence; sharp, fragile, a laden cloud threatening to burst sutured skin.

Swarnakumari said with finality, 'Dal is dal.'

The others nodded.

'Shall we try the noodle bar on Mill Road, then?' asked Eileen.

Heera spoke slowly, ignoring Eileen's question. 'You know, girls, there is a big difference between being an Asian born here, coming from East Africa and coming from India out of choice and free will. When you come here from India, even if you try, India doesn't let you go. It's funny, but after all these years I still automatically convert English money into rupees sometimes.' She chuckled. 'And I keep a rupee coin in my purse for good luck. Shall I tell you something else? Sometimes I go into the Grafton Centre on a Saturday just to be in a crowd again. Not for shopping. I want to be pushed and shoved by everyone, but then I start searching for the old faces that I know I will never find there. And in any case, no one pushes me, and if I push them by mistake, *they* say "Sorry" to *me*! It must be the same for you, Swarna, we both came here only because of our husbands – but maybe it's difficult for Durga to understand.'

Had Durga spoken, the words would have stretched

191

all the way round the room, each letter bold on a fluttering white square, boxed row upon row until, forming a chain, they seized an open window and trailed behind a plane soaring in the distance. Letters in the sky appeared smaller, but lived longer.

'So when are we going out?' persisted Eileen.

'I will ask Your Uncle and let you know, *hanh*. Lunchtime will be good, evening time is difficult for me.'

'Before I forget, anyone interested in buying my friend Rama Prasanna's book on South Indian cooking? She's giving a discount – normally it is £6.99. If you buy two, then it'll be £5.99 for each,' said Heera.

'Why to take two? It's the same book, *na*?' Swarnakumari was puzzled.

'Like crutches,' said Durga helpfully.

'*Arre* no, what's this nonsense about crutches all the time, Durga? I mean two copies in case you want to give someone else a Diwali or Christmas present. I promised her I would ask you girls, but I also told her straight, no Asian will spend money on cooking books. At the most, one *bakra* – one sucker – will buy and then everyone else will borrow. A friend of hers called Aparna even bought the book and then gave it back and coolly took a refund the next day. What a cheeky monkey! Poor Rama was quite upset, but I told her, "Straight case of book photocopying by Aparna's husband in the office. Nothing you can do about it." Eileen, you must be thinking we are all mad. Even when we're not eating, we still talk about food.'

Diana had previously attempted to manoeuvre Eileen out of the Thursday shift and into the Monday slot with Betty and Mary, but Eileen had refused, a steely edge to her voice. She would work on a Thursday, or not at all.

'Has Mrs Wellington-Smythe said anything about the Christmas decorations for the shop? We must start soon, *na*.' Swarnakumari deflected the conversation away from the cookery book she did not plan to purchase.

'Relax, it's only October. What's your hurry? Who feels Christmassy in the wind and autumn leaves? *Arre*, let Diwali come first. Why would anyone want to buy Christmas wrap just now?' Heera paused. 'Actually, I could be wrong. A cheap and cheerful nine-metre roll might interest a few early birds,' she said meaningfully.

'Present company excluded, of course,' retaliated Durga.

'We should be the first with the Christmas window display,' continued Swarnakumari earnestly.

'By the way, I put the blond wig in the window on the way out, Swarna. Don't worry, it won't disturb your display,' said Durga reassuringly, as they cleared the lunch table.

'No prizes for guessing who it is this time,' laughed Heera as the telephone rang. 'IndiaNeed, good afternoon . . . Yes, Mrs Wellington-Smythe, it's Heera here . . . Yes, we just had a photograph taken for the paper . . . But you told me not to disturb you and that's why I didn't ring . . . You've already told the photographer not to use it? Yes, I understand . . . Yes, I've been here all the time during shop hours . . . Yes, I've locked up every Thursday this month . . . Yes, *of course*, I'm here all the time, and the rest of the volunteers come and go . . . Yes, sometimes I *do* buy things from the shop, but I always . . . *I always pay*. Yes, I remember we talked about those thefts . . . No, I didn't realise it was always on a Thursday . . . Yes, I know it's a Thursday today . . . Yes, I will tell everyone to look out for anything unusual today . . . Yes, *of course* I'm closing at five . . . No, I'm not leaving early. Yes, I will call if . . .' She replaced the receiver in a daze, turning to the three women. 'Did you hear that? Did you hear that? She thinks I'm the thief.'

Swarnakumari asked, 'What are you saying?'

Heera's voice rose. 'She thinks I'm a bloody thief! You heard, didn't you, just now? Girls, she is saying I am a thief!'

'Are you sure?' asked Swarnakumari.

'Yes. You know how she is. First she ticked me off *again* for opening the shop ten minutes late. It was only ten minutes. You three were standing outside waiting for me and you didn't complain, so what's her problem? Then she changed the subject, talking about the thief and Thursdays, so smooth, and she said, "Do be extra careful, watch the customers today, and don't forget to report anything unusual," but girls, I know she meant me.' Tears of outrage shimmered in her eyes.

Swarnakumari trembled. 'A thief in the shop today? What will he do to me?'

'Let's see, the thief could be male or female, of any age, size, shape, weight or colour, shabby or well-dressed, a batty old man, a student, young mother, anyone at all. Or maybe there's a whole gang out there. But I doubt anyone would want to attack you, Swarna, for reasons that I won't go into now,' said Durga comfortably.

Heera called out impatiently, 'Girls, girls, aren't you listening? What d'you think I'm telling you? She suspects me! Who the hell does she think she is? I'm telling you, I've had enough now. I live a comfortable life, and I am not doing this for the money. I took this job only because I needed to sort something for myself in my mind. Looks like I made the wrong choice, didn't I? I ended up sorting other people's rejects instead. What's a charity shop, after all?'

'A symbol of the Diaspora, failed dreams and of what we can't have or hold any more, a domain of collective hope and renewed, recycled life,' said Durga.

'I come here for a laugh, the customers give me respect and I help deserving people in India, but now this is a question of my reputation. I'm not leaving until I've cleared my name.'

There was silence in the shop as the women absorbed the significance of Heera's announcement.

'She hasn't exactly accused you—' began Durga, but Heera interrupted fiercely, 'You wouldn't be saying that if she had talked to you instead of me. And that thin, cutting voice of hers like sharp ice . . .'

Swarnakumari soothed, 'Heera, some people are like that only. You cannot change them, so you have to protect yourself. What is the point of getting angry? Guru Ma says anger always destroys. It will eat and eat inside, and you will be the one to suffer. And in every situation you must always think of why the other person is acting like that, *na*. Guru Ma explains this very well in her chapter on understanding. You know the word "understand". It means to "stand under", to feel how it must be inside the other person's skin. We must try to understand Mrs Wellington-Smythe. I think she has some problems. She is not looking happy – something is wrong.'

'You could be right, Swarna,' Eileen admitted.

Heera was incensed. 'What? Are all three of you taking her side? All this Guru Ma stuff has made mango pickle out of your brain, Swarna. How can you feel sorry for Lady Di, of all people? I feel really let down, girls. What is this behaviour? If you were in my place, I would definitely support you.'

'We are supporting you, but what can we do?' asked Swarnakumari without conviction.

'*Chors*, bloody thieves run around in this world doing dishonest things, but no, that Lady Di has to catch me instead. I'm telling you, I'm going to do something about this. I'm wondering now – what if this thief really does come in on a Thursday, just after we close the shop at five, just so it doesn't look suspicious?'

Swarnakumari was sceptical. 'But how can a thief break in just like that? People would see, *na*.'

Heera silently absorbed the truth of Swarnakumari's words. Mill Road was unlike other roads in Cambridge in that there was life after dark; soon after the bookbinders had closed and the florist had stored away the buckets and unhooked the yellow and white striped awning, the pawnshop had reluctantly locked its doors and the charity shops had removed any precious items from their windows, the curry houses and restaurants rolled up their shutters, ready for the evening trade.

She spoke slowly, voicing her thoughts. 'Yes, but what if the thief is so clever he isn't breaking in? He must be coming in some other way, but how?' She continued, 'Tell you what, we are going to find out, girls. Today after we close the shop we'll stay on a little longer, and see what happens. And don't you dare say you're not going to wait; if you're my friends, you'll help me.'

It was Eileen who was the first to agree.

CHAPTER ELEVEN

What goes up must come down

EILEEN OPENED THE shop door on her way out to buy stamps at the local post office at the moment when a frail old lady entered, holding a large purse, and headed purposefully for the counter, settling on the chair at the till.

'Madam, you can't go there, that area is for staff only. May I help you?' asked Heera.

'Eh?' The elderly lady adjusted her hearing aid, and slowly removed several folded carrier bags from her purse. She set them out on the counter; each was meticulously flattened into a neat square.

Heera whispered to Durga, 'Why does she have so many carrier bags? D'you think she plans to steal something?'

'No, she looks plain batty to me. And too feeble to carry away the video recorder. She can't possibly be the thief.'

'Yeah, she looks like she's not wired right. She needs carrying herself. She reminds me of my Aunty Buddi Mai. D'you know what Aunty said to me when I got married? "Just make your home so happy that your man wants to come every night to your bed." Poor

Buddi Mai – they say she poisoned her husband's second wife,' confided Heera.

Durga was staring intently at the elderly lady. 'Was your Aunty Buddi Mai as dozy as this one?'

Heera shrugged her shoulders in incomprehension. 'Maybe it's a trick, and she'll suddenly wake up and start nicking things when we're not looking.'

Durga peered closer, giving the old lady a nudge. She slumped lower. Durga felt her pulse. 'She certainly won't need anything from the shop where she's going. Not even an old cardigan.'

'What?' asked Heera, startled.

'Well, it's not far, is it – six feet under.'

'Talk straight, Durga.' Heera walked away to a corner near the display window, beckoning. 'What are you saying?' she hissed.

'One could, of course, ignore random disruptions, refute the notion of finality and adopt a metaphysical determinant of consciousness. All right, she's dead,' said Durga.

'Dead? The old lady? Oh my God, what a situation!' Heera pulled herself together. 'All right, so we ring. Who do we ring first? Lady Di or the police? Should we call an ambulance? But what about Swarna?' She paused before continuing briskly, 'The thing is, sales have been slow all day, and this old lady, bless her soul, is already dead, so we could wait a bit before we tell anyone, right? Or does that sound too mean?'

Durga shook her head.

'So then, let Eileen and Swarna just carry on as usual. We need them to act normally.' Heera was thinking rapidly. 'But what if Swarna sees the old lady? She'll either scream for England or wash her hands ten times.

No, Durga. You and I will have to put the old lady somewhere out of sight for now.' Heera cast a desperate glance around the shop. 'It will be safe in the changing room. C'mon.'

The two swiftly heaved the body onto the wheelchair and propelled it into the changing room, zigzagging their way through the clothes racks, and then returned to the till. Meanwhile, Swarnakumari turned to another customer and asked, 'Tell me, do you come in on a Thursday only, or other days also? What about this coat – you like it? Nice colour, *na*? Come with me, there are many more in this section. We have a changing room if you want to try on anything. We sold a new Marks & Spencer cardigan just last week, otherwise I could have shown it to you.'

Heera and Durga fled to the changing room to wheel the body out.

Heera warned, 'That silly Swarna is taking this whole thief thing so seriously she will send all the customers to the changing room just so that she can check their belongings. Such an *eediot*! She's ruining everything. Maybe we should tell Eileen when she returns. That way at least she can stop Swarna messing up.'

'Too late for all that,' said Durga. 'Let's just take the old lady to the window.'

'Brilliant. Yeah, let's do that,' agreed Heera in relief.

They wheeled the body into the display area while Swarnakumari attempted to interest the customer in a Royal Doulton figurine. Heera was panting as they reached the window, and fumbled with her free hand to retrieve a ringing mobile phone from her trouser pocket. 'Yes, Bob, what is it? *Jaan*, do you realise what a difficult position I'm in right now? I really can't talk now. Bye.'

She turned to Durga, still breathless. 'Sorry about that. It was Bob.'

'Men! They never get the timing right,' replied Durga.

'Here, pass me the blond wig,' urged Heera, and she placed it at a rakish angle on the elderly lady's head.

'I know blondes have more fun, but are you sure the timing's right for *her*?'

'Pass me the hat. Quickly, that long scarf too – it will be good for covering her face,' hissed Heera. 'And that cardie there. I'll drape it over her arms.'

Durga murmured as she bent over the corpse, 'Forgive me, for truly I know not what I do.'

Swarnakumari pointed to a porcelain shepherdess. 'What about something like this for your mother's next birthday? I know what you must be thinking, but do you know, you really can save a lot of money when you buy from here. We keep only quality things in this shop, and many times they are completely brand new. I would not work here otherwise, *na*.' She spotted the pram. 'Oh, nice large pram, you can put many things next to the baby. Can I just see how much space you have got inside?'

A well-dressed customer entered, along with Eileen, who began to shadow her, but the woman took a dislike to being trailed and left immediately.

Struggling with the body in the window, Durga cried indignantly, 'Hang on a sec, that's my cardigan! How did it get here? I left it right there on that chair when I went out for the milk.'

'Strange things happen. In this shop, in life and

201

death,' murmured Heera. 'We'll sort it out later, Durga. Let's just leave it on her for now.'

The two hastily left the window display area and returned to the till as the shop bell tinkled and Swarnakumari's customer departed. Swarnakumari was relieved. 'I checked. That customer was not the thief, *hanh*! We are safe.'

The shop bell tinkled again, and a dapper man entered, nursing an umbrella with a wooden handle. 'Oh hello,' he began nervously. 'I was just passing by the window when I saw . . . well, I was wondering if you could show me the binoculars you have there. And the blond wig too, if you please.'

'Yes,' replied Eileen.

'No. There is no wig there,' denied Durga.

'Oh, but there is! It's on your mannequin. Shall I show you?' asked the customer.

'Please don't, I'll get both for you. Kindly wait here. Durga, could you take the gentleman to the counter?' asked Heera hastily.

The wig was removed and brought to the counter along with the binoculars. Durga tenderly wrapped the wig in a carrier bag belonging to the elderly lady.

'Thank you so much for helping IndiaNeed today with your purchase,' chorused Heera and Durga, escorting him to the door.

'What was that all about?' demanded Eileen curiously. 'Why are you two behaving so strangely? Has everyone gone mad in the shop today?'

Heera stared meaningfully. As soon as the last customer had left, she snapped, 'Quick, Swarna, it's five! Turn the shop sign to *Closed*. Lock the door, Durga, and Eileen, turn down the blinds! Swarna and Eileen, switch off the lights and then go to the Staff Area, we're coming too, in just a minute.'

Swarnakumari looked bewildered, Eileen looked suspicous, but following Heera's instructions both obediently disappeared behind the curtain. Heera and Durga raced to the window and wheeled the elderly lady backwards, propping her frame upright in the centre of the shop. They followed Swarnakumari into the Staff Area and waited in the dark. Time passed.

'Heera, we have been just sitting for fifteen minutes already. What is this – how long are we to wait? I cannot even phone Your Uncle to tell him I will be late, because he will tell me to come home immediately. I always make hot food for him and Mallika, *na*. And Heera, now I am thinking, why did that customer want the blond wig? He had so much of his own hair. He was asking for the binoculars, but then why did he only buy the wig? Could it be *he* is the thief and it is his disguise?' Swarnakumari jumped, startled. 'What was that?'

'What?' asked Durga.

'That sound. At the back.'

Durga was reassuring. 'Only a ghost.'

Swarnakumari emitted a strangled sound. 'A ghost!'

'Oh, didn't I tell you? The charity shop has been erected on troubled ground. It was built at the very spot where a student was hanged for troublemaking in 1265 by order of the King's Justices. Up until the six-teenth century, several undergraduates were living in lodgings around the town. His wandering ghost is still seen in the shops of Mill Road. He has a frayed piece of noose around his neck,' explained Durga. 'Perhaps the thief is none other than the ghost? Incidentally, did you know Peterhouse had an eighteenth-century ghost? A Mr Dawes, the Bursar. Hanged himself.'

'I am not staying now. You are frightening me, Durga.'

There was a thud. Swarnakumari squealed.

'That must be a poltergeist,' said Durga.

'*Hanh?*'

'Haven't you ever heard of them, Swarna?' inquired Eileen.

'Peterhouse once had a poltergeist, too, apparently. They had to remove it from a student's room,' said Durga with relish.

'What's a polta-whatever?' inquired Heera.

'German word for noisy and troublesome spirits,' replied Durga.

'Oh, *those*, is that what they are called? D'you know, there were these polta-thingies in a house near us in Hyderabad. My mother's friend got married, and she lived there with her husband and his mother-in-law and his two brothers and three sisters. Poor thing, she was very young, and she had a terrible time there. Anyway, suddenly a lot of strange things started happening. When they woke up in the morning, each and every chair was smashed. Then all the clothes started getting holes. Can you imagine, all their clothes, even new ones in the wardrobe! They blamed it on the daughter-in-law,' said Heera.

'Naturally,' said Durga.

'But then they realised she couldn't be doing all those things by herself. In front of their eyes there were solid objects flying in the air. Once a heavy teak cabinet just lifted by itself and walked to the other end of the room. Then the dishes got smashed, and they heard loud bangs. The lamps used to swing, there were electrical fuses, and then the funny voices started. They heard male and female voices giving curses. The family got really frightened. The police didn't really believe these people, but then the policeman who stayed there the night got holes in his clothes too. So then they decided that my mother's friend must be a witch,' concluded Heera dramatically.

'Naturally,' repeated Durga.

'What happened next?' asked Eileen.

'One night those polta-thingies set fire to their clothes. My mother's friend rushed to try and save her husband's clothes from burning—'

'Not her own? How noble!' interrupted Durga.

'And a sister-in-law just pushed her onto the flames,' finished Heera.

There was silence as they digested the horror of the woman's plight. Heera's mobile rang, and Swarnakumari jumped.

'Yes, Bob . . . No, I think I'm busy tomorrow evening, too. The WI meeting – it gets over late. Tell you what, why don't you call sometime in the weekend? . . . Bye!'

Heera continued, 'Where was I? No, no, it's not a tragedy. It could have been, but my mother was there, and she was very brave. She pulled her friend out before she got badly burned. The funny thing is, my mother used to be very shy and meek, and now suddenly she just yelled at her friend's in-laws. Afterwards, she told everyone to keep quiet, and she began talking in a very calm voice; she was reaching out to those polta-thingy spirits. She kept telling them their work was done, and to leave everyone in peace. And suddenly the lamps

205

stopped swinging and the fire burned out. The ashes made a very strange pattern, my mother said.'

'I'm feeling very cold,' confessed Swarnakumari in a small, shivering voice.

'Then there must certainly be a ghost around. Did you know the temperature is always lower when there's a ghost in the air? Cambridge, with all its fens and marshes, is an ideal breeding ground for them. They like the damp,' Durga added. 'I've got an idea – let's go on a Cambridge Ghost Walk, and then we'll all join the Ghost Club. A curry club is so predictable. Let's tell Lady Di to call us her little "Ghost Club" instead.'

Heera intervened. 'She's just winding you up. Relax, Swarna. The sound came from upstairs, can't you tell? It's the DIY bloke again.'

'If poltergeists were in here, would they make holes in the net curtains?' pondered Durga. 'What would you do if the net curtains looked the same from the inside and outside, Swarna?'

'*Baba*, enough, Durga! You don't know when to stop. I am really frightened. I don't like sitting here in the dark.' Swarnakumari screamed and pointed to a shadow on the wall. 'Look, there is a knife! Look . . . sticking out!'

'Give me your torch, Swarna!' commanded Heera. She shone it on the object. 'What a silly thing you are! How can you think the hanger was a knife, honestly!'

'Heera, conscience calls. Aren't you going to ring about the old lady?' warned Durga.

Eileen was suspicious. 'What old lady?'

'Ignore her. She's just winding us all up again.' Heera turned urgently to Durga. 'If I ring now, my plan will be ruined. The thief won't show up if there's a police car outside.'

Durga was insistent. 'You wouldn't leave your old Aunty Buddi Mai like that, now would you, Heera?'

Swarnakumari quavered. 'Police car? What are you talking about?'

'I suppose you're right. I'll ring,' agreed Heera.

She moved towards the telephone, and in the silence there was the sound of the unlocking of the shop door; the bell tinkled. The four women looked at each other in tacit agreement as Heera grabbed the torch and led them to the curtain. They saw a man bending over a box, and Heera moved forward with her torch as the others followed fearfully. The man turned, and Swarna-kumari panicked, grabbed a saucepan and hit him on the head. As he tried to escape, there was the sound of something tearing, he tripped over an object in the centre of the room and there was a crash as he hit the floor. Heera switched on the lights.

'Well done, Swarna! Knocked him out! Your Guru Ma would be proud of you,' she cried.

Swarnakumari responded shakily, pleased. 'Really? But I hit one person only. How come two are there now? Heera, Durga, tell me. I hit one person, *na*? This same person. But why is he lying on top of this old lady?'

Durga explained, 'Two lovers with a single death wish.'

'What to do with this girl! Durga, do not tease me. I do not understand anything at all. Tell me first, are there two thieves or only one?'

'Look, the young man you knocked out is the thief. The old lady is dead. She's been dead for some time. Why they ended up in a passionate clinch on the floor is a long, long story. But anyway, well done, that was a nifty little blow you gave him,' said Durga.

'But . . .'

'Seriously, great job, Swarna. And look, you've ripped his jeans, too!'

Swarnakumari was bewildered. 'God and Guru Ma save me, *eita ki hochche*? What is happening?'

'Shouldn't we see who he is? C'mon, help me!' ordered Heera.

Heera and Eileen heaved him over as Swarnakumari looked on in horror, and Durga peered down at him. 'Young bloke, seen him before. Wait a minute, there's no need to call in the police just yet. Do you know who we've got here?'

'W-W-Who?' asked Swarnakumari.

'You'll never guess — it's Lady Di's son!' announced Durga.

'What?' Heera yelled.

'It's Lady Di's son,' repeated Durga.

Swarnakumari asked in hushed tones, 'Are you sure?'

'This Hugh Grant wannabe hangs about near the Mill pub at the river after school. He's in the Sixth Form. I know a student who is a friend of his,' replied Durga. 'What? Don't you believe me? Can't you see the spitting resemblance to his mother?'

'But how did he get in? We heard the sound of the key turning, didn't we?' asked Heera.

'His mother's, of course,' deduced Eileen.

'Anyway, terrific initiative, Swarna. You can explain to Lady Di you killed him in self-defence,' said Durga.

'What are you saying? Oh God, save me, how was I to know . . .'

208

Durga relented. 'I was only teasing, Swarna. You've only knocked him out, that's all. Serves him right.'

'He's breathing,' said Eileen.

'Oh, what a big scare I got, and my heart is beating so fast! Durga, you frightened me, but I forgive you. I am wondering, why does a boy from such a good family steal from this charity shop?'

'Drugs,' said Durga.

'Drugs?' Swarnakumari was speechless. 'But why? Must be these English boarding schools. Children are lonely without their parents, *na*. And by the time they are seventeen, eighteen, they have picked up all the bad habits. Smoking, drinking . . .'

'Wild sex.'

'All right – yes, Durga, that also. But you know, I am thinking now I know why Mrs Wellington-Smythe must be worried about this naughty boy. Now I know why she is looking upset all the time.'

'Perhaps he's only a harmless modern-day Samuel Coleridge – the poet was a colourful character in his undergraduate days at Jesus College, you know. Ran up a pile of debts, and had to leave.'

Heera thundered, 'What are you two on about? Don't you realise what this means, girls? We've caught the thief, and he's her son, of all people. Can you imagine her face when she sees it's her own little samosa?' She paused triumphantly. 'Girls, girls, oh what sweet revenge, what a day this has been!'

'Could he be wearing something he's stolen from the shop?' speculated Eileen.

Heera and Eileen inspected the young man while Swarnakumari paced the floor.

'Does this striped shirt look familiar to you, Durga?' asked Heera.

'Yes, it's a Paul Smith.'

Swarnakumari fretted, 'Such a good, aristocratic family, and poor boy, no one to give him proper guidance. If the parents are too busy, or not caring about the problem, at least there should be grandparents like in our Indian families, *na*, to advise this poor boy.'

'Do you have any idea how many young Asians do drugs?' asked Durga.

'*Hanh?*'

'And how many Asian parents deny the problem exists?'

'Girls, girls, we have caught the thief, and it's Lady Di's son. That's all that matters,' Heera reminded them.

'Will he return my reading glasses?' asked Swarnakumari hopefully.

'Come here, girls, I'm dialling Lady Di's number. Now just watch the fun.' They gathered near the till.

'Daina?' Heera said quickly, deliberately mispronouncing her employer's first name to dispense with protocol. 'Heera here – you know, you call me Helen – from the shop again. Yes, I'm sorry to disturb you . . . No, I didn't know you had important guests for dinner, but you told me to ring you . . . Yes, I will ring Sue Carter in the evenings from now on. Yes, I have her number . . . Yes, this *is* an emergency. You told me to call you about the burglary, and well, I now know who it is, and we have also caught him. He is right here in the shop . . . Yes, of course I can do that, but I think you should accompany the thief to the police station yourself along with the police.'

Heera was oblivious of the frantic signals from Swarnakumari and Durga as the young man raised himself in a daze and bolted out of the door, leaving it ajar. 'If you are there, who knows, maybe the *Evening News* will want a photograph of you.' She smiled, satisfied. 'You are coming in twenty minutes? Yes, I'll wait . . . Yes, actually we're all still here. It's past closing time, you know, it's nearly six o'clock . . . Yes, everything is under control, I am waiting in the shop for you . . . We are waiting, goodbye!'

'Heera, he's gone,' said Swarnakumari.

Heera looked in disbelief at the empty space on the floor. 'Oh my God! Gone! How could he just get up and run off like that? Swarna, you're useless. I thought you gave him a nasty blow, but I should've guessed, naturally you wouldn't do it properly. Why didn't you stop him? Durga, why didn't *you* stop him?'

Swarnakumari was relieved. '*Baba*, now what has happened has happened. It was good I didn't hurt him, *na*. After all, it is no less than the son of Mrs Wellington-Smythe. Guru Ma says violence . . .'

Heera raged. 'Pardon my language, but to hell with your Guru Ma, is she going to help us now? No. So, what are we going to do?'

'God will give us the strength to find the way,' said Eileen calmly.

Swarnakumari agreed, 'Yes, be calm, be calm. While you are thinking about what you are going to say to Mrs Wellington-Smythe, I am just going to wash my hands, *hanh*.'

'What d'you mean? You're not going anywhere, Swarna. No handwashing allowed. You stay right here. I'm not doing this alone. Let's think about what we are going to say to her. We're in this together, and we're all going to wait for her to arrive. We were so close – we were *this* close to catching him.' Heera stepped on a set of keys. 'What's this? Keys to the shop? They must be the ones he took from his mother, and they dropped out of his pocket when he fell. Girls, now we have proof it was him. *Arre*, watch the fun when Lady Di arrives. She will have a lot of explaining to do.'

'But do you not think that Mrs Wellington-Smythe might say *you* stole her keys from her? How can you prove it was her boy?' asked Swarnakumari.

'You're right.' Heera was crestfallen.

'For once,' said Durga.

'What are we going to do?' despaired Heera.

Durga prodded, 'What are we going to do about the *old lady*?'

Heera and Durga heaved the body back onto the wheelchair. The handbag on the corpse fell open and a mirror and a pair of gloves tumbled to the floor.

'Swarna, gloves! Do you want them for sorting the bags?' cried Durga.

As she spoke, a man entered through the open door. 'Evenin'. Sorry I'm late,' he said. 'Traffic on Milton Road's shocking tonight. Got to collect a wheelchair for the Arthur Rank Hospice.'

Swarnakumari, Heera and Eileen froze, but Durga straightened and moved forward. 'Oh, there you are. She's been waiting for you.' She bent over the old lady solicitously. 'Haven't you, angel? Off you go, my dear. Now, take good care of yourself where you're going. Goodbye!' She turned to the man. 'She's all yours.'

'Got orders to pick up a wheelchair,' repeated the man, perplexed.

'A wheelchair. Yes, with her in it. She's taking a nap, the old dear. She's been travelling back and forth such a lot lately, poor thing. Let me help you wheel her out, that's it. Could you hold the door open for me? Easy does it . . . Right. Goodbye.'

'Wait, take her crutches too,' said Eileen, handing them abruptly to the man.

'Yes,' agreed Durga. 'Wouldn't want to leave them behind, would we?'

Still perplexed, the man left with the elderly lady in the wheelchair, the crutches placed neatly across her lap.

Swarnakumari spoke slowly. 'My heart is beating very fast, *baba*. What is all this happening? I need to sit down. Where did the young man go? Where did the old lady go? Where did this other man go?'

'Oh no, I forgot to tell the man the brake on the wheelchair isn't working. That was why some *eediot* had donated it to us in the first place,' lamented Heera.

'And I forgot to get my cardigan back,' added Durga regretfully.

Heera fumed, 'Forget the bloody cardigan. Lady Di will be here any minute. Girls, what are we going to do?'

The shop bell tinkled again, and before their worried eyes, the *Cambridge Evening News* photographer entered. 'Hiya, *Cambridge Evening News* again. How are the four lovely ladies? Got a call from your boss. She's coming down here. Had a lot of excitement lately, haven't yer? Where's the bloke you caught?'

Durga moved forward again. 'It frequently happens that the signifier slips and evades the grasp of the signified in a poststructuralist site of unintentional fallacy.

It must be remembered that we live in a society of simulacrum, free of connection to reality. One should therefore desist from further discourse.'

'Er . . .' mumbled the photographer, lost.

'Hang on, what's this?' she exclaimed as she spotted an object lying on the floor, and scooped it into her hands. 'A wallet. Whose?'

'Maybe a customer lost it?' suggested Swarnakumari.

'There's only one way to find out,' advised Eileen.

Durga flicked it open and paused for dramatic effect. 'We've got the proof although we don't have the pudding.'

'Talk straight!' commanded Heera.

'Is this a hanger I see before me? Nay, behold, 'tis the purse of the noble lord.'

Heera spluttered, 'You mean . . .? Oh my God, this is brilliant. Brilliant. It must have fallen, but how? When Swarna ripped his jeans? Oh my God. Yes!'

'Good "back pocket" job on the trousers, Swarna,' applauded Durga. 'Your people in Kolkata would be proud of you.'

Swarnakumari looked pleased. 'Really? You, and Mallika, you young girls are clever, but I am no less, *na*. But I still do not understand what is going on. First that young man falls on that poor lady, and then another man takes her away in the wheelchair. Who *are* these men?'

'Rivals, both, for her love,' quipped Durga.

'What a story I will have to tell Mallika and Your Uncle. He has already been in the shop today, and so much has happened, *na*. How is he going to believe that so much more happened in one single day? Actually I still do not understand what happened, but

214

anyway . . . Oh, I am so late! I have to make the dinner.' Swarnakumari paused. 'Never mind, they should wait this time, *na*?' she added, with a smile in Durga's direction.

Durga smiled back. She had a sudden thought, speaking decisively to the photographer. 'Mrs Wellington-Smythe would surely wish to capture this for posterity, since this is the moment we found proof of the thief's identity and guilt. We're ready for our photograph.' She mimicked the photographer's earlier instructions. 'We'll pose here, right under the shop sign *IndiaNeed*. Brilliant.'

When the phone rang, Heera hesitated. It finally hiccuped into silence as her mobile phone took over.

Durga urged, 'Heera, come on, in the centre, that's it. Now, why don't you three lovely ladies display something that doesn't belong to the shop? Ah, that's it, the wallet. Could you hold it up so Mr Photographer can get a good close-up?'

Mesmerised by her authoritative tone, the photographer clicked obediently.

'Did you get it, love? Now another one of the four of us. C'mon Swarna, heroine of the hour, c'mon Heera, Eileen, we can do better than that. We are the "Cambridge Curry Club". United we stand, though we may fall or fail. Right – we're ready.' They posed, beaming at the camera.

The photographer clicked again to the accompaniment of a thunderous crash upstairs. A shower of golden dust sprayed the group, followed by another and yet another, until they stood choking and gasping, ghostly apparitions – victims of DIY floor lamination.

A large, jagged hole had formed in the ceiling of the

charity shop. As they gazed upwards in mute horror, a fresh mound of rubble fell through, knocking the wallet out of Heera's hand and burying it beneath a pile of bricks and dust. A tousled head appeared directly above, and a Yorkshire-accented voice said cheerily, 'Eh oop! Sorry about that. Everyone down there all reet?'

The shop was plunged into darkness.

Epilogue

————◦◉◦————

SIX WEEKS LATER, spangled golden Christmas lights winked at the thronging shoppers in the city centre as the Salvation Army band struck up a carol outside Lion's Yard. Not far away, Mill Road carried its own festive look; bunting, miniature Christmas trees and snowmen decorated the shop windows, but the book-binder was closed; Wright, the elderly owner, had an inflamed knee. The wistful blonde florist turned contemplative; the boyfriend had not proposed, but there was always next year. The grocers Veejay had artfully placed mulled wine sachets above the coriander and ginger. A brand-new pizza and kebab takeaway called Bytes4U was proving popular with the residents; a special promotion offered a large pizza at £9.99 with free fries and a Coke and a red-and-white candy stick that said *Xmas Xtra*. Its predecessor, IndiaNeed, could never have offered such inducements, and had humbly surrendered to the takeaway's gleaming ovens, chrome counters and sunshine teenagers in perky caps and aprons.

Swarnakumari and Mr Chatterjee were away, holi-daying in Kolkata over Christmas. Their sudden decision to leave Cambridge could be traced to Mr Banerjee's brush with fate in early November. He had been walking along Queen Edith's Way on a Sunday afternoon in the fading light, admiring flowering winter jasmine in a passing garden when a sharp object was thrust into his back, and a voice commanded him to hand over his money without turning round. Banerjee froze before removing his wallet containing a pound in change and a smiling photograph of Heinz and Madhumita, and turned. The next moment he lay on the ground, writhing, as his attacker fled. A resident sounded the alarm, but Banerjee lay unconscious until the ambulance arrived. The young thug sped away, cursing as he found the meagre coins, flinging the wallet into thick shrubbery at the junction of the road. Unknown to Banerjee, the worn Indian leather wallet and the smiling photograph of Heinz and Madhumita were to nestle for several years among the leaves, along with an abandoned packet of salt and vinegar crisps, unnoticed by the human eye.

It was difficult to ascertain whether it was Banerjee or Mr Chatterjee who was left more shaken by the incident. But for an urgent letter to be written to the City Council complaining about a faulty streetlamp on Newton Square, Mr Chatterjee would have been Banerjee's companion on Sunday's fateful walk. Mr Chatterjee lay sleepless as tortured thoughts encircled his pillow; would the assailant have attacked two elderly men on a walk, or only one? Would the thug have targeted him more brutally than Banerjee for not carrying his wallet at all, and would he have been left to bleed, a cracked skull, life ebbing on the Cambridge pavement of a Neighbourhood Watch street?

Madhumita, Banerjee's daughter, was tearfully apologetic. She would have flown out immediately, but their schedules were 'real tough'; neither she nor Heinz had leave for the rest of the year. Mr Chatterjee had pursed his lips silently at the thought of the ketchup clown, although Banerjee was more understanding. Heinz was going to buy a new car next summer and the couple had planned a holiday to Europe, he explained. Banerjee was simply too blind to see how foolish it was to rely on offspring to sweeten old age, thought Mr Chatterjee with sudden insight. Children were like the books he borrowed from the Rock Road Library: to be kept only for a limited period. He nevertheless viewed Mallika's application to Stanford on the recommendation of her supervisors with anxiety; in geographical location, it was dangerously close to San Ramon.

Banerjee was in pain, and waiting for an operation on the National Health Service to his shoulder, but no date had been provided. The uncertainty was already taking its toll. Mrs Banerjee's military-style ministrations added to the general discomfort, and it was impossible to tell which was more intolerable. Banerjee's malt whisky had been banned and banished; medicine and alcohol were a lethal combination, bellowed his commanding officer.

A witness to Banerjee's tribulations, Mr Chatterjee was deeply alarmed on several counts. The assailant could still be concealed in the bushes, ready to pounce. In the meanwhile, Mr Chatterjee read about another attack, reported in the *Cambridge Evening News*, on a blind woman who was out walking. Two youths kicked away her cane and snatched her purse. Mr Chatterjee was shaken to the core, as he lay in his bed staring at the ceiling that night. This was not the Britain he had dreamed of as a boy growing up in Calcutta, this was not the country of Shakespeare and Keats and Shelley and Wordsworth. It was a wasteland, he thought. It had become a council estate wasteland and Hooligan's Choice – not Hobson's – before his very eyes.

Banerjee's NHS wait was deplorable; this could not be permitted to happen in the country that rationed his friend's pension and had swallowed his tax contributions. Mr Chatterjee felt unease, betrayal, and as a consequence the Neighbourhood Watch duties were no longer challenging; it seemed irrelevant and futile to invest in securing other homes with his own still at risk. Old age had always been a worry to Mr Chatterjee; now he was deeply troubled. For some days, he had not bothered to glance at the magazines on the top shelf at the newsagent, nor had he scanned the headlines in his Bengali paper with the same relish.

Returning late from a Diwali party in Girton two days after the Banerjee incident, he was surprised to see a police checkpoint on Trumpington Road. As he fearfully rolled down his car window, the officer inquired about the extent of his consumption of alcohol earlier that evening.

Unfamilarity with the situation made Mr Chatterjee, a man of legal precision, respond meekly and weakly, 'Not much.' He watched miserably as other cars were let through. Recovering his wits as the officer approached him with the breath-testing unit, he supplied quickly, 'I remember now. It was one glass of whisky.'

It was too late. The officer took no notice, proceeding with rapid instructions that left Mr Chatterjee trembling like the Japanese wind chimes in his conservatory. He blew into the tube, cupping it with both hands. The officer shook his head. 'That's no good, sir. Try again.' Mr Chatterjee continued to quiver while Swarnakumari sat wordlessly beside him. The second attempt failed. 'No, don't hold it sir. Just blow. Blow!' Mr Chatterjee humbly confessed that his nervousness prevented him from fully comprehending what he had to do. Could the officer explain slowly? he asked, whereupon the officer warned him that if he did not blow properly one last time, he would be under arrest.

Mr Chatterjee had spoken the truth about his intake that evening; the officer eventually let them pass. The couple did not speak as they negotiated the Long Road bridge. Mr Chatterjee's hands clutched his dignity on the steering wheel, as he drove steadily past the Sixth Form College and Tennis Centre.

He recalled an incident from the time his cousin Palash Ghosh was visiting from Jamshedpur. Mr Chatterjee had extolled the English way of life with enthusiasm. 'Observe the immaculate dress of the English. Even coach drivers wear black suits. Observe how respectful they are towards cultured Indians. My postman calls me "sir" just for giving me the post – the accountant, the busdriver, all of them say "sir" to me.' Ghosh had agreed; English civility was exemplary. Ghosh had been equally impressed by the English roundabout.

Swarnakumari looked ahead; her fingers unclenched eastward. Mr Chatterjee's fingers were perspiring over the wheel. He now sensed that 'sir' had more inflections than one.

Mr Chatterjee's changing moods mirrored the dreary

winter landscape. When he continued to stare at the leafless trees outside as he sat at his desk on a Monday, his Parker pen idle in his hands, Swarnakumari produced the telephone number of Heera's Essex travel agent who specialised in cheap fares to India. Mr Chatterjee protested over the stops at three Middle Eastern destinations en route, but the persuasive Gujarati man pointed out reasonably that it was high season with low availability. Mallika would invite an Indian friend to stay, and look after the house; the neighbours, including Joseph, had offered to keep an eye. Mr Chatterjee demurred but Swarnakumari, now calm, referred him to the chapter on parenting in the missing prayer book. When a bird was ready to fly, said Guru Ma, a sloping nest was never a deterrent.

Swarnakumari's skilful manoeuvres infused new vigour in Mr Chatterjee, who now believed that the holiday in India had always been his suggestion. He took enthusiastic control, checking the locks on windows and doors, pruning the bushes and clearing away the leaves, switching off the fountain feature and storing the garden Aphrodite in the garage. The neat bundles of junk mail in there reminded him to instruct Mallika to stack the post neatly on his desk during their absence. He organised the payment of the utility bills and discontinued the Bengali newspaper for a month, glancing only out of habit at the magazine covers turned upside down.

'Going home?' asked the envious newsagent.

It was eight years since the Patels had returned to Gujarat on holiday. The shop was only closed half-days on Sundays, and there was no one to take command if they went on holiday; the son was at university and had already expressed his lack of interest in his father's enterprise, and Mr Patel's brother and nephews ran shops of their own in Ealing and Wembley. Mr Chatterjee was startled by the newsagent's wistful reference to 'home'.

After the holiday in India with Swarnakumari, Mr Chatterjee's life would chart a different path. The passengers had arrived in Kolkata fifteen minutes ahead of schedule. The pilot had mentioned strong tail winds.

Bob was unlikely to patronise the Bytes4U takeaway. He was no lover of fast food. He was pining for Indian food, Heera's food. Repeated calls to her after the shop's closure traced her to a Tupperware demonstration in Farida Nayak's living room. Standing on a familiar doorstep a week later, he fumbled ruefully for his key before ringing the doorbell instead. The hallway still carried lingering odours of spice.

They sat at the kitchen table with a fruit bowl in its centre. El Salvio loved red seedless grapes, he thought, before realising he had transposed two realities and two households, two lives and a split existence. How easy it would have been not to leave at all, to share a convivial pot of Chinese green tea with Heera and put the rubbish out in the bin in the frost-covered patio, and climb the stairs to sleep and never have climbed down again.

He noticed, heart sinking, that she offered him the Wedgwood cup and saucer reserved for guests. She sat stiffly on the kitchen stool, regal and resolute in her shapeless kaftan. Staring at the turmeric stain below her shoulder, he was mesmerised by its yellowness as it engorged, swelling into a flame of orange hope. He began slowly in a quiet voice, telling her of his childhood in the dank cottage on the moor, the rooms filled with reproach, his confusion, the beatings and his cowed resistance, the city, the unending questions of who and what and why he was, and his fear of the ending of the world and his life without knowing, the struggle, the battle to find his self, himself. He loved her utterly, he knew that now.

Heera rose to fill the kettle and in the rising steam recalled her meeting with Javed in the cosy Turkish restaurant on King Street. The flickering candlelight had enacted a shadow dance on his face; the mystery of the missing card on the bouquet now solved, he recited the Urdu couplet, soft, baritone, seductive. He had penned additional lyrics for the occasion in praise of steadfastness, and she had listened spellbound. They had laughed at each other's slide into middle age; she patted the rolls of flesh around her hips and he pointed wryly to his chin and his protruding stomach. When she shut the door firmly later that evening, he lingered outside her house under the moonlight on the gravel path, looked up at the night sky and knew she had set him free.

Heera sat down at the kitchen table again. She told Bob that nothing had changed; she was still his wife, and he her husband. She had her self-esteem and dignity and her standing in the community, and just as a decision to leave had not been taken hastily, so was his desire to return to be weighed with care. If he returned, she said firmly, it would be on her terms. With a compassion that left him wordless, she said she knew he was not ready, whatever he might profess to the contrary, and the matter of the mortgage should be settled in the meanwhile; the house on Tenison Road would be sold, and she would move into a small flat. A small flat? he asked, dazed. It was not a split decision, she said, smiling. There was always a right action and a wrong one; the right action was the one that never seemed to be so at the time.

He stayed until midnight, boldly uncorking a Merlot from his wine rack. He narrated his battles with El Salvio, and she laughed, tears streaming. As he left, carrying the bunch of red seedless grapes she had hastily packed into a Tesco carrier bag, he turned to see her in the hallway, her reddish hair framed by its light. From where he was standing it looked like a halo.

The day after he first met Durga, Roman waited impatiently in the travel section at Heffers. It had been a mistake for him to suggest the bookshop, he realised. Teresa might be lurking behind the shelves, red and ready. He decided not to look at his watch again. It would only confirm one fact: Durga was not coming. She was already an hour and ten minutes late, and there could be no mistake about the place or time. Although he had supplied his telephone number, she had merely stated cryptically that she would be there.

He walked away, through All Saint's Passage, turning right onto Sidney Street, and up St Andrew's Street and Regent Street, turning left at Gonville Place, past the Parkside swimming pool and onto Mill Road, his steps treading a furious mile.

He stood speechless, staring at the exterior of the charity shop. A red and white ticker tape had been placed around the entrance, sealing all access. The ceiling appeared to have collapsed; all he could see was debris inside the shop. Fear seized him as he stared, all recrimination and reproach banished.

The blonde florist at Sunflowers was happy to tell him the sad news; the entire ceiling had caved in that morning, but the shop had already been closed. A small part of it had collapsed the previous evening while the volunteers were still inside, but they were unharmed. The police had already visited and so had the shop's director. The secretary at the solicitor's firm two doors down was of the opinion that IndiaNeed would not re-open, she added.

Roman was calming a thumping heart. Where were the volunteers? he asked. Were they operating out of other premises? Did she know the woman called Durga? He began to describe her – slim, tall, shiny shoulder-length hair, dark-brown eyes, full lips – and the blonde florist turned more wistful as she saw the soft light in his eyes matching the velvet of the scarlet blooms. He dashed out of the shop when she could help no further, having spotted her freckled assistant moodily scuffing a shoe against the pavement.

'Hi, remember me?' said Roman urgently. 'I delivered your roses for you to that shop over there. I met you yesterday. I delivered the bouquet for you, remember? You had to see your girlfriend. It was only yesterday. Wake up, man!' Roman smacked the lad's cheeks between his hands.

'She dumped me,' said the lad morosely.

'That's too bad. Listen, did you know Durga, who worked at IndiaNeed? She's Indian. Slim, beautiful, shoulder-length black hair? Did you know any of the people there? Do you know where they live – anything? Come on, man.'

The lad was unable to oblige, sinking into a witless stupor. Roman felt a sudden compassion for the woe-begone Cupid. 'Listen, man, you've got to pull yourself together,' he advised. 'If you really love her, then you'll find a way. Give her a dozen red roses. Don't you get a discount? Plus chocolates and a heart-shaped card. Maybe a big red balloon too? You're a good-looking fella, bet you know what to do. Go for it.'

The freckled lad listened before slumping moodily again against the unforgiving wall as Roman returned to the blonde florist.

'Nick's a good lad, but a bit slow,' she said when he reported the failure of his efforts. 'Why did you ask him? He wouldn't know a thing. Oh, did I tell you the director's name was Diana Wellington-Smythe? Everyone's heard of her – maybe you should get in touch.'

Diana was at a trendy salon off Market Square, enjoying a vigorous Indian head massage to restore her jangled nerves. IndiaNeed was gone, had vanished in a little puff and cloud of dust. Immediately after the collapse of the ceiling the next day, she and other members of the Board of IndiaNeed had declared the items beyond recovery; salvage was too much trouble and money. An electrician surveying the damage had handed her a long-stemmed rose he had found nestling behind a twisted wooden rack. It was still a perfect bloom, he had said wonderingly. She twirled it for a moment and placed it on the debris as she left. The 'Cambridge Curry Club' had been disbanded without ceremony.

Rupert was away in London, as usual, staying overnight at the little flat in Chelsea, and James had not returned home, either; he was probably staying with his awful friend Henry. It was all so tiresome.

Her mobile rang and she answered, hair oily and wild, as the masseuse paused and stepped back respectfully. 'Diana Wellington-Smythe . . . Who? . . . Tempest? Dr Tempest? You are from where, did you say? . . . Oh, I see . . . No, that's all right, I like to leave my mobile number on the answerphone. People should feel they can reach me quickly, or what's the point . . . Yes, it was a disaster, quite appalling, very distressing indeed . . . In touch with whom? . . . Dewga? Dugga? No, I don't recall that name. Do you mean the Indian woman who was doing the research for a television company – the Cambridge graduate? Yes? In that case, Helen would know how to contact her – you know, my manager . . . *Her* home number? No, I'm afraid I can't remember. It would be in the files, but it's been such a dreadful business with the debris, can't find a thing . . . Her last name? I simply can't remember . . . You're welcome. Dr Tempest, you sound American. Are you? . . . How interesting! Are you staying over Christmas? If so, perhaps you would like to join us for dinner some day . . . We would love to have you at our table. Rupert and I regularly entertain Cambridge Faculty. Do give me a ring, won't you? Goodbye.'

Roman turned to the blonde florist in desperation. 'Do you know the shop manager Helen? What does she look like?'

'She's of South Asian origin, not tall, not slim, and the surname is Moore. An Asian gentleman sent her roses yesterday,' replied the politically correct florist. 'Helen . . . Funny, I'm sure her name was Heera,' she added.

'Heera, that's the one! Moore, did you say, as in M-o-o-r-e? That's an English surname.' Roman asked for the directory again.

There was something in his desperately seeking voice that prompted Heera to give him Durga's address.

'There's someone downstairs who wants to see you. He said his name was Dr Tempest. Shall I let him in?' asked Atul.

Durga dropped a startled ladle into the cooking pot. 'No, tell him to wait downstairs. He's . . . he's in a hurry. I've got to give him a message. I'll be right back.'

They met outside under a clear night sky near the neat lawn overlooked by the block of flats, camouflaged by the communal bins. They gazed at each other until he said, 'I guess you didn't want to be found.'

'No.'

'When I was a kid, I used to play detective. I had a rusty bunch of keys on a wire. They unravelled every mystery, and I solved every crime in the neighbourhood. My mom found them lying around one day and threw them away. They were just a bunch of old keys to her, but they were the shiniest, newest keys in the whole wide world to me. I should have found out where she got rid of them, and I should have kept looking.'

She remained silent.

'Well, anyway, here I am,' he said.

'Yes.'

'I need to get something straight. You didn't show up, and I've been through a helluva lot of trouble tracing you here. It's a long story, like the one with the florist, and I think that's two reasons to still meet for

229

dinner. I wasn't imagining it yesterday. There's something I felt that maybe you felt too . . .'

'Yes.'

He moved closer. 'Then why didn't you show up? Cold feet? Did you look me up on the Internet and discover my Cactus Cowboys Escorts Service? Damn, I should've known you'd find out who I really am.' He searched her face. 'Who's that guy who answered when I buzzed you downstairs?'

'My husband.'

He stepped backwards with an exaggerated gesture of disbelief. 'A husband?' He stood silent, considering. 'I'm okay with that, too. Things aren't going quite the way I planned, but no problem. How about you, your husband and me go out to dinner? A bit crowded at a cosy table for two, but I think an extra chair just might be arranged if we move the window.'

'I'm sorry.'

'Why? Because you didn't think it was important enough to tell me? That you didn't tell me? No problem. How about I come up for dinner, then? What's cooking?'

'Vangebhaji and amti and bhaat. Aubergines, dal and rice.'

'This vangerber stuff sounds good to me. Is he good to you?'

'Yes.'

'Why didn't you tell me?' he asked softly.

'I wanted to help you find a cactus.'

They spoke under a spell in the darkness.

'And I thought I'd found one, and didn't want to lose it,' he said.

She shook her head, moving away.

'Do you always follow your head?'

She shook her head again. 'This is madness.'

'Have you never given in to the madness, the crazed dance, raced the rushing blood to the horizon?'

She looked away.

'Well, my speech is over, my lines are laid to rest. You have my number, coyote. If you want to, give me a call.' He strode away into the light.

Durga lay awake next to her husband, coiled in the memory of Roman and the burst of stars. She waited, still, in the silence. A plaintive saxophone played softly across from the apartment opposite. It was never the same sound every night and always the same sweet blue riff of curling desire.

The volunteers and the photographer had staggered out of the shop the previous evening, choking with dust, helped out by passersby. Swarnakumari had looked shocked, and the secretary at the solicitor's firm, staying late to type a client's will, offered tea in her office.

'First things first, girls: what did we lose? The Fire Brigade man said he would try to recover all the missing items I mentioned, but was there anything we forgot?' asked Heera later.

Swarnakumari was still in a daze, and Eileen whispered, 'Her Guru Ma prayer book.'

'Of course, I forgot all about it. She hasn't mentioned it, though. I think she's still in shock, poor thing. This time it might never be found,' replied Heera in a low voice. She looked at the three women. 'Cheer up, girls! At least the collapsible bed's gone as well. Someone's nicked it.'

'Shouldn't Mrs Wellington-Smythe be here by now?'

interrupted the solicitor's secretary sharply. 'I've got to lock up, it's getting late.'

'Yes, it's quite late. I think you should all go now. I'll wait outside until she arrives,' agreed Heera.

They put on their coats as the secretary tidied her desk.

'I'll wait with you,' offered Eileen. 'I only live round the corner.'

'What should I tell her?' asked Heera slowly. 'I mean about the wallet, and her son.'

'The truth, of course,' replied Eileen, puzzled. 'Why do you ask?'

'See, the thing is, the wallet is gone, right? It's somewhere under the debris. The ceiling's gone as well, and everything's a mess. It's going to take them a while to clear all that up – who's liable, who's going to pay for the damage, all that sort of thing. It's clear that we can't go back in to work for a long time, and who knows when that will be? Who knows what's going to happen to us, and to the shop? So what does it matter in the end?'

She turned to the others, pausing for breath. 'Girls, let's not tell Lady Di it was her son. We really can't prove it unless the wallet is found, in any case, and she's going to get a nasty shock seeing the shop, as it is. She had planned to have Lady What's-It come by tomorrow – it was going to be her big day. Maybe Swarna's right. Maybe she's having a rough time already, who knows? What if her son really is on drugs? Anyway, let's forget it, shall we? Simply drop the whole thing. I'll just say the thief ran away when the ceiling came down and that's that. Let it go.'

'No,' said Eileen forcefully. 'She should get what she deserves.'

The others digested her words in silence, surprised by their flinty weight.

Swarnakumari's stomach rumbled loudly. She had been fasting all day for Guru Ma's birthday. It had been one of the most eventful days of Swarnakumari's life; so coloured, it was now a white blur.

'What do you think, Swarna?' asked Heera.

'*Ami arr parchi na,*' croaked Swarnakumari fuzzily. 'I can't, I just can't cope . . .'

Durga was inclined to agree with Eileen; the wallet episode should not be dropped. To resolve the issue in democratic mode, Heera suggested a secret vote, much to the irritation of the solicitor's secretary, now regretting her impulsive gesture of goodwill. She would not be paid overtime for her Samaritan spirit. As Heera read the four hastily written slips a few minutes later, she beamed. 'We *are* a club. Unanimous vote not to tell Lady Di.'

The day after their meeting near the black bins in the darkness, Durga found Roman in the fading light and hushed leaves outside Darwin College. They walked through Malting Lane and Ridley Hall Road, turning right onto the Backs, stopping on Clare College Bridge. In the end, it was the most natural place, and a knowing of the place for the first time, for her to move closer into his arms.

At first he did not ask, nor did she want to talk about her life with her husband. It did not matter in the walks over the Grantchester fields and the Fens, or as they rummaged in Waterstone's and Heffers, or huddled in the cold of a college garden.

'Don't you read any poetry? Elizabeth Barrett

Browning, Christina Rossetti, Emily Dickinson? I thought you would go for Sylvia Plath,' he teased.

'I like to laugh,' she replied.

Atul was a good, upright man, said Durga, conscientious and competent in his work, respected by his colleagues, liked by his friends, and loved by his family. He was also handsome, she added. Roman waited patiently for her to continue, and as he held her hands firmly between his own, she spoke of her childhood in England, of India and her teachers, her spiteful schoolmates, of college, her parents and relatives, of Malabar Hill, the sea and Vivek. The sea was not a painter's sea, she reminisced, but magnificent in the monsoon when the tall waves crashed and pounded the rocks and shoreline, spraying the city's waterfront promenades and the flimsy stalls selling corn on the cob and coconut water. The monsoon was the time for romance, she said wistfully.

Vivek was no longer in the matchbox business; his family had acquired a chain of luxury hotels. He was married and had a baby. She had met him in London at a café overlooking Green Park. Roman watched her face closely as she said Vivek no longer did silly things, and was content. Life had moved them both along.

She talked of her research for the television documentary on charities and her role as a Thursday volunteer in the shop, marking time before the job in London. Her eyes glinted as she talked of the customer searching for electric blankets, and the bizarre death of an elderly lady who was to have been the shop's newest volunteer.

'What do you think it was Arthur always used to say?' she asked, waiting patiently for his reply.

'Is this a trick question? Somehow, I get the feeling my answer is important to you. I guess I should make Arthur say a whole bunch of witty stuff about kings and round tables, but basically, I think he used to say that the true love of a man or a woman was all the blanket anyone would ever need.'

She shot him a smile, and he felt he had passed a test as challenging as a driving test for British roads. He had a teaser of his own, he said, retaliating. A road sign near Stamford in Lincolnshire announced *St Martin's Without*. Without what? He chuckled and spluttered before she could answer.

'Oops, I've just thought of what St Martin could be without. How interesting. Roman, you naughty, naughty boy!' He slapped his wrist. 'Okay, drop that one. Tell me how to get off a roundabout.'

'You have to know where you're coming from. And you have to know where you are going,' she said slowly.

She drew sharp, witty portraits of Swarnakumari, Heera and Eileen, saying she would probably never meet them again once she started work, blinking fiercely, unwilling to let him see her face, but in the end the words tumbled in tearful laughter as she recounted the bizarre events of their last day at the shop. In the end it seemed as if her entire life was about letting go of everything, she said wryly, dust to dust, rot to rust, what must end must. *I must and I must increase my bust* had failed too. She spoke of Atul's family, of his mother, sister Archana and cloying cousin Shreya, and the time that had passed, sand in a glass between her and her husband, was the unease of strangers in a lift between floors.

'I wouldn't be so hard on your sister-in-law Archie,'

he said. 'Why should she be the one stuck holding the weepy Oedipal mother-in-law while you guys have fun in Cambridge? She just needs to get a life. What she really needs is a man. If Archie babe were back home, I'd fix her up, but say, why doesn't that woman you told me about, the fat scheming matchmaker, get her together with the moody guy in New Jersey who shouts and yells?'

He laughed at his own wit, and then quietened. 'I have a confession to make – I shouted and yelled a lot. At Kathy. I also yelled into the desert. It was ugly. *I* was ugly. Shouting is cowardice, isn't it? A fear of losing control, so you end up losing all control. But maybe Archie babe should still give it a shot with the New Jersey dude if she's got a pair of sturdy earplugs.' Roman continued, 'Sounds like the green-eyed cousin with the secret uterine infection needs a man too. Is she a first, second or third cousin? These things matter.'

'I'm not sure. I'm not sure he likes her that much, either,' Durga's tone was edgy.

'He does, but I guess it's just not the right time, right place.'

She had turned prickly, and Roman wondered why, and what he could do. He would always feel he had been to blame for what happened with Kathy, but he had laid his own demons to rest: they had been pulverised and scattered somewhere over San Francisco and Arizona. Atonement, repentance, penitence for all things past, he was going to Durga in wonder and in trust, and he could never have imagined that he would meet her, only known that when he did she was real. Nothing and everything was wrong about her

236

marriage, but it was not for him to decide its thudding dullness or its sanity.

A month and a half later, Christmas shoppers thronged Market Square, hungrily sniffing the warm smell of doughnuts at a corner stall. Durga hurried towards Roman, who was waiting near a Guildhall festooned with golden lights.

'What's up?'

'How do you know something's up?' she replied.

'Whatever it is, I want to hold you and wish it away,' he said.

'This is too big. There was a phone call from his sister in the middle of the night. Atul's rushing back to India. His mother's unwell, and apparently she's been like this for a long, long time with a mysterious ailment, but Archana didn't tell him, and the mother's been having all sorts of tests and examinations, and the doctors there think it's time Atul should be with her for reassurance. I'm fine with him going to hold her hand, of course, but the thing is, Archana says his dad wants him to stay on and take over the Maternity Clinic and not return to Cambridge at all. Atul has finished his fieldwork and case studies, you see, so technically he could stay on in India and complete from there. It's all very confusing, a big mess. He's busy checking flights and packing.'

'What about you?'

'What about me? Got to go, too,' she said dully. 'He says I should follow after we've sorted out everything. There's the flat we're renting – we have to give notice. I was going to start my new job . . .' She looked at him, eyes moist. 'I'm such a loser. I've just drifted through

237

my life, a Peter Pan of academia. I've done nothing with my life but study one thing after another – foreign languages, English and German Literature, Political and Social Sciences. Even being at Cambridge was so weird. I thought it would be different, but I was never part of student life at all. And now, just when I thought I'd be doing something for myself in London, it's all changed. Back to Pune.'

He caught her wrist and stopped outside Great St Mary's Church, but she twisted free, eyes brimming. 'And you – what am I doing with you? My life's already complicated. I'm *married*. I'm supposed to be thinking of my querulous mother-in-law in a creepy ancestral house in Pune. Where does this thing with you lead? Nowhere.'

He held her close, speaking earnestly. 'As I see it, you've got a choice. Maybe for the first time in your life. You don't have to do what he wants you to do. He'll cope – the clan's there, and they need *him* right now, not you. And maybe he and they don't really need you in the long term, either, and maybe you don't need him? Think about it. You can choose to go or not go, you can choose to be or not be with him. As for this thing with me, if it bothers you that much, you can choose to end wherever and whatever you want. You don't *have* to do anything.'

Durga stood at the window of her flat, looking at the neatly parked cars in the street below. Despite Roman's stirring words, she would go to India, remain by Atul's side and nurse his mother. Roman belonged to a society that encouraged individuals to seek their own paths, one in which a path that did not lead anywhere could be dropped, she reasoned. But could a relationship, a marriage be dropped simply because it was dull? Her own parents had worked at staying together, and wasn't marriage about imperfections and warts and fissures and cracks and packs of Band Aid? It was ironic, deeply ironic, she thought, that it was she, not Swarnakumari, who had travelled across the world with a suitcase packed with tradition and values, too afraid to unlock and unpack its contents. And now it was to be carried back, handled with care across the Arabian Sea and over the craggy Deccan mountains to Pune, to be set down with an obedient sigh to mop a moping brow.

In the end she discovered it was quite simple. It was not about his family; it was Atul she found boring and boorish and not the man she thought he would be. Now that she had met Roman, she would no longer think miserably about the years and the life stretching ahead with Atul. Roman could not last, passion did not last; she would soon find something she didn't like about him. Perhaps he needed more space than she did, and in any case there were worlds to cross, and it was no longer easy to stay flippant – and what if he went away at Christmas, in the spring, one day, never to return? Far better to leave first, to hold on to the memory of him on a hot, hellish night in Pune when the mosquito bites and the angry red blisters on her skin became too much to bear. Then she would never let him go.

That evening she told her husband she could not leave Cambridge in a hurry. There was the flat to vacate, bank balances to be transferred, belongings to be shipped. They would understand in Pune, if he would. She needed time.

Atul left the next day, obediently following the

239

thoughts that had already arrived safely in India before him. His chinos were waiting in his father's cupboard on the shelf below the Johnnie Walker Black Label whisky. An unwilling Nikhil had carried them a year earlier to Delhi, from where they accompanied a Grant Medical College friend a month later to Pune, along with Atul's instructions to his mother to have them dry cleaned. His frugal sister gave them to the dhobi instead, who arrived every Monday with the bundle of the previous week's washed and ironed clothes. Squatting expectantly in the hallway, the wrinkled man looked expressionlessly at the pickle-stained chinos. Customers often expected miracles he could not deliver.

Upgraded to Business Class for his cleancut looks and air of authority, Dr Atul Patwardhan was seated next to an attractive, wealthy young woman with natural cleavage and symmetrical white teeth, the kind that bit into an apple or flesh leaving a perfect dent. She was from Goa, and suffered from chronic thyroid problems. She felt completely at ease discussing her condition with the polite, handsome doctor. She listened to his advice and fluttered near his shoulder.

He thought of Durga and the feel of her silky hair and the look on her solemn, puckered face. He thought of her with the sudden panic of having abandoned his hair-trimming scissors that he wished he could have carried on board, but should at least have packed into his luggage. His companion leaned over comfortingly. The French red wine had complemented her meal.

Roman chose the same day to place his hand over his heart and bend a knee on the cold stone floor of a college archway. He had prepared to recite a long passage from Thoreau, but in the end the words were his own. He shivered, but he would stay on that stone until he froze, he declared, the damp grey cold seeping into his bones, turning hot blood into icy deliberation; he would stay there on that stone and become a stalagmite, which was more or less the same shape as a cactus. The word 'stalagmite' was derived from the Greek *stalagmos* or 'something dropped', he told her with chattering teeth. Was she ready to drop something else and take his heart instead? His was a healthy heart, bronzed and glowing: would she hold his heart in hers and take both into the Mumbai monsoon?

He swore that he did not care if he never saw another cactus again, unless it was with her by his side, and a desert was only a desert unless he saw it with her colours, and what they really needed was a collapsible bed, because they would travel to the ends of the earth together for the rest of their married lives, because that was what he was proposing – marriage – or why would he be on his knees turning to stone on the stone, and he didn't care if the three Furies from Pune pursued him through tempest, wind and fire, if Tisiphone, Alecto and Megaera castrated him with their tongues for his abduction of Durga, his goddess whom he adored, his protector of the good and pure, destroyer of evil, destroyer of the demon Mahishasura, destroyer of negation, at whose feet he worshipped, humble and devout.

He paused for breath. His knee was soon going to be frost-bitten, he warned. He was no match for a dishy doctor, he admitted, but if she was going to choose, he thought she should know that he, Roman, was pure, delectable, melting, swirling, sinful, brownest of brown chocolate. She had laughed, heard the sound in the echoing courtyard, and her eyes were soft as she said she loved chocolate, how did he know, she needed time.

Eileen lived on David Street, an arterial road near the charity shops. She had witnessed the transformation of IndiaNeed into the pizza and kebab takeaway, Bytes4U, with loyal disapproval. The overpowering smell of charcoaled kebabs sent her scurrying to the newsagent to purchase her first lottery ticket – after apologising to the spirit of her Catholic mother.

She had stood in the shop, a wispy-haired woman lost in calculations before she carefully made her selection, and was only mildly surprised at the winnings of twenty thousand pounds. Danny Watts was delighted; it was a neat little sum for retirement, and they could even nip across to the Algarve every year, two weeks in the sun, quiet hotel by the beach, half-board. Her silent response was to seek an interview with the loans department of her local bank, where she impressed the manager with her figures and forecasts. Six months later, in the hall of the church round the corner, she was running a successful after-school club called Kids Love Maths with a year's waiting list. She had been saved by numbers.

The hairdresser James (Juan) had dreamed of the Costa del Sol every Christmas as he went home to his cantankerous mother in Glasgow instead. Then on another windy morning two days after IndiaNeed closed, a Spanish woman visited his salon; he carefully highlighted her blond hair as she chattered, and forgot his accent as he watched her smile in the mirror. Events moved along so rapidly that, shortly afterwards, he accompanied her to Barcelona, instructing the estate agent to advertise the sale of his salon.

Mr Khan of Waterford Way already owned two take-aways in Cambridge. He knew his neighbours resented the parked delivery van outside his residence, but Mr Khan had other things on his mind and his eye on Mill Road, and once the salon was on the market he lost no time in making a successful bid as a cash buyer. The salon space was ideally suited to an Indian restaurant.

Meticulous to the last detail, Mr Khan aimed to provide authentic cuisine; not for him new-fangled dishes such as Indian-style pasta, nor would he ever serve curries, burger and pizza under one roof. He carefully proofread the menu for errors, changing *motor panir* to read *matar panir* instead.

The name of the restaurant was initially a challenge; Mr Khan had proposed Koh-i-noor and The Taj, but these were already in existence, as were The Gandhi, Curry Palace, India Gate, India House, Indian Garden, Royal Tandoori, Raj Mahal, Raj Villa, The Mogul, Spice City, the Bottisham Tandoori, Downham Tandoori and Romano's Histon Village Tandoori Restaurant.

In an inspired moment while painting on top of a ladder in the restaurant, Mr Khan tumbled upon the name. He would call it The Cambridge, like the popular pub that went by the name of The Granta at Newnham. A day later, his uncle from London suggested he add the word 'club' for an air of exclusivity and refinement. It was to be The Cambridge Club until Mrs Khan insisted that no flavour was possible without the word 'curry'. She always had the last word.

The Cambridge Curry Club opened in early December

and was taking bookings for Christmas. A gust of wind almost unhooked the sign; Mr Khan had it firmly nailed back the next day. The telephone staff occasionally stumbled over the long name and privately thought The Taj would have been snappier, but The Cambridge Curry Club it remained.

In the concluding chapter of the prayer book, Swarnakumari's Guru Ma had succinctly elucidated the transmutation and transformation of all matter over time:

Nothing ever died that had never lived, nothing lived that had never died, and nothing lived or died, that was not reborn.

All BlackAmber Books are available from your local bookshop.

For a regular update on BlackAmber's latest release, with extracts, reviews and events, visit:

www.blackamber.com